THE MYSTERIOUS ISLAND

JULES VERNE

The Mysterious Island is the sequel to Jules Verne's unforgettable novel, *20000 Leagues Under the Sea* and *In Search of the Castaways (The Children of Captain Grant)*

This is the story of five brave men on an uncharted island in the South Pacific. Five prisoners of war decides to escape by the unusual means of hijacking a balloon. The five are Cyrus Harding, a railroad engineer in the Union army, his black manservant Neb, the sailor Pencroft, his protégé Herbert Brown, a young boy whom Pencroft raises as his own after the death of his father and the journalist Gideon Spilett. The company is completed by Cyrus's dog 'Top'.

The group crash-lands on a cliffbound, volcanic, unknown island. With the knowledge of engineer Harding, the five are able to sustain themselves on the island, producing fire, pottery, bricks, nitroglycerin, iron, a simple electric telegraph, a home on a stony cliffside called "Granite House", and even a seaworthy ship.

The mystery of the island seems inexplicable. The survival of Cyrus from his fall from the balloon, the mysterious rescue of his dog Top from a wild dugong, the presence of a box full of equipment (guns and ammunition, tools, etc.), the finding of a message in the sea calling for help, the finding of a lead bullet in the body of a young pig, and so on.

The secrets are revealed at the end. What happens at the end? What is the mystery of the island?

One of the great novels by Jules Verne. The gripping suspense makes it unputdownable till you reach the end of this complete & unabridged edition.

THE MYSTERIOUS ISLAND

JULES VERNE

Translated from the original by
Frederick Amadeus Malleson

PAPILIO

PAPILIO is an imprint of PROJAPOTI

The Mysterious Island
(L'Île mystérieuse)
was first published in 1874

This revised edition of *The Mysterious Island by Jules Verne*
is published by
PROJAPOTI 22 Sitaram Ghosh Street, Kolkata-700009. India
Printed in India

CTP IP 2/21

1 3 5 7 9 8 6 4 2

ISBN 10: 81-7606-023-2
ISBN 13: 978-81-7606-023-3

Jules Verne

(1828-1905)

Jules Verne was the founding father of science fiction with H. G. Wells. Verne's stories caught the spirit of the 19th century and it's fascination about scientific progress and inventions.

Jules Verne was born and raised in the port of Nantes. His father was a prosperous lawyer and to continue the practice, moved to Paris. Jules studied law there. In Paris, he also started to publish plays under the influence of such writers as Victor Hugo and Alexandre Dumas (fils). His one-act comedy, *The Broken Straws* was performed in Paris when he was 22. In spite of busy writing, Jules managed to pass his law degree.

In 1854 Charles Baudelaire translated Edgar Allan Poe's works into French. Verne became one of the most devoted admirers of the American author, and wrote his first science fiction tale, *A voyage in Balloon* (1851), under the influence of Poe. Later Verne would write a sequel to Poe's unfinished novel, *Narrative of A Gordon Pym*, entitled *The Sphinz of the Ice-Fileds* (1897). When his career as an author progressed slowly, Verne turned to stockbroking, an occupation which he held until his successful tale *Five Weeks in a Balloon* (1863) in the series 'Voyages Extraordinaries.' In 1862,Verne met Pierre Jules Hetzel, a publisher and writer for children. Hetzel started to publish Verne's 'Extraordinary Journeys'. This cooperation lasted until the end of Verne's career. Hetzel had also worked with Balzac and George Sand. He read Verne's manuscripts carefully and did not hesitate to suggest corrections. Verne's early work, *Paris in the Twentieth Century* was turned down by Hetzel. It did not appear until 1994.

Verne's novels gained a huge popularity throughout the world. Verne spent much of his time in research and tried to be realistic and practical in details. In *The First Men in the Moon*, H. G. Well's wrote about cavourite, a substance impervious to gravity. Verne was not satisfied. *A Journey to the Centre of the Earth* depicted an expedition that enters in the hollow heart of the Earth. In *Hector Servadac* (1877) a comet takes Hector and his servant on a trip around the Solar System. But *Around the World in Eighty Days* was about Philèas Fogg's daring but realistic travel based on a real journey by the US traveller George Francis Train (1829-1904).

Verne's imagination sometimes contradicted facts. In *From Earth to the Moon* a giant cannon shoots the protagonist into orbit. In reality, they would be killed by the initial acceleration. The idea of the space gun first appeared in print in the 18th Century. And before it, Cyrano de Bergerac wrote *Voyages to the Moon and Sun* (1655).

Verne's major works were written by 1880. In later novels the author's pessimism about the future of human civilization was reflected. In *Robur the Conqueror* (1886) Verne predicted the birth of heavier-than-air craft, but in the sequel, *Master of the World* (1904), the great inventor Robur suffers from megalomania, and plays cat-and-mouse game with authorities.

Verne travelled with his brother Paul in 1867 to the United States, visiting the Niagara falls. He made a boat trip around the Mediterranean. In 1871, he settled in Amiens and was elected councillor in 1888. Verne survived a murder attempt there in 1886. His paranoid nephew, Gaston, shot him in the leg and the authors was disabled for the rest of his life.

Jules Verne married Honorine de Viane at the age of 28. Although Verne wrote about exotic places, he travelled relatively little. He yachted occasionally. And his only balloon flight lasted twenty four minutes. Verne died in Amiens on March 24, 1905.

For over 40 years Verne published books on various subjects. His works include sixty five novels, some twenty short stories and essays, thirty plays, some geographical works, and also opera librettos.

Verne's works have inspired a number of film makers from Georges Méliès (A Trip to the Moon, 1902) and Walt Disney (20,000 Leagues Under the Sea, 1954) to such Hollywood directors as Henry Levin (Journey to the Centre of the Earth, 1959) and Irwin Allen (Five Weeks in a Balloon, 1962).

Further reading:

Jules Verne by Kenneth Allott (1940);
Jules Verne and His Works by I. O. Evans (1966);
Jules Verne by B. Becker (1966);
Le Trés Curieux Jules Verne by M. More (1969);
The Political and Social Ideas of Jules Verne by Jean Chesneaux (1972);
Jules Verne by Jean-Jules Verne (1976),
Jules Verne by Peter Costello (1978);
Jules Verne's Journey to the Centre of the Self by William Butcher (1990);

PART ONE

DROPPED FROM THE CLOUDS

Chapter 1

'Are we rising again?'

'No. On the contrary.'

'Are we descending?'

'Worse than that, captain! we are falling!' '

For Heaven's sake heave out the ballast!'

'There! the last sack is empty!'

'Does the balloon rise?'

'No!'

'I hear a noise like the dashing of waves. The sea is below the car! It cannot be more than 500 feet from us!'

'Overboard with every weight! ...everything!'

Such were the loud and startling words which resounded through the air, above the vast watery desert of the Pacific, about four o'clock in the evening of the 23rd of March, 1865.

Few can possibly have forgAotten the terrible storm from the northeast, in the middle of the equinox of that year. The tempest raged without intermission from the 18th to the 26th of March. Its ravages were terrible in America, Europe, and Asia, covering a distance of eighteen hundred miles, and extending obliquely to the equator from the thirty-fifth north parallel to the fortieth south parallel. Towns were overthrown, forests uprooted, coasts devastated by the mountains of water which were precipitated on them, vessels cast on the shore, which the published accounts numbered by hundreds, whole districts levelled by waterspouts which destroyed everything they passed over, several thousand people crushed on land or drowned at sea; such were the traces of its fury, left by this devastating tempest. It surpassed in disasters those which so frightfully ravaged Havana and Guadalupe, one on the 25th of October, 1810, the other on the 26th of July, 1825.

But while so many catastrophes were taking place on land and at sea, a drama not less exciting was being enacted in the agitated air.

In fact, a balloon, as a ball might be carried on the summit of a waterspout, had been taken into the circling movement of a column of air and had traversed space at the rate of ninety miles an hour, turning round and round as if seized by some aerial maelstrom.

Beneath the lower point of the balloon swung a car, containing five passengers, scarcely visible in the midst of the thick vapour mingled with spray which hung over the surface of the ocean.

Whence, it may be asked, had come that plaything of the tempest? From what part of the world did it rise? It surely could not have started during the storm. But the storm had raged five days already, and the first symptoms were manifested on the 18th. It cannot be doubted that the balloon came from a great distance, for it could not have travelled less than two thousand miles in twenty-four hours.

At any rate the passengers, destitute of all marks for their guidance, could not have possessed the means of reckoning the route traversed since their departure. It was a remarkable fact that, although in the very midst of the furious tempest, they did not suffer from it. They were thrown about and whirled round and round without feeling the rotation in the slightest degree, or being sensible that they were removed from a horizontal position.

Their eyes could not pierce through the thick mist which had gathered beneath the car. Dark vapour was all around them. Such was the density of the atmosphere that they could not be certain whether it was day or night. No reflection of light, no sound from inhabited land, no roaring of the ocean could have reached them, through the obscurity, while suspended in those elevated zones. Their rapid descent alone had informed them of the dangers which they ran from the waves. However, the balloon, lightened of heavy articles, such as ammunition, arms, and provisions, had risen into the higher layers of the atmosphere, to a height of 4,500 feet. The voyagers, after having discovered that the sea extended beneath them, and thinking the dangers above less dreadful than those below, did not hesitate to throw overboard even their most useful articles, while they endeavoured to lose no more of that fluid, the life of their enterprise, which sustained them above the abyss.

The night passed in the midst of alarms which would have been death to less energetic souls. Again the day appeared and with it the tempest began to moderate. From the beginning of that day, the 24th of March, it showed symptoms of abating. At dawn, some of the lighter clouds had risen into the more lofty regions of the air. In a few hours the wind had changed from a hurricane to a fresh breeze, that is to say, the rate of the transit of the atmospheric layers was diminished by half. It was still what sailors call 'a close-reeved topsail breeze,' but the commotion in the elements had none the less considerably diminished.

Towards eleven o'clock, the lower region of the air was sensibly clearer. The atmosphere threw off that chilly dampness which is felt after the passage of a great meteor. The storm did not seem to have gone farther to the west. It appeared to have exhausted itself. Could it have passed away in electric sheets, as is sometimes the case with regard to the typhoons of the Indian Ocean?

But at the same time, it was also evident that the balloon was again slowly descending with a regular movement. It appeared as if it were, little by little, collapsing, and that its case was lengthening and extending, passing from a spherical to an oval form. Towards midday the balloon was hovering above the sea at a height of only 2,000 feet. It contained 50,000 cubic feet of gas, and, thanks to its capacity, it could maintain itself a long time in the air, although it should reach a great altitude or might be thrown into a horizontal position.

Perceiving their danger, the passengers cast away the last articles which still weighed down the car, the few provisions they had kept, everything, even to their pocketknives, and one of them, having hoisted himself on to the circles which united the cords of the net, tried to secure more firmly the lower point of the balloon.

It was, however, evident to the voyagers that the gas was failing, and that the balloon could no longer be sustained in the higher regions. They must infallibly perish!

There was not a continent, nor even an island, visible beneath them. The watery expanse did not present a single speck of land, not a solid surface upon which their anchor could hold.

It was the open sea, whose waves were still dashing with tremendous violence! It was the ocean, without any visible limits, even for those whose gaze, from their commanding position, extended over a radius of forty miles. The vast liquid plain, lashed without mercy by the storm, appeared as if covered with herds of furious chargers, whose white and dishevelled crests were streaming in the wind. No land was in sight, not a solitary ship could be seen. It was necessary at any cost to arrest their downward course, and to prevent the balloon from being engulfed in the waves. The voyagers directed all their energies to this urgent work. But, notwithstanding their efforts, the balloon still fell, and at the same time shifted with the greatest rapidity, following the direction of the wind, that is to say, from the northeast to the southwest.

Frightful indeed was the situation of these unfortunate men. They were evidently no longer masters of the machine. All their attempts were useless. The case of the balloon collapsed more and more. The gas escaped without any possibility of retaining it. Their descent was visibly accelerated, and soon after midday the car hung within 600 feet of the ocean.

It was impossible to prevent the escape of gas, which rushed through a large rent in the silk. By lightening the car of all the articles which it contained, the passengers had been able to prolong their suspension in the air for a few hours. But the inevitable catastrophe could only be retarded, and if land did not appear before night, voyagers, car, and balloon must to a certainty vanish beneath the waves.

They now resorted to the only remaining expedient. They were truly dauntless men, who knew how to look death in the face. Not a single murmur escaped from their lips. They were determined to struggle to the last minute, to do anything to retard their fall. The car was only a sort of willow basket, unable to float, and there was not the slightest possibility of maintaining it on the surface of the sea.

Two more hours passed and the balloon was scarcely 400 feet above the water.

At that moment a loud voice, the voice of a man whose heart was inaccessible to fear, was heard. To this voice responded others not less determined. 'Is everything thrown out?' 'No, here are still 2,000 dollars in gold.' A heavy bag immediately plunged into the sea. 'Does the balloon rise?' 'A little, but it will not be long before it falls again.' 'What still remains to be thrown out?' 'Nothing.' 'Yes! the car!' 'Let us catch hold of the net, and into the sea with the car.'

This was, in fact, the last and only mode of lightening the balloon. The ropes which held the car were cut, and the balloon, after its fall, mounted 2,000 feet. The five voyagers had hoisted themselves into the net, and clung to the meshes, gazing at the abyss.

The delicate sensibility of balloons is well known. It is sufficient to throw out the lightest article to produce a difference in its vertical position. The apparatus in the air is like a balance of mathematical precision. It can be thus easily understood that when it is lightened of any considerable weight its movement will be impetuous and sudden. So it happened on this occasion. But after being suspended for an instant aloft, the balloon began to redescend, the gas escaping by the rent which it was impossible to repair.

The men had done all that men could do. No human efforts could save them now.

They must trust to the mercy of Him who rules the elements.

At four o'clock the balloon was only 500 feet above the surface of the water.

A loud barking was heard. A dog accompanied the voyagers, and was held pressed close to his master in the meshes of the net.

'Top has seen something,' cried one of the men. Then immediately a loud voice shouted,—

'Land! land!' The balloon, which the wind still drove towards the southwest, had since daybreak gone a considerable distance, which might be reckoned by hundreds of miles, and a tolerably high land had, in fact, appeared in that direction. But this land was still thirty miles off. It would not take less than an hour to get to it, and then there was the chance of falling to leeward.

An hour! Might not the balloon before that be emptied of all the fluid it yet retained?

Such was the terrible question! The voyagers could distinctly see that solid spot which they must reach at any cost. They were ignorant of what it was, whether an island or a continent, for they did not know to what part of the world the hurricane had driven them. But they must reach this land, whether inhabited or desolate, whether hospitable or not.

It was evident that the balloon could no longer support itself! Several times already had the crests of the enormous billows licked the bottom of the net, making it still heavier, and the balloon only half rose, like a bird with a wounded wing. Half an hour later the land was not more than a mile off, but the balloon, exhausted, flabby, hanging in great folds, had gas in its upper part alone. The voyagers, clinging to the net, were still too heavy for it, and soon, half plunged into the sea, they were beaten by the furious waves. The balloon-case bulged out again, and the wind, taking it, drove it along like a vessel. Might it not possibly thus reach the land?

But, when only two fathoms off, terrible cries resounded from four pairs of lungs at once. The balloon, which had appeared as if it would never again rise, suddenly made an unexpected bound, after having been struck by a tremendous sea. As if it had been at that instant relieved of a new part of its weight, it mounted to a height of 1,500 feet, and here it met a current of wind, which instead of taking it directly to the coast, carried it in a nearly parallel direction.

At last, two minutes later, it reproached obliquely, and finally fell on a sandy beach, out of the reach of the waves.

The voyagers, aiding each other, managed to disengage themselves from the meshes of the net. The balloon, relieved of their weight, was taken by the wind, and like a wounded bird which revives for an instant, disappeared into space.

But the car had contained five passengers, with a dog, and the balloon only left four on the shore.

The missing person had evidently been swept off by the sea, which had just struck the net, and it was owing to this circumstance that the lightened balloon rose the last time, and then soon after reached the land. Scarcely had the four castaways set foot on firm ground, than they all, thinking of the absent one, simultaneously exclaimed, 'Perhaps he will try to swim to land! Let us save him! let us save him!'

Chapter 2

Those whom the hurricane had just thrown on this coast were neither aeronauts by profession nor amateurs. They were prisoners of war whose boldness had induced them to escape in this extraordinary manner.

A hundred times they had almost perished! A hundred times had they almost fallen from their torn balloon into the depths of the ocean. But Heaven had reserved them for a strange destiny, and after having, on the 20th of March, escaped from Richmond, besieged by the troops of General Ulysses Grant, they found themselves seven thousand miles from the capital of Virginia, which was the principal stronghold of the South, during the terrible War of Secession. Their aerial voyage had lasted five days.

The curious circumstances which led to the escape of the prisoners were as follows:

That same year, in the month of February, 1865, in one of the coups de main by which General Grant attempted, though in vain, to possess himself of Richmond, several of his officers fell into the power of the enemy and were detained in the town. One of the most distinguished was Captain Cyrus Harding. He was a native of Massachusetts, a first-class engineer, to whom the government had confided, during the war, the direction of the railways, which were so important at that time. A true Northerner, thin, bony, lean, about forty-five years of age; his close-cut hair and his beard, of which he only kept a thick moustache, were already getting gray. He had one-of those finely-developed heads which appear made to be struck on a medal, piercing eyes, a serious mouth, the physiognomy of a clever man of the military school. He was one of those engineers who began by handling the hammer and pickaxe, like generals who first act as common soldiers. Besides mental power, he also possessed great manual dexterity. His muscles exhibited remarkable proofs of tenacity. A man of action as well as a man of thought, all he did was without effort to one of his vigorous and sanguine temperament. Learned, clear-headed, and practical, he fulfilled in all emergencies those three conditions which united ought to insure human success—activity of mind and body, impetuous wishes, and powerful will. He might have taken for his motto that of William of Orange in the 17th century: 'I can undertake and persevere even without hope of success.' Cyrus Harding was courage personified. He had been in all the battles of that war. After having begun as a volunteer at Illinois, under Ulysses Grant, he fought at Paducah, Belmont, Pittsburg Landing, at the siege of Corinth, Port Gibson, Black River, Chattanooga, the Wilderness, on the Potomac, everywhere and valiantly, a soldier worthy of the general who said, 'I never count my dead!' And hundreds of times Captain Harding had almost been among those who were not counted by the terrible Grant; but in these combats where he never spared himself, fortune favoured him till the moment when he was wounded and taken prisoner on the field of battle near Richmond. At the same time and on the same day another important personage fell into the hands of the Southerners. This was no other than Gideon Spilen, a reporter for the New York Herald, who had been ordered to follow the changes of the war in the midst of the Northern armies.

Gideon Spilett was one of that race of indomitable English or American chroniclers, like Stanley and others, who stop at nothing to obtain exact information, and transmit it to their journal in the shortest possible time. The newspapers of the Union, such as the New York Herald, are genuine powers, and their reporters are men to be reckoned with. Gideon Spilett ranked among the first of those reporters: a man of great merit, energetic, prompt and ready for anything, full of ideas, having travelled over the whole world, soldier and artist, enthusiastic in council, resolute in action, caring neither for trouble, fatigue, nor danger, when in pursuit of information, for himself first, and then for his journal, a perfect treasury of knowledge on all sorts of curious subjects, of the unpublished, of the unknown, and of the impossible. He was one of those intrepid observers who write under fire, 'reporting' among bullets, and to whom every danger is welcome.

He also had been in all the battles, in the first rank, revolver in one hand, notebook in the other; grapeshot never made his pencil tremble. He did not fatigue the wires with incessant telegrams, like those who speak when they have nothing to say, but each of his notes, short, decisive, and clear, threw light on some important point. Besides, he was not wanting in humour. It was he who, after the affair of the Black River, determined at any cost to keep his place at the wicket of the telegraph office, and after having announced to his journal the result of the battle, telegraphed for two hours the first chapters of the Bible. It cost the New York Herald two thousand dollars, but the New York Herald published the first intelligence.

Gideon Spilett was tall. He was rather more than forty years of age. Light whiskers bordering on red surrounded his face. His eye was steady, lively, rapid in its changes. It was the eye of a man accustomed to take in at a glance all the details of a scene. Well built, he was inured to all climates, like a bar of steel hardened in cold water.

For ten years Gideon Spilett had been the reporter of the New York Herald, which he enriched by his letters and drawings, for he was as skilful in the use of the pencil as of the pen. When be was captured, he was in the act of making a description and sketch of the battle. The last words in his notebook were these: 'A Southern rifleman has just taken aim at me, but—' The Southerner notwithstanding missed Gideon Spilett, who, with his usual fortune, came out of this affair without a scratch.

Cyrus Harding and Gideon Spilett, who did not know each other except by reputation, had both been carried to Richmond. The engineer's wounds rapidly healed, and it was during his convalescence that he made acquaintance with the reporter. The two men then learned to appreciate each other. Soon their common aim had but one object, that of escaping, rejoining Grant's army, and fighting together in the ranks of the Federals.

The two Americans had from the first determined to seize every chance; but although they were allowed to wander at liberty in the town, Richmond was so strictly guarded, that escape appeared impossible. In the meanwhile Captain Harding was rejoined by a servant who was devoted to him in life and in death. This intrepid fellow was a Negro born on the engineer's estate, of a slave father and mother, but to whom Cyrus, who was an Abolitionist from conviction and heart, had long since given his freedom. The once slave, though free, would not leave his master. He would have died for him. He was a man of about thirty, vigorous, active, clever, intelligent, gentle, and calm, sometimes naive, always merry, obliging, and honest. His name was Nebuchadnezzar, but he only answered to the familiar abbreviation of Neb.

When Neb heard that his master had been made prisoner, he left Massachusetts without hesitating an instant, arrived before Richmond, and by dint of stratagem and shrewdness, after having risked his life twenty times over, managed to penetrate into the besieged town. The pleasure of Harding on seeing his servant, and the joy of Neb at finding his master, can scarcely be described.

But though Neb had been able to make his way into Richmond, it was quite another thing to get out again, for the Northern prisoners were very strictly watched. Some extraordinary opportunity was needed to make the attempt with any chance of success, and this opportunity not only did not present itself, but was very difficult to find.

Meanwhile Grant continued his energetic operations. The victory of Petersburg had been very dearly bought. His forces, united to those of Butler, had as yet been unsuccessful before Richmond, and nothing gave the prisoners any hope of a speedy deliverance.

The reporter, to whom his tedious captivity did not offer a single incident worthy of note, could stand it no longer. His usually active mind was occupied with one sole thought—how he might get out of Richmond at any cost. Several times had he even made the attempt, but was stopped by some insurmountable obstacle. However, the siege continued; and if the prisoners were anxious to escape and join Grant's army, certain of the besieged were no less anxious to join the Southern forces. Among them was one Jonathan Forster, a determined Southerner. The truth was, that if the prisoners of the Secessionists could not leave the town, neither could the Secessionists themselves while the Northern army invested it. The Governor of Richmond for a long time had been unable to communicate with General Lee, and he very much wished to make known to him the situation of the town, so as to hasten the march of the army to their relief. Thus Jonathan Forster accordingly conceived the idea of rising in a balloon, so as to pass over the besieging lines, and in that way reach the Secessionist camp.

The Governor authorized the attempt. A balloon was manufactured and placed at the disposal of Forster, who was to be accompanied by five other persons. They were furnished with arms in case they might have to defend themselves when they alighted, and provisions in the event of their aerial voyage being prolonged.

The departure of the balloon was fixed for the 18th of March. It should be effected during the night, with a northwest wind of moderate force, and the aeronauts calculated that they would reach General Lee's camp in a few hours.

But this northwest wind was not a simple breeze. From the 18th it was evident that it was changing to a hurricane. The tempest soon became such that Forster's departure was deferred, for it was impossible to risk the balloon and those whom it carried in the midst of the furious elements.

The balloon, inflated on the great square of Richmond, was ready to depart on the first abatement of the wind, and, as may be supposed, the impatience among the besieged to see the storm moderate was very great.

The 18th, the 19th of March passed without any alteration in the weather. There was even great difficulty in keeping the balloon fastened to the ground, as the squalls dashed it furiously about.

The night of the 19th passed, but the next morning the storm blew with redoubled force. The departure of the balloon was impossible.

On that day the engineer, Cyrus Harding, was accosted in one of the streets of Richmond by a person whom he did not in the least know. This was a sailor named Pencroft, a man of about thirty-five or forty years of age, strongly built, very sunburnt, and possessed of a pair of bright sparkling eyes and a remarkably good physiognomy. Pencroft was an American from the North, who had sailed all the ocean over, and who had gone through every possible and almost impossible adventure that a being with two feet and no wings would encounter. It is needless to say that he was a bold, dashing fellow, ready to dare anything and was astonished at nothing. Pencroft at the beginning of the year had gone to Richmond on business, with a young boy of fifteen from New Jersey, son of a former captain, an orphan, whom he loved as if he had been his own child. Not having been able to leave the town before the first operations of the siege, he found himself shut up, to his great disgust; but, not accustomed to succumb to difficulties, he resolved to escape by some means or other. He knew the engineer-officer by reputation; he knew with what impatience that determined man chafed under his restraint. On this day he did not, therefore, hesitate to accost him, saying, without circumlocution, 'Have you had enough of Richmond, captain?'

The engineer looked fixedly at the man who spoke, and who added, in a low voice,—

'Captain Harding, will you try to escape?'

'When?' asked the engineer quickly, and it was evident that this question was uttered without consideration, for he had not yet examined the stranger who addressed him. But after having with a penetrating eye observed the open face of the sailor, he was convinced that he had before him an honest man.

'Who are you?' he asked briefly.

Pencroft made himself known.

'Well,' replied Harding, 'and in what way do you propose to escape?'

'By that lazy balloon which is left there doing nothing, and which looks to me as if it was waiting on purpose for us—'

There was no necessity for the sailor to finish his sentence. The engineer understood him at once. He seized Pencroft by the arm, and dragged him to his house. There the sailor developed his project, which was indeed extremely simple. They risked nothing but their lives in its execution. The hurricane was in all its violence, it is true, but so clever and daring an engineer as Cyrus Harding knew perfectly well how to manage a balloon. Had he himself been as well acquainted with the art of sailing in the air as he was with the navigation of a ship, Pencroft would not have hesitated to set out, of course taking his young friend Herbert with him; for, accustomed to brave the fiercest tempests of the ocean, he was not to be hindered on account of the hurricane.

Captain Harding had listened to the sailor without saying a word, but his eyes shone with satisfaction. Here was the long-sought-for opportunity—he was not a man to let it pass. The plan was feasible, though, it must be confessed, dangerous in the extreme. In the night, in spite of their guards, they might approach the balloon, slip into the car, and then cut the cords which held it. There was no doubt that they might be killed, but on the other hand they might succeed, and without this storm!—Without this storm the balloon would have started already and the looked-for opportunity would not have then presented itself.

'I am not alone!' said Harding at last.

'How many people do you wish to bring with you?' asked the sailor.

'Two; my friend Spilett, and my servant Neb.'

'That will be three,' replied Pencroft; 'and with Herbert and me five. But the balloon will hold six—'

'That will be enough, we will go,' answered Harding in a firm voice.

This 'we' included Spilett, for the reporter, as his friend well knew, was not a man to draw back, and when the project was communicated to him he approved of it unreservedly. What astonished him was, that so simple an idea had not occurred to him before. As to Neb, he followed his master wherever his master wished to go.

'This evening, then,' said Pencroft, 'we will all meet out there.'

'This evening, at ten o'clock,' replied Captain Harding; 'and Heaven grant that the storm does not abate before our departure.

Pencroft took leave of the two friends, and returned to his lodging, where young Herbert Brown had remained. The courageous boy knew of the sailor's plan, and it was not without anxiety that he awaited the result of the proposal being made to the engineer. Thus five determined persons were about to abandon themselves to the mercy of the tempestuous elements!

No! the storm did not abate, and neither Jonathan Forster nor his companions dreamed of confronting it in that frail car.

It would be a terrible journey. The engineer only feared one thing; it was that the balloon, held to the ground and dashed about by the wind, would be torn into shreds. For several hours he roamed round the nearly-deserted square, surveying the apparatus. Pencroft did the same on his side, his hands in his pockets, yawning now and then like a man who did not know how to kill the time, but really dreading, like his friend, either the escape or destruction of the balloon. Evening arrived. The night was dark in the extreme. Thick mists passed like clouds close to the ground. Rain fell mingled with snow. it was very cold. A mist hung over Richmond. it seemed as if the violent storm had produced a truce between the besiegers and the besieged, and that the cannon were silenced by the louder detonations of the storm. The streets of the town were deserted. It had not even appeared necessary in that horrible weather to place a guard in the square, in the midst of which plunged the balloon. Everything favoured the departure of the prisoners, but what might possibly be the termination of the hazardous voyage they contemplated in the midst of the furious elements?—

'Dirty weather!' exclaimed Pencroft, fixing his hat firmly on his head with a blow of his fist; 'but pshaw, we shall succeed all the same!'

At half-past nine, Harding and his companions glided from different directions into the square, which the gas-lamps, extinguished by the wind, had left in total obscurity. Even the enormous balloon, almost beaten to the ground, could not be seen. Independently of the sacks of ballast, to which the cords of the net were fastened, the car was held by a strong cable passed through a ring in the pavement. The five prisoners met by the car. They had not been perceived, and such was the darkness that they could not even see each other.

Without speaking a word, Harding, Spilett, Neb, and Herbert took their places in the car, while Pencroft by the engineer's order detached successively the bags of ballast. It was the work of a few minutes only, and the sailor rejoined his companions.

The balloon was then only held by the cable, and the engineer had nothing to do but to give the word.

At that moment a dog sprang with a bound into the car. It was Top, a favourite of the engineer. The faithful creature, having broken his chain, had followed his master. He, however, fearing that its additional weight might impede their ascent, wished to send away the animal.

'One more will make but little difference, poor beast!' exclaimed Pencroft, heaving out two bags of sand, and as he spoke letting go the cable; the balloon ascending in an oblique direction, disappeared, after having dashed the car against two chimneys, which it threw down as it swept by them.

Then, indeed, the full rage of the hurricane was exhibited to the voyagers. During the night the engineer could not dream of descending, and when day broke, even a glimpse of the earth below was intercepted by fog.

Five days had passed when a partial clearing allowed them to see the wide extending ocean beneath their feet, now lashed into the maddest fury by the gale.

Our readers will recollect what befell these five daring individuals who set out on their hazardous expedition in the balloon on the 20th of March. Five days afterwards four of them were thrown on a desert coast, seven thousand miles from their country! But one of their number was missing, the man who was to be their guide, their leading spirit, the engineer, Captain Harding! The instant they had recovered their feet, they all hurried to the beach in the hopes of rendering him assistance.

Chapter 3

The engineer, the meshes of the net having given way, had been carried off by a wave. His dog also had disappeared. The faithful animal had voluntarily leaped out to help his master. 'Forward,' cried the reporter; and all four, Spilett, Herbert, Pencroft, and Neb, forgetting their fatigue, began their search. Poor Neb shed bitter tears, giving way to despair at the thought of having lost the only being he loved on earth.

Only two minutes had passed from the time when Cyrus Harding disappeared to the moment when his companions set foot on the ground. They had hopes therefore of arriving in time to save him. 'Let us look for him! let us look for him!' cried Neb.

'Yes, Neb,' replied Gideon Spilett, 'and we will find him too!'

'Living, I trust!'

'Still living!'

'Can he swim?' asked Pencroft.

'Yes,' replied Neb, 'and besides, Top is there.'

The sailor, observing the heavy surf on the shore, shook his head.

The engineer had disappeared to the north of the shore, and nearly half a mile from the place where the castaways had landed. The nearest point of the beach he could reach was thus fully that distance off.

It was then nearly six o'clock. A thick fog made the night very dark. The castaways proceeded toward the north of the land on which chance had thrown them, an unknown region, the geographical situation of which they could not even guess. They were walking upon a sandy soil, mingled with stones, which appeared destitute of any sort of vegetation. The ground, very unequal and rough, was in some places perfectly riddled with holes, making walking extremely painful. From these holes escaped every minute great birds of clumsy flight, which flew in all directions. Others, more active, rose in flocks and passed in clouds over their heads. The sailor thought he recognized gulls and cormorants, whose shrill cries rose above the roaring of the sea.

From time to time the castaways stopped and shouted, then listened for some response from the ocean, for they thought that if the engineer had landed, and they had been near to the place, they would have heard the barking of the dog Top, even should Harding himself have been unable to give any sign of existence. They stopped to listen, but no sound arose above the roaring of the waves and the dashing of the surf. The little band then continued their march forward, searching into every hollow of the shore.

After walking for twenty minutes, the four castaways were suddenly brought to a standstill by the sight of foaming billows close to their feet. The solid ground ended here. They found themselves at the extremity of a sharp point on which the sea broke furiously.

'It is a promontory,' said the sailor; 'we must retrace our steps, holding towards the right, and we shall thus gain the mainland.'

'But if he is there,' said Neb, pointing to the ocean, whose waves shone of a snowy white in the darkness. 'Well, let us call again,' and all uniting their voices, they gave a vigorous shout, but there came no reply. They waited for a lull, then began again; still no reply.

The castaways accordingly returned, following the opposite side of the promontory, over a soil equally sandy and rugged. However, Pencroft observed that the shore was more equal, that the ground rose, and he declared that it was joined by a long slope to a hill, whose massive front he thought that he could see looming indistinctly through the mist. The birds were less numerous on this part of the shore; the sea was also less tumultuous, and they observed that the agitation of the waves was diminished. The noise of the surf was scarcely heard. This side of the promontory evidently formed a semicircular bay, which the sharp point sheltered from the breakers of the open sea. But to follow this direction was to go south, exactly opposite to that part of the coast where Harding might have landed. After a walk of a mile and a half, the shore presented no curve which would permit them to return to the north. This promontory, of which they had turned the point, must be attached to the mainland. The castaways, although their strength was nearly exhausted, still marched courageously forward, hoping every moment to meet with a sudden angle which would set them in the first direction. What was their disappointment, when, after trudging nearly two miles, having reached an elevated point composed of slippery rocks, they found themselves again stopped by the sea.

'We are on an islet,' said Pencroft, 'and we have surveyed it from one extremity to the other.'

The sailor was right; they had been thrown, not on a continent, not even on an island, but on an islet which was not more than two miles in length, with even a less breadth.

Was this barren spot the desolate refuge of sea-birds, strewn with stones and destitute of vegetation, attached to a more important archipelago? It was impossible to say. When the voyagers from their car saw the land through the mist, they had not been able to reconnoitre it sufficiently. However, Pencroft, accustomed with his sailor eyes to piece through the gloom, was almost certain that he could clearly distinguish in the west confused masses which indicated an elevated coast. But they could not in the dark determine whether it was a single island, or connected with others. They could not leave it either, as the sea surrounded them; they must therefore put off till the next day their search for the engineer, from whom, alas! not a single cry had reached them to show that he was still in existence.

'The silence of our friend proves nothing,' said the reporter. 'Perhaps he has fainted or is wounded, and unable to reply directly, so we will not despair.

The reporter then proposed to light a fire on a point of the islet, which would serve as a signal to the engineer. But they searched in vain for wood or dry brambles; nothing but sand and stones were to be found. The grief of Neb and his companions, who were all strongly attached to the intrepid Harding, can be better pictured than described. It was too evident that they were powerless to help him. They must wait with what patience they could for daylight. Either the engineer had been able to save himself, and had already found a refuge on some point of the coast, or he was lost for ever! The long and painful hours passed by. The cold was intense. The castaways suffered cruelly, but they scarcely perceived it. They did not even think of taking a minute's rest. Forgetting everything but their chief, hoping or wishing to hope on, they continued to walk up and down on this sterile spot, always returning to its northern point, where they could approach nearest to the scene of the catastrophe. They listened, they called, and then uniting their voices, they endeavoured to raise even a louder shout than before, which would be transmitted to a great distance. The wind had now fallen almost to a calm, and the noise of the sea began also to subside. One of Neb's shouts even appeared to produce an echo. Herbert directed Pencroft's attention to it, adding, 'That proves that there is a coast to the west, at no great distance.' The sailor nodded; besides, his eyes could not deceive him. If he had discovered land, however indistinct it might appear, land was sure to be there. But that distant echo was the only response produced by Neb's shouts, while a heavy gloom hung over all the part east of the island.

Meanwhile, the sky was clearing little by little. Towards midnight the stars shone out, and if the engineer had been there with his companions he would have remarked that these stars did not belong to the Northern Hemisphere. The Polar Star was not visible, the constellations were not those which they had been accustomed to see in the United States; the Southern Cross glittered brightly in the sky.

The night passed away. Towards five o'clock in the morning of the 25th of March, the sky began to lighten; the horizon still remained dark, but with daybreak a thick mist rose from the sea, so that the eye could scarcely penetrate beyond twenty feet or so from where they stood. At length the fog gradually unrolled itself in great heavily moving waves.

It was unfortunate, however, that the castaways could distinguish nothing around them. While the gaze of the reporter and Neb were cast upon the ocean, the sailor and Herbert looked eagerly for the coast in the west. But not a speck of land was visible. 'Never mind,' said Pencroft, 'though I do not see the land, I feel it... it is there... there... as sure as the fact that we are no longer at Richmond.' But the fog was not long in rising. it was only a fine-weather mist. A hot sun soon penetrated to the surface of the island. About half-past six, three-quarters of an hour after sunrise, the mist became more transparent. It grew thicker above, but cleared away below. Soon the isle appeared as if it had descended from a cloud, then the sea showed itself around them, spreading far away towards the east, but bounded on the west by an abrupt and precipitous coast.

Yes! the land was there. Their safety was at least provisionally insured. The islet and the coast were separated by a channel about half a mile in breadth, through which rushed an extremely rapid current.

However, one of the castaways, following the impulse of his heart, immediately threw himself into the current, without consulting his companions, without saying a single word. It was Neb. He was in haste to be on the other side, and to climb towards the north. It had been impossible to hold him back. Pencroft called him in vain. The reporter prepared to follow him, but Pencroft stopped him. 'Do you want to cross the channel?' he asked. 'Yes,' replied Spilett. 'All right!' said the seaman; 'wait a bit; Neb is well able to carry help to his master. If we venture into the channel, we risk being carried into the open sea by the current, which is running very strong; but, if I'm not wrong, it is ebbing. See, the tide is going down over the sand. Let us have patience, and at low water it is possible we may find a fordable passage.' 'You are right,' replied the reporter, 'we will not separate more than we can help.'

During this time Neb was struggling vigorously against the current. He was crossing in an oblique direction. His black shoulders could be seen emerging at each stroke. He was carried down very quickly, but he also made way towards the shore. It took more than half an hour to cross from the islet to the land, and he reached the shore several hundred feet from the place which was opposite to the point from which he had started.

Landing at the foot of a high wall of granite, he shook himself vigorously; and then, setting off running, soon disappeared behind a rocky point, which projected to nearly the height of the northern extremity of the islet.

Neb's companions had watched his daring attempt with painful anxiety, and when he was out of sight, they fixed their attention on the land where their hope of safety lay, while eating some shell-fish with which the sand was strewn. It was a wretched repast, but still it was better than nothing. The opposite coast formed one vast bay, terminating on the south by a very sharp point, which was destitute of all vegetation, and was of a very wild aspect. This point abutted on the shore in a grotesque outline of high granite rocks. Towards the north, on the contrary, the bay widened, and a more rounded coast appeared, trending from the southwest to the northeast, and terminating in a slender cape. The distance between these two extremities, which made the bow of the bay, was about eight miles. Half a mile from the shore rose the islet, which somewhat resembled the carcass of a gigantic whale. its extreme breadth was not more than a quarter of a mile.

Opposite the islet, the beach consisted first of sand, covered with black stones, which were now appearing little by little above the retreating tide. The second level was separated by a perpendicular granite cliff, terminated at the top by an unequal edge at a height of at least 300 feet. It continued thus for a length of three miles, ending suddenly on the right with a precipice which looked as if cut by the hand of man. On the left, above the promontory, this irregular and jagged cliff descended by a long slope of conglomerated rocks till it mingled with the ground of the southern point. On the upper plateau of the coast not a tree appeared. It was a flat tableland like that above Cape Town at the Cape of Good Hope, but of reduced proportions; at least so it appeared seen from the islet. However, verdure was not wanting to the right beyond the precipice. They could easily distinguish a confused mass of great trees, which extended beyond the limits of their view. This verdure relieved the eye, so long wearied by the continued ranges of granite. Lastly, beyond and above the plateau, in a northwesterly direction and at a distance of at least seven miles, glittered a white summit which reflected the sun's rays. It was that of a lofty mountain, capped with snow.

The question could not at present be decided whether this land formed an island, or whether it belonged to a continent. But on beholding the convulsed masses heaped up on the left, no geologist would have hesitated to give them a volcanic origin, for they were unquestionably the work of subterranean convulsions.

Gideon Spilett, Pencroft, and Herbert attentively examined this land, on which they might perhaps have to live many long years; on which indeed they might even die, should it be out of the usual track of vessels, as was likely to be the case.

'Well,' asked Herbert, 'what do you say, Pencroft?'

'There is some good and some bad, as in everything,' replied the sailor. 'We shall see. But now the ebb is evidently making. In three hours we will attempt the passage, and once on the other side, we will try to get out of this scrape, and I hope may find the captain.' Pencroft was not wrong in his anticipations. Three hours later at low tide, the greater part of the sand forming the bed of the channel was uncovered. Between the islet and the coast there only remained a narrow channel which would no doubt be easy to cross.

About ten o'clock, Gideon Spilett and his companions stripped themselves of their clothes, which they placed in bundles on their heads, and then ventured into the water, which was not more than five feet deep. Herbert, for whom it was too deep, swam like a fish, and got through capitally. All three arrived without difficulty on the opposite shore. Quickly drying themselves in the sun, they put on their clothes, which they had preserved from contact with the water, and sat down to take counsel together what to do next.

Chapter 4

All at once the reporter sprang up, and telling the sailor that he would rejoin them at that same place, he climbed the cliff in the direction which the Negro Neb had taken a few hours before. Anxiety hastened his steps, for he longed to obtain news of his friend, and he soon disappeared round an angle of the cliff. Herbert wished to accompany him.

'Stop here, my boy,' said the sailor; 'we have to prepare an encampment, and to try and find rather better grub than these shell-fish. Our friends will want something when they come back. There is work for everybody.'

'I am ready,' replied Herbert.

'All right,' said the sailor; 'that will do. We must set about it regularly. We are tired, cold, and hungry; therefore we must have shelter, fire, and food. There is wood in the forest, and eggs in nests; we have only to find a house.'

'Very well,' returned Herbert, 'I will look for a cove among the rocks, and I shall be sure to discover some hole into which we can creep.'

'All right,' said Pencroft; 'go on, my boy.'

They both walked to the foot of the enormous wall over the beach, far from which the tide had now retreated; but instead of going towards the north, they went southward. Pencroft had remarked, several hundred feet from the place at which they landed, a narrow cutting, out of which he thought a river or stream might issue. Now, on the one hand it was important to settle themselves in the neighbourhood of a good stream of water, and on the other it was possible that the current had thrown Cyrus Harding on the shore there.

The cliff, as has been said, rose to a height of three hundred feet, but the mass was unbroken throughout, and even at its base, scarcely washed by the sea, it did not offer the smallest fissure which would serve as a dwelling. It was a perpendicular wall of very hard granite, which even the waves had not worn away. Towards the summit fluttered myriads of sea-fowl, and especially those of the web-footed species with long, flat, pointed beaks—a clamorous tribe, bold in the presence of man, who probably for the first time thus invaded their domains. Pencroft recognized the skua and other gulls among them, the voracious little sea-mew, which in great numbers nestled in the crevices of the granite. A shot fired among this swarm would have killed a great number, but to fire a shot a gun was needed, and neither Pencroft nor Herbert had one; besides this, gulls and sea-mews are scarcely eatable, and even their eggs have a detestable taste. However, Herbert, who had gone forward a little more to the left, soon came upon rocks covered with sea-weed, which, some hours later, would be hidden by the high tide. On these rocks, in the midst of slippery wrack, abounded bivalve shell-fish, not to be despised by starving people. Herbert called Pencroft, who ran up hastily.

'Here are mussels!' cried the sailor; 'these will do instead of eggs!'

'They are not mussels,' replied Herbert, who was attentively examining the molluscs attached to the rocks; 'they are lithodomes.'

'Are they good to eat?' asked Pencroft.

'Perfectly so.'

'Then let us eat some lithodomes.'

The sailor could rely upon Herbert; the young boy was well up in natural history, and always had had quite a passion for the science. His father had encouraged him in it, by letting him attend the lectures of the best professors in Boston, who were very fond of the intelligent, industrious lad. And his turn for natural history was, more than once in the course of time, of great use, and he was not mistaken in this instance. These lithodomes were oblong shells, suspended in clusters and adhering very tightly to the rocks. They belong to that species of molluscous perforators which excavate holes in the hardest stone; their shell is rounded at both ends, a feature which is not remarked in the common mussel.

Pencroft and Herbert made a good meal of the lithodomes, which were then half opened to the sun. They ate them as oysters, and as they had a strong peppery taste, they were palatable without condiments of any sort.

Their hunger was thus appeased for the time, but not their thirst, which increased after eating these naturally-spiced molluscs. They had then to find fresh water, and it was not likely that it would be wanting in such a capriciously uneven region. Pencroft and Herbert, after having taken the precaution of collecting an ample supply of lithodomes, with which they filled their pockets and handkerchiefs, regained the foot of the cliff.

Two hundred paces farther they arrived at the cutting, through which, as Pencroft had guessed, ran a stream of water, whether fresh or not was to be ascertained. At this place the wall appeared to have been separated by some violent subterranean force. At its base was hollowed out a little creek, the farthest part of which formed a tolerably sharp angle. The watercourse at that part measured one hundred feet in breadth, and its two banks on each side were scarcely twenty feet high. The river became strong almost directly between the two walls of granite, which began to sink above the mouth; it then suddenly turned and disappeared beneath a wood of stunted trees half a mile off.

'Here is the water, and yonder is the wood we require!' said Pencroft. 'Well, Herbert, now we only want the house.'

The water of the river was limpid. The sailor ascertained that at this time—that is to say, at low tide, when the rising floods did not reach it —it was sweet. This important point established, Herbert looked for some cavity which would serve them as a retreat, but in vain; everywhere the wall appeared smooth, plain, and perpendicular.

However, at the mouth of the watercourse and above the reach of the high tide, the convulsions of nature had formed, not a grotto, but a pile of enormous rocks, such as are often met with in granite countries and which bear the name of 'Chimneys.'

Pencroft and Herbert penetrated quite far in among the rocks, by sandy passages in which light was not wanting, for it entered through the openings which were left between the blocks, of which some were only sustained by a miracle of equilibrium; but with the light came also air—a regular corridor-gale—and with the wind the sharp cold from the exterior. However, the sailor thought that by stopping-up some of the openings with a mixture of stones and sand, the Chimneys could be rendered habitable. Their geometrical plan represented the typographical sign '&,' which signifies 'et cetera' abridged, but by isolating the upper mouth of the sign, through which the south and west winds blew so strongly, they could succeed in making the lower part of use.

'Here's our work,' said Pencroft, 'and if we ever see Captain Harding again, he will know how to make something of this labyrinth.'

'We shall see him again, Pencroft,' cried Herbert, 'and when be returns he must find a tolerable dwelling here. It will be so, if we can make a fireplace in the left passage and keep an opening for the smoke.'

'So we can, my boy,' replied the sailor, 'and these Chimneys will serve our turn. Let us set to work, but first come and get a store of fuel. I think some branches will be very useful in stopping up these openings, through which the wind shrieks like so many fiends.'

Herbert and Pencroft left the Chimneys, and, turning the angle, they began to climb the left bank of the river. The current here was quite rapid, and drifted down some dead wood. The rising tide—and it could already be perceived—must drive it back with force to a considerable distance. The sailor then thought that they could utilize this ebb and flow for the transport of heavy objects.

After having walked for a quarter of an hour, the sailor and the boy arrived at the angle which the river made in turning towards the left. From this point its course was pursued through a forest of magnificent trees. These trees still retained their verdure, notwithstanding the advanced season, for they belonged to the family of 'coniferae,' which is spread over all the regions of the globe, from northern climates to the tropics. The young naturalist recognized especially the 'deedara,' which are very numerous in the Himalayan zone, and which spread around them a most agreeable odour. Between these beautiful trees sprang up clusters of firs, whose opaque open parasol boughs spread wide around. Among the long grass, Pencroft felt that his feet were crushing dry branches which crackled like fireworks.

'Well, my boy,' said he to Herbert, 'if I don't know the name of these trees, at any rate I reckon that we may call them 'burning wood,' and just now that's the chief thing we want.'

'Let us get a supply,' replied Herbert, who immediately set to work.

The collection was easily made. It was not even necessary to lop the trees, for enormous quantities of dead wood were lying at their feet; but if fuel was not wanting, the means of transporting it was not yet found. The wood, being very dry, would burn rapidly; it was therefore necessary to carry to the Chimneys a considerable quantity, and the loads of two men would not be sufficient. Herbert remarked this.

'Well, my boy,' replied the sailor, 'there must be some way of carrying this wood; there is always a way of doing everything. If we had a cart or a boat, it would be easy enough.'

'But we have the river,' said Herbert.

'Right,' replied Pencroft; 'the river will be to us like a road which carries of itself, and rafts have not been invented for nothing.'

'Only,' observed Herbert, 'at this moment our road is going the wrong way, for the tide is rising!'

'We shall be all right if we wait till it ebbs,' replied the sailor, 'and then we will trust it to carry our fuel to the Chimneys. Let us get the raft ready.'

The sailor, followed by Herbert, directed his steps towards the river. They both carried, each in proportion to his strength, a load of wood bound in faggots. They found on the bank also a great quantity of dead branches in the midst of grass, among which the foot of man had probably never before trod. Pencroft began directly to make his raft. In a kind of little bay, created by a point of the shore which broke the current, the sailor and the lad placed some good-sized pieces of wood, which they had fastened together with dry creepers. A raft was thus formed, on which they stacked all they had collected, sufficient, indeed, to have loaded at least twenty men. In an hour the work was finished, and the raft moored to the bank, awaited the turning of the tide.

There were still several hours to be occupied, and with one consent Pencroft and Herbert resolved to gain the upper plateau, so as to have a more extended view of the surrounding country.

Exactly two hundred feet behind the angle formed by the river, the wall, terminated by a fall of rocks, died away in a gentle slope to the edge of the forest. It was a natural staircase. Herbert and the sailor began their ascent; thanks to the vigour of their muscles they reached the summit in a few minutes; and proceeded to the point above the mouth of the river.

On attaining it, their first look was cast upon the ocean which not long before they had traversed in such a terrible condition. They observed, with emotion, all that part to the north of the coast on which the catastrophe had taken place. It was there that Cyrus Harding had disappeared. They looked to see if some portion of their balloon, to which a man might possibly cling, yet existed. Nothing! The sea was but one vast watery desert. As to the coast, it was solitary also. Neither the reporter nor Neb could be anywhere seen. But it was possible that at this time they were both too far away to be perceived.

'Something tells me,' cried Herbert, 'that a man as energetic as Captain Harding would not let himself be drowned like other people. He must have reached some point of the shore; don't you think so, Pencroft?'

The sailor shook his head sadly. He little expected ever to see Cyrus Harding again; but wishing to leave some hope to Herbert: 'Doubtless, doubtless,' said he; 'our engineer is a man who would get out of a scrape to which any one else would yield.'

In the meantime he examined the coast with great attention. Stretched out below them was the sandy shore, bounded on the right of the river's mouth by lines of breakers. The rocks which were visible appeared like amphibious monsters reposing in the surf. Beyond the reef, the sea sparkled beneath the sun's rays. To the south a sharp point closed the horizon, and it could not be seen if the land was prolonged in that direction, or if it ran southeast and southwest, which would have made this coast a very long peninsula. At the northern extremity of the bay the outline of the shore was continued to a great distance in a wider curve. There the shore was low, flat, without cliffs, and with great banks of sand, which the tide left uncovered. Pencroft and Herbert then returned towards the west. Their attention was first arrested by the snow-topped mountain which rose at a distance of six or seven miles. From its first declivities to within two miles of the coast were spread vast masses of wood, relieved by large green patches, caused by the presence of evergreen trees. Then, from the edge of this forest to the shore extended a plain, scattered irregularly with groups of trees. Here and there on the left sparkled through glades the waters of the little river; they could trace its winding course back towards the spurs of the mountain, among which it seemed to spring. At the point where the sailor had left his raft of wood, it began to run between the two high granite walls; but if on the left bank the wall remained clear and abrupt, on the right bank, on the contrary, it sank gradually, the massive sides changed to isolated rocks, the rocks to stones, the stones to shingle running to the extremity of the point.

'Are we on an island?' murmured the sailor.

'At any rate, it seems to be big enough,' replied the lad.

'An island, ever so big, is an island all the same!' said Pencroft.

But this important question could not yet be answered. A more perfect survey had to be made to settle the point. As to the land itself, island or continent, it appeared fertile, agreeable in its aspect, and varied in its productions.

'This is satisfactory,' observed Pencroft; 'and in our misfortune, we must thank Providence for it.'

'God be praised!' responded Herbert, whose pious heart was full of gratitude to the Author of all things.

Pencroft and Herbert examined for some time the country on which they had been cast; but it was difficult to guess after so hasty an inspection what the future had in store for them.

They then returned, following the southern crest of the granite platform, bordered by a long fringe of jagged rocks, of the most whimsical shapes. Some hundreds of birds lived there nestled in the holes of the stone; Herbert, jumping over the rocks, startled a whole flock of these winged creatures.

'Oh!' cried he, 'those are not gulls nor sea-mews!'

'What are they then?' asked Pencroft.

'Upon my word, one would say they were pigeons!'

'Just so, but these are wild or rock pigeons. I recognize them by the double band of black on the wing, by the white tail, and by their slate-coloured plumage. But if the rock-pigeon is good to eat, its eggs must be excellent, and we will soon see how many they may have left in their nests!'

'We will not give them time to hatch, unless it is in the shape of an omelette!' replied Pencroft merrily.

'But what will you make your omelette in?' asked Herbert; 'in your hat?'

'Well!' replied the sailor, 'I am not quite conjuror enough for that; we must come down to eggs in the shell, my boy, and I will undertake to despatch the hardest!'

Pencroft and Herbert attentively examined the cavities in the granite, and they really found eggs in some of the hollows. A few dozen being collected, were packed in the sailor's handkerchief, and as the time when the tide would be full was approaching, Pencroft and Herbert began to redescend towards the watercourse. When they arrived there, it was an hour after midday. The tide had already turned. They must now avail themselves of the ebb to take the wood to the mouth. Pencroft did not intend to let the raft go away in the current without guidance, neither did he mean to embark on it himself to steer it. But a sailor is never at a loss when there is a question of cables or ropes, and Pencroft rapidly twisted a cord, a few fathoms long, made of dry creepers. This vegetable cable was fastened to the after-part of the raft, and the sailor held it in his hand while Herbert, pushing off the raft with a long pole, kept it in the current. This succeeded capitally. The enormous load of wood drifted down the current. The bank was very equal; there was no fear that the raft would run aground, and before two o'clock they arrived at the river's mouth, a few paces from the Chimneys.

Chapter 5

Pencroft's first care, after unloading the raft, was to render the cave habitable by stopping up all the holes which made it draughty. Sand, stones, twisted branches, wet clay, closed up the galleries open to the south winds. One narrow and winding opening at the side was kept, to lead out the smoke and to make the fire draw. The cave was thus divided into three or four rooms, if such dark dens with which a donkey would scarcely have been contented deserved the name. But they were dry, and there was space to stand upright, at least in the principal room, which occupied the centre. The floor was covered with fine sand, and taking all in all they were well pleased with it for want of a better.

'Perhaps,' said Herbert, while he and Pencroft were working, 'our companions have found a superior place to ours.'

'Very likely,' replied the seaman; 'but, as we don't know, we must work all the same. Better to have two strings to one's bow than no string at all!'

'Oh!' exclaimed Herbert, 'how jolly it will be if they were to find Captain Harding and were to bring him back with them!'

'Yes, indeed!' said Pencroft, 'that was a man of the right sort.'

'Was!' exclaimed Herbert, 'do you despair of ever seeing him again?'

'God forbid!' replied the sailor. Their work was soon done, and Pencroft declared himself very well satisfied.

'Now,' said he, 'our friends can come back when they like. They will find a good enough shelter.'

They now had only to make a fireplace and to prepare the supper—an easy task. Large flat stones were placed on the ground at the opening of the narrow passage which had been kept. This, if the smoke did not take the heat out with it, would be enough to maintain an equal temperature inside. Their wood was stowed away in one of the rooms, and the sailor laid in the fireplace some logs and brushwood. The seaman was busy with this, when Herbert asked him if he had any matches.

'Certainly,' replied Pencroft, 'and I may say happily, for without matches or tinder we should be in a fix.'

'Still we might get fire as the savages do,' replied Herbert, 'by rubbing two bits of dry stick one against the other.'

'All right; try, my boy, and let's see if you can do anything besides exercising your arms.'

'Well, it's a very simple proceeding, and much used in the islands of the Pacific.'

'I don't deny it,' replied Pencroft, 'but the savages must know how to do it or employ a peculiar wood, for more than once I have tried to get fire in that way, but I could never manage it. I must say I prefer matches. By the bye, where are my matches?'

Pencroft searched in his waistcoat for the box, which was always there, for he was a confirmed smoker. He could not find it; he rummaged the pockets of his trousers, but, to his horror, he could nowhere discover the box.

'Here's a go!' said he, looking at Herbert. 'The box must have fallen out of my pocket and got lost! Surely, Herbert, you must have something—a tinderbox—anything that can possibly make fire!'

'No, I haven't, Pencroft.'

The sailor rushed out, followed by the boy. On the sand, among the rocks, near the river's bank, they both searched carefully, but in vain. The box was of copper, and therefore would have been easily seen.

'Pencroft,' asked Herbert, 'didn't you throw it out of the car?'

'I knew better than that,' replied the sailor; 'but such a small article could easily disappear in the tumbling about we have gone through. I would rather even have lost my pipe! Confound the box! Where can it be?'

'Look here, the tide is going down,' said Herbert; 'let's run to the place where we landed.'

It was scarcely probable that they would find the box, which the waves had rolled about among the pebbles, at high tide, but it was as well to try. Herbert and Pencroft walked rapidly to the point where they had landed the day before, about two hundred feet from the cave. They hunted there, among the shingle, in the clefts of the rocks, but found nothing. If the box had fallen at this place it must have been swept away by the waves. As the sea went down, they searched every little crevice with no result. It was a grave loss in their circumstances, and for the time irreparable. Pencroft could not hide his vexation; he looked very anxious, but said not a word. Herbert tried to console him by observing, that if they had found the matches, they would, very likely, have been wetted by the sea and useless.

'No, my boy,' replied the sailor; 'they were in a copper box which shut very tightly; and now what are we to do?'

'We shall certainly find some way of making a fire,' said Herbert. 'Captain Harding or Mr. Spilett will not be without them.'

'Yes,' replied Pencroft; 'but in the meantime we are without fire, and our companions will find but a sorry repast on their return.'

'But,' said Herbert quickly, 'do you think it possible that they have no tinder or matches?'

'I doubt it,' replied the sailor, shaking his head, 'for neither Neb nor Captain Harding smoke, and I believe that Mr. Spilett would rather keep his notebook than his matchbox.'

Herbert did not reply. The loss of the box was certainly to be regretted, but the boy was still sure of procuring fire in some way or other. Pencroft, more experienced, did not think so, although he was not a man to trouble himself about a small or great grievance. At any rate, there was only one thing to be done—to await the return of Neb and the reporter; but they must give up the feast of hard eggs which they had meant to prepare, and a meal of raw flesh was not an agreeable prospect either for themselves or for the others.

Before returning to the cave, the sailor and Herbert, in the event of fire being positively unattainable, collected some more shell-fish, and then silently retraced their steps to their dwelling.

Pencroft, his eyes fixed on the ground, still looked for his box. He even climbed up the left bank of the river from its mouth to the angle where the raft had been moored. He returned to the plateau, went over it in every direction, searched among the high grass on the border of the forest, all in vain.

It was five in the evening when he and Herbert re-entered the cave. It is useless to say that the darkest corners of the passages were ransacked before they were obliged to give it up in despair. Towards six o'clock, when the sun was disappearing behind the high lands of the west, Herbert, who was walking up and down on the strand, signalized the return of Neb and Spilett.

They were returning alone!... The boy's heart sank; the sailor had not been deceived in his forebodings; the engineer, Cyrus Harding, had not been found!

The reporter, on his arrival, sat down on a rock, without saying anything. Exhausted with fatigue, dying of hunger, he had not strength to utter a word.

As to Neb, his red eyes showed how he had cried, and the tears which he could not restrain told too clearly that he had lost all hope.

The reporter recounted all that they had done in their attempt to recover Cyrus Harding. He and Neb had surveyed the coast for a distance of eight miles and consequently much beyond the place where the balloon had fallen the last time but one, a fall which was followed by the disappearance of the engineer and the dog Top. The shore was solitary; not a vestige of a mark. Not even a pebble recently displaced; not a trace on the sand; not a human footstep on all that part of the beach. It was clear that that portion of the shore had never been visited by a human being. The sea was as deserted as the land, and it was there, a few hundred feet from the coast, that the engineer must have found a tomb.

As Spilett ended his account, Neb jumped up, exclaiming in a voice which showed how hope struggled within him, 'No! he is not dead! he can't be dead! It might happen to any one else, but never to him! He could get out of anything!' Then his strength forsaking him, 'Oh! I can do no more!' he murmured.

'Neb,' said Herbert, running to him, 'we will find him! God will give him back to us! But in the meantime you are hungry, and you must eat something.'

So saying, he offered the poor Negro a few handfuls of shell-fish, which was indeed wretched and insufficient food. Neb had not eaten anything for several hours, but he refused them. He could not, would not live without his master.

As to Gideon Spilett, he devoured the shell-fish, then he laid himself down on the sand, at the foot of a rock. He was very weak, but calm. Herbert went up to him, and taking his hand, 'Sir,' said he, 'we have found a shelter which will be better than lying here. Night is advancing. Come and rest! Tomorrow we will search farther.'

The reporter got up, and guided by the boy went towards the cave. On the way, Pencroft asked him in the most natural tone, if by chance he happened to have a match or two.

The reporter stopped, felt in his pockets, but finding nothing said, 'I had some, but I must have thrown them away.'

The seaman then put the same question to Neb and received the same answer.

'Confound it!' exclaimed the sailor.

The reporter heard him and seizing his arm, 'Have you no matches?' he asked.

'Not one, and no fire in consequence.'

'Ah!' cried Neb, 'if my master was here, he would know what to do!'

The four castaways remained motionless, looking uneasily at each other. Herbert was the first to break the silence by saying, 'Mr. Spilett, you are a smoker and always have matches about you; perhaps you haven't looked well, try again, a single match will be enough!'

The reporter hunted again in the pockets of his trousers, waistcoat, and greatcoat, and at last to Pencroft's great joy, no less to his extreme surprise, he felt a tiny piece of wood entangled in the lining of his waistcoat. He seized it with his fingers through the stuff, but he could not get it out. If this was a match and a single one, it was of great importance not to rub off the phosphorus.

'Will you let me try?' said the boy, and very cleverly, without breaking it, he managed to draw out the wretched yet precious little bit of wood which was of such great importance to these poor men. It was unused.

'Hurrah!' cried Pencroft; 'it is as good as having a whole cargo!' He took the match, and, followed by his companions, entered the cave.

This small piece of wood, of which so many in an inhabited country are wasted with indifference and are of no value, must here be used with the greatest caution.

The sailor first made sure that it was quite dry; that done, 'We must have some paper,' said he.

'Here,' replied Spilett, after some hesitation tearing a leaf out of his notebook.

Pencroft took the piece of paper which the reporter held out to him, and knelt down before the fireplace. Some handfuls of grass, leaves, and dry moss were placed under the faggots and disposed in such a way that the air could easily circulate, and the dry wood would rapidly catch fire.

Pencroft then twisted the piece of paper into the shape of a cone, as smokers do in a high wind, and poked it in among the moss. Taking a small, rough stone, he wiped it carefully, and with a beating heart, holding his breath, he gently rubbed the match. The first attempt did not produce any effect. Pencroft had not struck hard enough, fearing to rub off the phosphorus.

'No, I can't do it,' said he, 'my hand trembles, the match has missed fire; I cannot, I will not!' and rising, he told Herbert to take his place.

Certainly the boy had never in all his life been so nervous. Prometheus going to steal the fire from heaven could not have been more anxious. He did not hesitate, however, but struck the match directly.

A little spluttering was heard and a tiny blue flame sprang up, making a choking smoke. Herbert quickly turned the match so as to augment the flame, and then slipped it into the paper cone, which in a few seconds too caught fire, and then the moss.

A minute later the dry wood crackled and a cheerful flame, assisted by the vigorous blowing of the sailor, sprang up in the midst of the darkness.

'At last!' cried Pencroft, getting up; 'I was never so nervous before in all my life!'

The flat stones made a capital fireplace. The smoke went quite easily out at the narrow passage, the chimney drew, and an agreeable warmth was not long in being felt.

They must now take great care not to let the fire go out, and always to keep some embers alight. It only needed care and attention, as they had plenty of wood and could renew their store at any time.

Pencroft's first thought was to use the fire by preparing a more nourishing supper than a dish of shell-fish. Two dozen eggs were brought by Herbert. The reporter leaning up in a corner, watched these preparations without saying anything. A threefold thought weighed on his mind. Was Cyrus still alive? If he was alive, where was he? If he had survived from his fall, how was it that he had not found some means of making known his existence? As to Neb, he was roaming about the shore. He was like a body without a soul.

Pencroft knew fifty ways of cooking eggs, but this time he had no choice, and was obliged to content himself with roasting them under the hot cinders. In a few minutes the cooking was done, and the seaman invited the reporter to take his share of the supper. Such was the first repast of the castaways on this unknown coast. The hard eggs were excellent, and as eggs contain everything indispensable to man's nourishment, these poor people thought themselves well off, and were much strengthened by them. Oh! if only one of them had not been missing at this meal! If the five prisoners who escaped from Richmond had been all there, under the piled-up rocks, before this clear, crackling fire on the dry sand, what thanksgiving must they have rendered to Heaven! But the most ingenious, the most learned, he who was their unquestioned chief, Cyrus Harding, was, alas! missing, and his body had not even obtained a burial-place.

Thus passed the 25th of March. Night had come on. Outside could be heard the howling of the wind and the monotonous sound of the surf breaking on the shore. The waves rolled the shingle backwards and forwards with a deafening noise.

The reporter retired into a dark corner after having shortly noted down the occurrences of the day; the first appearance of this new land, the loss of their leader, the exploration of the coast, the incident of the matches, etc.; and then overcome by fatigue, he managed to forget his sorrows in sleep. Herbert went to sleep directly. As to the sailor, he passed the night with one eye on the fire, on which he did not spare fuel. But one of the castaways did not sleep in the cave. The inconsolable, despairing Neb, notwithstanding all that his companions could say to induce him to take some rest, wandered all night long on the shore calling on his master.

Chapter 6

The inventory of the articles possessed by these castaways from the clouds, thrown upon a coast which appeared to be uninhabited, was soon made out. They had nothing, save the clothes which they were wearing at the time of the catastrophe. We must mention, however, a notebook and a watch which Gideon Spilett had kept, doubtless by inadvertence, not a weapon, not a tool, not even a pocket-knife; for while in the car they had thrown out everything to lighten the balloon. The imaginary heroes of Daniel Defoe or of Wyss, as well as Selkirk and Raynal shipwrecked on Juan Fernandez and on the archipelago of the Aucklands, were never in such absolute destitution. Either they had abundant resources from their stranded vessels, in grain, cattle, tools, ammunition, or else some things were thrown up on the coast which supplied them with all the first necessities of life. But here, not any instrument whatever, not a utensil. From nothing they must supply themselves with everything.

And yet, if Cyrus Harding had been with them, if the engineer could have brought his practical science, his inventive mind to bear on their situation, perhaps all hope would not have been lost. Alas! they must hope no longer again to see Cyrus Harding. The castaways could expect nothing but from themselves and from that Providence which never abandons those whose faith is sincere.

But ought they to establish themselves on this part of the coast, without trying to know to what continent it belonged, if it was inhabited, or if they were on the shore of a desert island?

It was an important question, and should be solved with the shortest possible delay. From its answer they would know what measures to take. However, according to Pencroft's advice, it appeared best to wait a few days before commencing an exploration. They must, in fact, prepare some provisions and procure more strengthening food than eggs and molluscs. The explorers, before undertaking new fatigues, must first of all recruit their strength.

The Chimneys offered a retreat sufficient for the present. The fire was lighted, and it was easy to preserve some embers. There were plenty of shell-fish and eggs among the rocks and on the beach. It would be easy to kill a few of the pigeons which were flying by hundreds about the summit of the plateau, either with sticks or stones. Perhaps the trees of the neighbouring forest would supply them with eatable fruit. Lastly, the sweet water was there.

It was accordingly settled that for a few days they would remain at the Chimneys so as to prepare themselves for an expedition, either along the shore or into the interior of the country. This plan suited Neb particularly. As obstinate in his ideas as in his presentiments, he was in no haste to abandon this part of the coast, the scene of the catastrophe. He did not, he would not believe in the loss of Cyrus Harding. No, it did not seem to him possible that such a man had ended in this vulgar fashion, carried away by a wave, drowned in the floods, a few hundred feet from a shore. As long as the waves had not cast up the body of the engineer, as long as he, Neb, had not seen with his eyes, touched with his hands the corpse of his master, he would not believe in his death! And this idea rooted itself deeper than ever in his determined heart. An illusion perhaps, but still an illusion to be respected, and one which the sailor did not wish to destroy. As for him, he hoped no longer, but there was no use in arguing with Neb. He was like the dog who will not leave the place where his master is buried, and his grief was such that most probably he would not survive him.

This same morning, the 26th of March, at daybreak, Neb had set out on the shore in a northerly direction, and he had returned to the spot where the sea, no doubt, had closed over the unfortunate Harding.

That day's breakfast was composed solely of pigeon's eggs and lithodomes. Herbert had found some salt deposited by evapouration in the hollows of the rocks, and this mineral was very welcome.

The repast ended, Pencroft asked the reporter if he wished to accompany Herbert and himself to the forest, where they were going to try to hunt. But on consideration, it was thought necessary that someone should remain to keep in the fire, and to be at hand in the highly improbable event of Neb requiring aid. The reporter accordingly remained behind.

'To the chase, Herbert,' said the sailor. 'We shall find ammunition on our way, and cut our weapons in the forest.' But at the moment of starting, Herbert observed, that since they had no tinder, it would perhaps be prudent to replace it by another substance.

'What?' asked Pencroft.

'Burnt linen,' replied the boy. 'That could in case of need serve for tinder.'

The sailor thought it very sensible advice. Only it had the inconvenience of necessitating the sacrifice of a piece of handkerchief. Notwithstanding, the thing was well worth while trying, and a part of Pencroft's large checked handkerchief was soon reduced to the state of a half-burnt rag. This inflammable material was placed in the central chamber at the bottom of a little cavity in the rock, sheltered from all wind and damp.

It was nine o'clock in the morning. The weather was threatening and the breeze blew from the southeast. Herbert and Pencroft turned the angle of the Chimneys, not without having cast a look at the smoke which, just at that place, curled round a point of rock: they ascended the left bank of the river.

Arrived at the forest, Pencroft broke from the first tree two stout branches which he transformed into clubs, the ends of which Herbert rubbed smooth on a rock. Oh! what would they not have given for a knife!

The two hunters now advanced among the long grass, following the bank. From the turning which directed its course to the southwest, the river narrowed gradually and the channel lay between high banks, over which the trees formed a double arch. Pencroft, lest they should lose themselves, resolved to follow the course of the stream, which would always lead them back to the point from which they started. But the bank was not without some obstacles: here, the flexible branches of the trees bent level with the current; there, creepers and thorns which they had to break down with their sticks. Herbert often glided among the broken stumps with the agility of a young cat, and disappeared in the underwood. But Pencroft called him back directly, begging him not to wander away. Meanwhile, the sailor attentively observed the disposition and nature of the surrounding country. On the left bank, the ground, which was flat and marshy, rose imperceptibly towards the interior. It looked there like a network of liquid threads which doubtless reached the river by some underground drain. Sometimes a stream ran through the underwood, which they crossed without difficulty. The opposite shore appeared to be more uneven, and the valley of which the river occupied the bottom was more clearly visible. The hill, covered with trees disposed in terraces, intercepted the view. On the right bank walking would have been difficult, for the declivities fell suddenly, and the trees bending over the water were only sustained by the strength of their roots.

It is needless to add that this forest, as well as the coast already surveyed, was destitute of any sign of human life. Pencroft only saw traces of quadrupeds, fresh footprints of animals, of which he could not recognize the species. In all probability, and such was also Herbert's opinion, some had been left by formidable wild beasts which doubtless would give them some trouble; but nowhere did they observe the mark of an axe on the trees, nor the ashes of a fire, nor the impression of a human foot. On this they might probably congratulate themselves, for on any land in the middle of the Pacific the presence of man was perhaps more to be feared than desired. Herbert and Pencroft speaking little, for the difficulties of the way were great, advanced very slowly, and after walking for an hour they had scarcely gone more than a mile. As yet the hunt had not been successful. However, some birds sang and fluttered in the foliage, and appeared very timid, as if man had inspired them with an instinctive fear. Among others, Herbert described, in a marshy part of the forest, a bird with a long pointed beak, closely resembling the kingfisher, but its plumage was not fine, though of a metallic brilliancy.

'That must be a jacamar,' said Herbert, trying to get nearer.

'This will be a good opportunity to taste jacamar,' replied the sailor, 'if that fellow is in a humour to be roasted!'

Just then, a stone cleverly thrown by the boy, struck the creature on the wing, but the blow did not disable it, and the jacamar ran off and disappeared in an instant.

'How clumsy I am!' cried Herbert.

'No, no, my boy!' replied the sailor. 'The blow was well aimed; many a one would have missed it altogether! Come, don't be vexed with yourself. We shall catch it another day!'

As the hunters advanced, the trees were found to be more scattered, many being magnificent, but none bore eatable fruit. Pencroft searched in vain for some of those precious palm-trees which am employed in so many ways in domestic life, and which have been found as far as the fortieth parallel in the Northern Hemisphere, and to the thirty-filth only in the Southern Hemisphere. But this forest was only composed of coniferae, such as deodaras, already recognized by Herbert, and Douglas pine, similar to those which grow on the northwest coast of America, and splendid firs, measuring a hundred and fifty feet in height.

At this moment a flock of birds, of a small size and pretty plumage, with long glancing tails, dispersed themselves among the branches strewing their feathers, which covered the ground as with fine down. Herbert picked up a few of these feathers, and after having examined them,—

'These are couroucous,' said he.

'I should prefer a moor-cock or guinea-fowl,' replied Pencroft, 'still, if they are good to eat—'

'They are good to eat, and also their flesh is very delicate,' replied Herbert. 'Besides, if I don't mistake, it is easy to approach and kill them with a stick.'

The sailor and the lad, creeping among the grass, arrived at the foot of a tree, whose lower branches were covered with little birds. The couroucous were waiting the passage of insects which served for their nourishment. Their feathery feet could be seen clasping the slender twigs which supported them.

The hunters then rose, and using their sticks like scythes, they mowed down whole rows of these couroucous, who never thought of flying away, and stupidly allowed themselves to be knocked off. A hundred were already heaped on the ground, before the others made up their minds to fly.

'Well,' said Pencroft, 'here is game, which is quite within the reach of hunters like us. We have only to put out our hands and take it!'

The sailor having strung the couroucous like larks on flexible twigs, they then continued their exploration. The stream here made a bend towards the south, but this detour was probably not prolonged for the river must have its source in the mountain, and be supplied by the melting of the snow which covered the sides of the central cone.

The particular object of their expedition was, as has been said, to procure the greatest possible quantity of game for the inhabitants of the Chimneys. It must be acknowledged that as yet this object had not been attained. So the sailor actively pursued his researches, though he exclaimed, when some animal which he had not even time to recognize fled into the long grass, 'If only we had had the dog Top!' But Top had disappeared at the same time as his master, and had probably perished with him.

Towards three o'clock new flocks of birds were seen through certain trees, at whose aromatic berries they were pecking, those of the juniper-tree among others. Suddenly a loud trumpet call resounded through the forest. This strange and sonorous cry was produced by a game bird called grouse in the United States. They soon saw several couples, whose plumage was rich chestnut-brown mottled with dark brown, and tail of the same colour. Herbert recognized the males by the two wing-like appendages raised on the neck. Pencroft determined to get hold of at least one of these gallinaceae, which were as large as a fowl, and whose flesh is better than that of a pullet. But it was difficult, for they would not allow themselves to be approached. After several fruitless attempts, which resulted in nothing but scaring the grouse, the sailor said to the lad,—

'Decidedly, since we can't kill them on the wing, we must try to take them with a line.'

'Like a fish?' cried Herbert, much surprised at the proposal.

'Like a fish,' replied the sailor quite seriously. Pencroft had found among the grass half a dozen grouse nests, each having three or four eggs.

He took great care not to touch these nests, to which their proprietors would not fail to return. It was around these that he meant to stretch his lines, not snares, but real fishing-lines. He took Herbert to some distance from the nests, and there prepared his singular apparatus with all the care which a disciple of Izaak Walton would have used. Herbert watched the work with great interest, though rather doubting its success. The lines were made of fine creepers, fastened one to the other, of the length of fifteen or twenty feet. Thick, strong thorns, the points bent back (which were supplied from a dwarf acacia bush) were fastened to the ends of the creepers, by way of hooks. Large red worms, which were crawling on the ground, furnished bait.

This done, Pencroft, passing among the grass and concealing himself skilfully, placed the end of his lines armed with hooks near the grouse nests; then he returned, took the other ends and hid with Herbert behind a large tree. There they both waited patiently; though, it must be said, that Herbert did not reckon much on the success of the inventive Pencroft.

A whole half-hour passed, but then, as the sailor had surmised, several couple of grouse returned to their nests. They walked along, pecking the ground, and not suspecting in any way the presence of the hunters, who, besides, had taken care to place themselves to leeward of the gallinaceae.

The lad felt at this moment highly interested. He held his breath, and Pencroft, his eyes staring, his mouth open, his lips advanced, as if about to taste a piece of grouse, scarcely breathed.

Meanwhile, the birds walked about the hooks, without taking any notice of them. Pencroft then gave little tugs which moved the bait as if the worms had been still alive.

The sailor undoubtedly felt much greater anxiety than does the fisherman, for he does not see his prey coming through the water. The jerks attracted the attention of the gallinaceae, and they attacked the hooks with their beaks. Three voracious grouse swallowed at the same moment bait and hook. Suddenly with a smart jerk, Pencroft 'struck' his line, and a flapping of wings showed that the birds were taken.

'Hurrah!' he cried, rushing towards the game, of which he made himself master in an instant.

Herbert clapped his hands. It was the first time that he had ever seen birds taken with a line, but the sailor modestly confessed that it was not his first attempt, and that besides he could not claim the merit of invention.

'And at any rate,' added he, 'situated as we are, we must hope to hit upon many other contrivances.'

The grouse were fastened by their claws, and Pencroft, delighted at not having to appear before their companions with empty hands, and observing that the day had begun to decline, judged it best to return to their dwelling.

The direction was indicated by the river, whose course they had only to follow, and, towards six o'clock, tired enough with their excursion, Herbert and Pencroft arrived at the Chimneys.

Chapter 7

Gideon Spilett was standing motionless on the shore, his arms crossed, gazing over the sea, the horizon of which was lost towards the east in a thick black cloud which was spreading rapidly towards the zenith. The wind was already strong, and increased with the decline of day. The whole sky was of a threatening aspect, and the first symptoms of a violent storm were clearly visible.

Herbert entered the Chimneys, and Pencroft went towards the reporter. The latter, deeply absorbed, did not see him approach.

'We are going to have a dirty night, Mr. Spilett!' said the sailor: 'Petrels delight in wind and rain.'

The reporter, turning at the moment, saw Pencroft, and his first words were,—

'At what distance from the coast would you say the car was, when the waves carried off our companion?'

The sailor had not expected this question. He reflected an instant and replied,—

'Two cables lengths at the most.'

'But what is a cable's length?' asked Gideon Spilett.

'About a hundred and twenty fathoms, or six hundred feet.'

'Then,' said the reporter, 'Cyrus Harding must have disappeared twelve hundred feet at the most from the shore?'

'About that,' replied Pencroft.

'And his dog also?'

'Also.'

'What astonishes me,' rejoined the reporter, 'while admitting that our companion has perished, is that Top has also met his death, and that neither the body of the dog nor of his master has been cast on the shore!'

'It is not astonishing, with such a heavy sea,' replied the sailor. 'Besides, it is possible that currents have carried them farther down the coast.'

'Then, it is your opinion that our friend has perished in the waves?' again asked the reporter.

'That is my opinion.'

'My own opinion,' said Gideon Spilett, 'with due deference to your experience, Pencroft, is that in the double fact of the absolute disappearance of Cyrus and Top, living or dead, there is something unaccountable and unlikely.'

'I wish I could think like you, Mr. Spilett,' replied Pencroft; 'unhappily, my mind is made up on this point.' Having said this, the sailor returned to the Chimneys. A good fire crackled on the hearth. Herbert had just thrown on an armful of dry wood, and the flame cast a bright light into the darkest parts of the passage.

Pencroft immediately began to prepare the dinner. It appeared best to introduce something solid into the bill of fare, for all needed to get up their strength. The strings of couroucous were kept for the next day, but they plucked a couple of grouse, which were soon spitted on a stick, and roasting before a blazing fire.

At seven in the evening Neb had not returned. The prolonged absence of the Negro made Pencroft very uneasy. It was to be feared that he had met with an accident on this unknown land, or that the unhappy fellow had been driven to some act of despair. But Herbert drew very different conclusions from this absence. According to him, Neb's delay was caused by some new circumstances which had induced him to prolong his search. Also, everything new must be to the advantage of Cyrus Harding. Why had Neb not returned unless hope still detained him? Perhaps he had found some mark, a footstep, a trace which had put him in the right path. Perhaps he was at this moment on a certain track. Perhaps even he was near his master.

Thus the lad reasoned. Thus he spoke. His companions let him talk. The reporter alone approved with a gesture. But what Pencroft thought most probable was, that Neb had pushed his researches on the shore farther than the day before, and that he had not as yet had time to return.

Herbert, however, agitated by vague presentiments, several times manifested an intention to go to meet Neb. But Pencroft assured him that that would be a useless course, that in the darkness and deplorable weather he could not find any traces of Neb, and that it would be much better to wait. If Neb had not made his appearance by the next day, Pencroft would not hesitate to join him in his search.

Gideon Spilett approved of the sailor's opinion that it was best not to divide, and Herbert was obliged to give up his project; but two large tears fell from his eyes.

The reporter could not refrain from embracing the generous boy.

Bad weather now set in. A furious gale from the southeast passed over the coast. The sea roared as it beat over the reef. Heavy rain was dashed by the storm into particles like dust. Ragged masses of vapour drove along the beach, on which the tormented shingles sounded as if poured out in cart- loads, while the sand raised by the wind added as it were mineral dust to that which was liquid, and rendered the united attack insupportable. Between the river's mouth and the end of the cliff, eddies of wind whirled and gusts from this maelstrom lashed the water which ran through the narrow valley. The smoke from the fireplace was also driven back through the opening, filling the passages and rendering them uninhabitable.

Therefore, as the grouse were cooked, Pencroft let the fire die away, and only preserved a few embers buried under the ashes.

At eight o'clock Neb had not appeared, but there was no doubt that the frightful weather alone hindered his return, and that he must have taken refuge in some cave, to await the end of the storm or at least the return of day. As to going to meet him, or attempting to find him, it was impossible.

The game constituted the only dish at supper; the meat was excellent, and Pencroft and Herbert, whose long excursion had rendered them very hungry, devoured it with infinite satisfaction.

Their meal concluded, each retired to the corner in which he had rested the preceding night, and Herbert was not long in going to sleep near the sailor, who had stretched himself beside the fireplace.

Outside, as the night advanced, the tempest also increased in strength, until it was equal to that which had carried the prisoners from Richmond to this land in the Pacific. The tempests which are frequent during the seasons of the equinox, and which are so prolific in catastrophes, are above all terrible over this immense ocean, which opposes no obstacle to their fury. No description can give an idea of the terrific violence of the gale as it beat upon the unprotected coast.

Happily the pile of rocks which formed the Chimneys was solid. It was composed of enormous blocks of granite, a few of which, insecurely balanced, seemed to tremble on their foundations, and Pencroft could feel rapid quiverings under his head as it rested on the rock. But he repeated to himself, and rightly, that there was nothing to fear, and that their retreat would not give way. However he heard the noise of stones torn from the summit of the plateau by the wind, falling down on to the beach. A few even rolled on to the upper part of the Chimneys, or flew off in fragments when they were projected perpendicularly. Twice the sailor rose and entrenched himself at the opening of the passage, so as to take a look in safety at the outside. But there was nothing to be feared from these showers, which were not considerable, and he returned to his couch before the fireplace, where the embers glowed beneath the ashes.

Notwithstanding the fury of the hurricane, the uproar of the tempest, the thunder, and the tumult, Herbert slept profoundly. Sleep at last took possession of Pencroft, whom a seafaring life had habituated to anything. Gideon Spilett alone was kept awake by anxiety. He reproached himself with not having accompanied Neb. It was evident that he had not abandoned all hope. The presentiments which had troubled Herbert did not cease to agitate him also. His thoughts were concentrated on Neb. Why had Neb not returned? He tossed about on his sandy couch, scarcely giving a thought to the struggle of the elements. Now and then, his eyes, heavy with fatigue, closed for an instant, but some sudden thought reopened them almost immediately.

Meanwhile the night advanced, and it was perhaps two hours from morning, when Pencroft, then sound asleep, was vigorously shaken.

'What's the matter?' he cried, rousing himself, and collecting his ideas with the promptitude usual to seamen.

The reporter was leaning over him, and saying,—

'Listen, Pencroft, listen!'

The sailor strained his ears, but could hear no noise beyond those caused by the storm.

'It is the wind,' said he.

'No,' replied Gideon Spilett, listening again, 'I thought I heard—'

'What?'

'The barking of a dog!'

'A dog!' cried Pencroft, springing up.

'Yes—barking—'

'It's not possible!' replied the sailor. 'And besides, how, in the roaring of the storm—'

'Stop—listen—' said the reporter.

Pencroft listened more attentively, and really thought he heard, during a lull, distant barking.

'Well!' said the reporter, pressing the sailor's hand.

'Yes—yes!' replied Pencroft.

'It is Top! It is Top!' cried Herbert, who had just awoke; and all three rushed towards the opening of the Chimneys. They had great difficulty in getting out. The wind drove them back. But at last they succeeded, and could only remain standing by leaning against the rocks. They looked about, but could not speak. The darkness was intense. The sea, the sky, the land were all mingled in one black mass. Not a speck of light was visible.

The reporter and his companions remained thus for a few minutes, overwhelmed by the wind, drenched by the rain, blinded by the sand.

Then, in a pause of the tumult, they again heard the barking, which they found must be at some distance.

It could only be Top! But was he alone or accompanied? He was most probably alone, for, if Neb had been with him, he would have made his way more directly towards the Chimneys. The sailor squeezed the reporter's hand, for he could not make himself heard, in a way which signified 'Wait!' then he re-entered the passage.

An instant after he issued with a lighted faggot, which he threw into the darkness, whistling shrilly.

It appeared as if this signal had been waited for; the barking immediately came nearer, and soon a dog bounded into the passage. Pencroft, Herbert, and Spilett entered after him.

An armful of dry wood was thrown on the embers. The passage was lighted up with a bright flame.

'It is Top!' cried Herbert.

It was indeed Top, a magnificent Anglo-Norman, who derived from these two races crossed the swiftness of foot and the acuteness of smell which are the preeminent qualities of coursing dogs. It was the dog of the engineer, Cyrus Harding. But he was alone! Neither Neb nor his master accompanied him!

How was it that his instinct had guided him straight to the Chimneys, which he did not know? It appeared inexplicable, above all, in the midst of this black night and in such a tempest! But what was still more inexplicable was, that Top was neither tired, nor exhausted, nor even soiled with mud or sand!—Herbert had drawn him towards him, and was patting his head, the dog rubbing his neck against the lad's hands.

'If the dog is found, the master will be found also!' said the reporter.

'God grant it!' responded Herbert. 'Let us set off! Top will guide us!'

Pencroft did not make any objection. He felt that Top's arrival contradicted his conjectures. 'Come along then!' said he.

Pencroft carefully covered the embers on the hearth. He placed a few pieces of wood among them, so as to keep in the fire until their return. Then, preceded by the dog, who seemed to invite them by short barks to come with him, and followed by the reporter and the boy, he dashed out, after having put up in his handkerchief the remains of the supper.

The storm was then in all its violence, and perhaps at its height. Not a single ray of light from the moon pierced through the clouds. To follow a straight course was difficult. It was best to rely on Top's instinct. They did so. The reporter and Herbert walked behind the dog, and the sailor brought up the rear. It was impossible to exchange a word. The rain was not very heavy, but the wind was terrific.

However, one circumstance favoured the seaman and his two companions. The wind being southeast, consequently blew on their backs. The clouds of sand, which otherwise would have been insupportable, from being received behind, did not in consequence impede their progress. In short, they sometimes went faster than they liked, and had some difficulty in keeping their feet; but hope gave them strength, for it was not at random that they made their way along the shore. They had no doubt that Neb had found his master, and that he had sent them the faithful dog. But was the engineer living, or had Neb only sent for his companions that they might render the last duties to the corpse of the unfortunate Harding?

After having passed the precipice, Herbert, the reporter, and Pencroft prudently stepped aside to stop and take breath. The turn of the rocks sheltered them from the wind, and they could breathe after this walk or rather run of a quarter of an hour.

They could now hear and reply to each other, and the lad having pronounced the name of Cyrus Harding, Top gave a few short barks, as much as to say that his master was saved.

'Saved, isn't he?' repeated Herbert; 'saved, Top?'

And the dog barked in reply.

They once more set out. The tide began to rise, and urged by the wind it threatened to be unusually high, as it was a spring tide. Great billows thundered against the reef with such violence that they probably passed entirely over the islet, then quite invisible. The mole no longer protected the coast, which was directly exposed to the attacks of the open sea.

As soon as the sailor and his companions left the precipice, the wind struck them again with renewed fury. Though bent under the gale they walked very quickly, following Top, who did not hesitate as to what direction to take.

They ascended towards the north, having on their left an interminable extent of billows, which broke with a deafening noise, and on their right a dark country, the aspect of which it was impossible to guess. But they felt that it was comparatively flat, for the wind passed completely over them, without being driven back as it was when it came in contact with the cliff.

At four o'clock in the morning, they reckoned that they had cleared about five miles. The clouds were slightly raised, and the wind, though less damp, was very sharp and cold. Insufficiently protected by their clothing, Pencroft, Herbert and Spilett suffered cruelly, but not a complaint escaped their lips. They were determined to follow Top, wherever the intelligent animal wished to lead them.

Towards five o'clock day began to break. At the zenith, where the fog was less thick, gray shades bordered the clouds; under an opaque belt, a luminous line clearly traced the horizon. The crests of the billows were tipped with a wild light, and the foam regained its whiteness. At the same time on the left the hilly parts of the coast could be seen, though very indistinctly.

At six o'clock day had broken. The clouds rapidly lifted. The seaman and his companions were then about six miles from the Chimneys. They were following a very flat shore bounded by a reef of rocks, whose heads scarcely emerged from the sea, for they were in deep water. On the left, the country appeared to be one vast extent of sandy downs, bristling with thistles. There was no cliff, and the shore offered no resistance to the ocean but a chain of irregular hillocks. Here and there grew two or three trees, inclined towards the west, their branches projecting in that direction. Quite behind, in the southwest, extended the border of the forest.

At this moment, Top became very excited. He ran forward, then returned, and seemed to entreat them to hasten their steps. The dog then left the beach, and guided by his wonderful instinct, without showing the least hesitation, went straight in among the downs. They followed him. The country appeared an absolute desert. Not a living creature was to be seen.

The downs, the extent of which was large, were composed of hillocks and even of hills, very irregularly distributed. They resembled a Switzerland modelled in sand, and only an amazing instinct could have possibly recognized the way.

Five minutes after having left the beach, the reporter and his two companions arrived at a sort of excavation, hollowed out at the back of a high mound. There Top stopped, and gave a loud, clear bark. Spilett, Herbert, and Pencroft dashed into the cave.

Neb was there, kneeling beside a body extended on a bed of grass.

The body was that of the engineer, Cyrus Harding.

Chapter 8

Neb did not move. Pencroft only uttered one word.

'Living?' he cried.

Neb did not reply. Spilett and the sailor turned pale. Herbert clasped his hands, and remained motionless. The poor Negro, absorbed in his grief, evidently had neither seen his companions nor heard the sailor speak.

The reporter knelt down beside the motionless body, and placed his ear to the engineer's chest, having first torn open his clothes.

A minute—an age!—passed, during which he endeavoured to catch the faintest throb of the heart.

Neb had raised himself a little and gazed without seeing. Despair had completely changed his countenance. He could scarcely be recognized, exhausted with fatigue, broken with grief. He believed his master was dead.

Gideon Spilett at last rose, after a long and attentive examination.

'He lives!' said he.

Pencroft knelt in his turn beside the engineer, he also heard a throbbing, and even felt a slight breath on his cheek.

Herbert at a word from the reporter ran out to look for water. He found, a hundred feet off, a limpid stream, which seemed to have been greatly increased by the rains, and which filtered through the sand; but nothing in which to put the water, not even a shell among the downs. The lad was obliged to content himself with dipping his handkerchief in the stream, and with it hastened back to the grotto.

Happily the wet handkerchief was enough for Gideon Spilett, who only wished to wet the engineer's lips. The cold water produced an almost immediate effect. His chest heaved and he seemed to try to speak.

'We will save him!' exclaimed the reporter.

At these words hope revived in Neb's heart. He undressed his master to see if he was wounded, but not so much as a bruise was to be found, either on the head, body, or limbs, which was surprising, as he must have been dashed against the rocks; even the hands were uninjured, and it was difficult to explain how the engineer showed no traces of the efforts which he must have made to get out of reach of the breakers.

But the explanation would come later. When Cyrus was able to speak he would say what had happened. For the present the question was, how to recall him to life, and it appeared likely that rubbing would bring this about; so they set to work with the sailor's jersey.

The engineer, revived by this rude shampooing, moved his arm slightly and began to breathe more regularly. He was sinking from exhaustion, and certainly, had not the reporter and his companions arrived, it would have been all over with Cyrus Harding.

'You thought your master was dead, didn't you?' said the seaman to Neb.

'Yes! quite dead!' replied Neb, 'and if Top had not found you, and brought you here, I should have buried my master, and then have lain down on his grave to die!'

It had indeed been a narrow escape for Cyrus Harding!

Neb then recounted what had happened. The day before, after having left the Chimneys at daybreak, he had ascended the coast in a northerly direction, and had reached that part of the shore which he had already visited.

There, without any hope he acknowledged, Neb had searched the beach, among the rocks, on the sand, for the smallest trace to guide him. He examined particularly that part of the beach which was not covered by the high tide, for near the sea the water would have obliterated all marks. Neb did not expect to find his master living. It was for a corpse that he searched, a corpse which he wished to bury with his own hands!

He sought long in vain. This desert coast appeared never to have been visited by a human creature. The shells, those which the sea had not reached, and which might be met with by millions above high-water mark, were untouched. Not a shell was broken.

Neb then resolved to walk along the beach for some miles. It was possible that the waves had carried the body to quite a distant point. When a corpse floats a little distance from a low shore, it rarely happens that the tide does not throw it up, sooner or later. This Neb knew, and he wished to see his master again for the last time.

'I went along the coast for another two miles, carefully examining the beach, both at high and low water, and I had despaired of finding anything, when yesterday, above five in the evening, I saw footprints on the sand.'

'Footprints?' exclaimed Pencroft.

'Yes!' replied Neb.

'Did these footprints begin at the water's edge?' asked the reporter.

'No,' replied Neb, 'only above high-water mark, for the others must have been washed out by the tide.'

'Go on, Neb,' said Spilett.

'I went half crazy when I saw these footprints. They were very clear and went towards the downs. I followed them for a quarter of a mile, running, but taking care not to destroy them. Five minutes after, as it was getting dark, I heard the barking of a dog. It was Top, and Top brought me here, to my master!'

Neb ended his account by saying what had been his grief at finding the inanimate body, in which he vainly sought for the least sign of life. Now that he had found him dead he longed for him to be alive. All his efforts were useless! Nothing remained to be done but to render the last duties to the one whom he had loved so much! Neb then thought of his companions. They, no doubt, would wish to see the unfortunate man again. Top was there. Could he not rely on the sagacity of the faithful animal? Neb several times pronounced the name of the reporter, the one among his companions whom Top knew best.

Then he pointed to the south, and the dog bounded off in the direction indicated to him.

We have heard how, guided by an instinct which might be looked upon almost as supernatural, Top had found them.

Neb's companions had listened with great attention to this account.

It was unaccountable to them how Cyrus Harding, after the efforts which he must have made to escape from the waves by crossing the rocks, had not received even a scratch. And what could not be explained either was how the engineer had managed to get to this cave in the downs, more than a mile from the shore.

'So, Neb,' said the reporter, 'it was not you who brought your master to this place.'

'No, it was not I,' replied the Negro.

'It's very clear that the captain came here by himself,' said Pencroft.

'It is clear in reality,' observed Spilett, 'but it is not credible!'

The explanation of this fact could only be produced from the engineer's own lips, and they must wait for that till speech returned. Rubbing had re-established the circulation of the blood. Cyrus Harding moved his arm again, then his head, and a few incomprehensible words escaped him.

Neb, who was bending over him, spoke, but the engineer did not appear to hear, and his eyes remained closed. Life was only exhibited in him by movement, his senses had not as yet been restored.

Pencroft much regretted not having either fire, or the means of procuring it, for he had, unfortunately, forgotten to bring the burnt linen, which would easily have ignited from the sparks produced by striking together two flints. As to the engineer's pockets, they were entirely empty, except that of his waistcoat, which contained his watch. It was necessary to carry Harding to the Chimneys, and that as soon as possible. This was the opinion of all.

Meanwhile, the care which was lavished on the engineer brought him back to consciousness sooner than they could have expected. The water with which they wetted his lips revived him gradually. Pencroft also thought of mixing with the water some moisture from the titra's flesh which he had brought. Herbert ran to the beach and returned with two large bivalve shells. The sailor concocted something which he introduced between the lips of the engineer, who eagerly drinking it opened his eyes.

Neb and the reporter were leaning over him.

'My master! my master!' cried Neb.

The engineer heard him. He recognized Neb and Spilett, then his other two companions, and his hand slightly pressed theirs.

A few words again escaped him, which showed what thoughts were, even then, troubling his brain. This time he was understood. Undoubtedly they were the same words he had before attempted to utter.

'Island or continent?' he murmured.

'Bother the continent,' cried Pencroft hastily; 'there is time enough to see about that, captain! we don't care for anything, provided you are living.'

The engineer nodded faintly, and then appeased to sleep.

They respected this sleep, and the reporter began immediately to make arrangements for transporting Harding to a more comfortable place. Neb, Herbert, and Pencroft left the cave and directed their steps towards a high mound crowned with a few distorted trees. On the way the sailor could not help repeating,—

'Island or continent! To think of that, when at one's last gasp! What a man!'

Arrived at the summit of the mound, Pencroft and his two companions set to work, with no other tools than their hands, to despoil of its principal branches a rather sickly tree, a sort of marine fir; with these branches they made a litter, on which, covered with grass and leaves, they could carry the engineer.

This occupied them nearly forty minutes, and it was ten o'clock when they returned to Cyrus Harding whom Spilett had not left.

The engineer was just awaking from the sleep, or rather from the drowsiness, in which they had found him. The colour was returning to his cheeks, which till now had been as pale as death. He raised himself a little, looked around him, and appeared to ask where he was.

'Can you listen to me without fatigue, Cyrus?' asked the reporter.

'Yes,' replied the engineer.

'It's my opinion,' said the sailor, 'that Captain Harding will be able to listen to you still better, if he will have some more grouse jelly,—for we have grouse, captain,' added he, presenting him with a little of this jelly, to which he this time added some of the flesh.

Cyrus Harding ate a little of the grouse, and the rest was divided among his companions, who found it but a meagre breakfast, for they were suffering extremely from hunger.

'Well!' said the sailor, 'there is plenty of food at the Chimneys, for you must know, captain, that down there, in the south, we have a house, with rooms, beds, and fireplace, and in the pantry, several dozen of birds, which our Herbert calls couroucous. Your litter is ready, and as soon as you feel strong enough we will carry you home.'

'Thanks, my friend,' replied the engineer; 'wait another hour or two, and then we will set out. And now speak, Spilett.'

The reporter then told him all that had occurred. He recounted all the events with which Cyrus was unacquainted, the last fall of the balloon, the landing on this unknown land, which appeared a desert (whatever it was, whether island or continent), the discovery of the Chimneys, the search for him, not forgetting of course Neb's devotion, the intelligence exhibited by the faithful Top, as well as many other matters.

'But,' asked Harding, in a still feeble voice, 'you did not, then, pick me up on the beach?'

'No,' replied the reporter.

'And did you not bring me to this cave?'

'No.'

'At what distance is this cave from the sea?'

'About a mile,' replied Pencroft; 'and if you are astonished, captain, we are not less surprised ourselves at seeing you in this place!'

'Indeed,' said the engineer, who was recovering gradually, and who took great interest in these details, 'indeed it is very singular!'

'But,' resumed the sailor, 'can you tell us what happened after you were carried off by the sea?'

Cyrus Harding considered. He knew very little. The wave had torn him from the balloon net. He sank at first several fathoms. On returning to the surface, in the half light, he felt a living creature struggling near him. It was Top, who had sprung to his help. He saw nothing of the balloon, which, lightened both of his weight and that of the dog, had darted away like an arrow.

There he was, in the midst of the angry sea, at a distance which could not be less than half a mile from the shore. He attempted to struggle against the billows by swimming vigorously. Top held him up by his clothes; but a strong current seized him and drove him towards the north, and after half an hour of exertion, he sank, dragging Top with him into the depths. From that moment to the moment in which he recovered to find himself in the arms of his friends he remembered nothing.

'However,' remarked Pencroft, 'you must have been thrown on to the beach, and you must have had strength to walk here, since Neb found your footmarks!'

'Yes... of course replied the engineer, thoughtfully; 'and you found no traces of human beings on this coast?'

'Not a trace,' replied the reporter; 'besides, if by chance you had met with some deliverer there, just in the nick of time, why should he have abandoned you after having saved you from the waves?'

'You are right, my dear Spilett. Tell me, Neb,' added the engineer, turning to his servant, 'it was not you who... you can't have had a moment of unconsciousness... during which no, that's absurd.... Do any of the footsteps still remain?' asked Harding.

'Yes, master, replied Neb; 'here, at the entrance, at the back of the mound, in a place sheltered from the rain and wind. The storm has destroyed the others.'

'Pencroft,' said Cyrus Harding, 'will you take my shoe and see if it fits exactly to the footprints?'

The sailor did as the engineer requested. While he and Herbert, guided by Neb, went to the place where the footprints were to be found, Cyrus remarked to the reporter,—

'It is a most extraordinary thing!'

'Perfectly inexplicable!' replied Gideon Spilett.

'But do not dwell upon it just now, my dear Spilett, we will talk about it by-and-by.'

A moment after the others entered.

There was no doubt about it. The engineer's shoe fitted exactly to the footmarks. It was therefore Cyrus Harding who had left them on the sand.

'Come,' said he, 'I must have experienced this unconsciousness which I attributed to Neb. I must have walked like a somnambulist, without any knowledge of my steps, and Top must have guided me here, after having dragged me from the waves... Come, Top! Come, old dog!'

The magnificent animal bounded barking to his master, and caresses were lavished on him. It was agreed that there was no other way of accounting for the rescue of Cyrus Harding, and that Top deserved all the honour of the affair.

Towards twelve o'clock, Pencroft having asked the engineer if they could now remove him, Harding, instead of replying, and by an effort which exhibited the most energetic will, got up. But he was obliged to lean on the sailor, or he would have fallen.

'Well done!' cried Pencroft; 'bring the captain's litter.'

The litter was brought; the transverse branches had been covered with leaves and long grass. Harding was laid on it, and Pencroft, having taken his place at one end and Neb at the other, they started towards the coast. There was a distance of eight miles to be accomplished; but, as they could not go fast, and it would perhaps be necessary to stop frequently, they reckoned that it would take at least six hours to reach the Chimneys. The wind was still strong, but fortunately it did not rain. Although lying down, the engineer, leaning on his elbow, observed the coast, particularly inland. He did not speak, but he gazed; and, no doubt, the appearance of the country, with its inequalities of ground, its forests, its various productions, were impressed on his mind. However, after traveling for two hours, fatigue overcame him, and he slept.

At half-past five the little band arrived at the precipice, and a short time after at the Chimneys.

They stopped, and the litter was placed on the sand; Cyrus Harding was sleeping profoundly, and did not awake.

Pencroft, to his extreme surprise, found that the terrible storm had quite altered the aspect of the place. Important changes had occurred; great blocks of stone lay on the beach, which was also covered with a thick carpet of sea-weed, algae, and wrack. Evidently the sea, passing over the islet, had been carried right up to the foot of the enormous curtain of granite. The soil in front of the cave had been torn away by the violence of the waves. A horrid presentiment flashed across Pencroft's mind. He rushed into the passage, but returned almost immediately, and stood motionless, staring at his companions.... The fire was out; the drowned cinders were nothing but mud; the burnt linen, which was to have served as tinder, had disappeared! The sea had penetrated to the end of the passages, and everything was overthrown and destroyed in the interior of the Chimneys!

Chapter 9

In a few words, Gideon Spilett, Herbert, and Neb were made acquainted with what had happened. This accident, which appeared so very serious to Pencroft, produced different effects on the companions of the honest sailor.

Neb, in his delight at having found his master, did not listen, or rather, did not care to trouble himself with what Pencroft was saying.

Herbert shared in some degree the sailor's feelings.

As to the reporter, he simply replied,—

'Upon my word, Pencroft, it's perfectly indifferent to me!'

'But, I repeat, that we haven't any fire!'

'Pooh!'

'Nor any means of relighting it!'

'Nonsense!'

'But I say, Mr. Spilett—'

'Isn't Cyrus here?' replied the reporter.

'Is not our engineer alive? He will soon find some way of making fire for us!'

'With what?'

'With nothing.'

What had Pencroft to say? He could say nothing, for, in the bottom of his heart he shared the confidence which his companions had in Cyrus Harding. The engineer was to them a microcosm, a compound of every science, a possessor of all human knowledge. It was better to be with Cyrus in a desert island, than without him in the most flourishing town in the United States. With him they could want nothing; with him they would never despair. If these brave men had been told that a volcanic eruption would destroy the land, that this land would be engulfed in the depths of the Pacific, they would have imperturbably replied,—

Cyrus is here!'

While in the palanquin, however, the engineer had again relapsed into unconsciousness, which the jolting to which he had been subjected during his journey had brought on, so that they could not now appeal to his ingenuity. The supper must necessarily be very meager. In fact, all the grouse flesh had been consumed, and there no longer existed any means of cooking more game. Besides, the couroucous which had been reserved had disappeared. They must consider what was to be done.

First of all, Cyrus Harding was carried into the central passage. There they managed to arrange for him a couch of sea-weed which still remained almost dry. The deep sleep which had overpowered him would no doubt be more beneficial to him than any nourishment.

Night had closed in, and the temperature, which had modified when the wind shifted to the northwest, again became extremely cold. Also, the sea having destroyed the partitions which Pencroft had put up in certain places in the passages, the Chimneys, on account of the draughts, had become scarcely habitable. The engineer's condition would, therefore, have been bad enough, if his companions had not carefully covered him with their coats and waistcoats.

Supper, this evening, was of course composed of the inevitable lithodomes, of which Herbert and Neb picked up a plentiful supply on the beach. However, to these molluscs, the lad added some edible sea-weed, which he gathered on high rocks, whose sides were only washed by the sea at the time of high tides. This sea-weed, which belongs to the order of Fucacae, of the genus Sargassum, produces, when dry, a gelatinous matter, rich and nutritious. The reporter and his companions, after having eaten a quantity of lithodomes, sucked the sargassum, of which the taste was very tolerable. It is used in parts of the East very considerably by the natives. 'Never mind!' said the sailor, 'the captain will help us soon.' Meanwhile the cold became very severe, and unhappily they had no means of defending themselves from it.

The sailor, extremely vexed, tried in all sorts of ways to procure fire. Neb helped him in this work. He found some dry moss, and by striking together two pebbles he obtained some sparks, but the moss, not being inflammable enough, did not take fire, for the sparks were really only incandescent, and not at all of the same consistency as those which are emitted from flint when struck in the same manner. The experiment, therefore, did not succeed.

Pencroft, although he had no confidence in the proceeding, then tried rubbing two pieces of dry wood together, as savages do. Certainly, the movement which he and Neb exhibited, if it had been transformed into heat, according to the new theory, would have been enough to heat the boiler of a steamer! It came to nothing. The bits of wood became hot, to be sure, but much less so than the operators themselves.

After working an hour, Pencroft, who was in a complete state of perspiration, threw down the pieces of wood in disgust.

'I can never be made to believe that savages light their fires in this way, let them say what they will,' he exclaimed. 'I could sooner light my arms by rubbing them against each other!'

The sailor was wrong to despise the proceeding. Savages often kindle wood by means of rapid rubbing. But every sort of wood does not answer for the purpose, and besides, there is 'the knack,' following the usual expression, and it is probable that Pencroft had not 'the knack.'

Pencroft's ill humour did not last long. Herbert had taken the bits of wood which he had turned down, and was exerting himself to rub them. The hardy sailor could not restrain a burst of laughter on seeing the efforts of the lad to succeed where he had failed.

'Rub, my boy, rub!' said he.

'I am rubbing,' replied Herbert, laughing, 'but I don't pretend to do anything else but warm myself instead of shivering, and soon I shall be as hot as you are, my good Pencroft!'

This soon happened. However, they were obliged to give up, for this night at least, the attempt to procure fire. Gideon Spilett repeated, for the twentieth time, that Cyrus Harding would not have been troubled for so small a difficulty. And, in the meantime, he stretched himself in one of the passages on his bed of sand. Herbert, Neb, and Pencroft did the same, while Top slept at his master's feet.

Next day, the 28th of March, when the engineer awoke, about eight in the morning, he saw his companions around him watching his sleep, and, as on the day before, his first words were:—

'Island or continent?' This was his uppermost thought.

'Well!' replied Pencroft, 'we don't know anything about it, captain!'

'You don't know yet?'

'But we shall know,' rejoined Pencroft, 'when you have guided us into the country.'

'I think I am able to try it,' replied the engineer, who, without much effort, rose and stood upright.

'That's capital!' cried the sailor.

'I feel dreadfully weak,' replied Harding. 'Give me something to eat, my friends, and it will soon go off. You have fire, haven't you?'

This question was not immediately replied to. But, in a few seconds—

'Alas! we have no fire,' said Pencroft, 'or rather, captain, we have it no longer!'

And the sailor recounted all that had passed the day before. He amused the engineer by the history of the single match, then his abortive attempt to procure fire in the savages' way.

'We shall consider,' replied the engineer, 'and if we do not find some substance similar to tinder—'

'Well?' asked the sailor.

'Well, we will make matches.

'Chemicals?'

'Chemicals!'

'It is not more difficult than that,' cried the reporter, striking the sailor on the shoulder.

The latter did not think it so simple, but he did not protest. All went out. The weather had become very fine. The sun was rising from the sea's horizon, and touched with golden spangles the prismatic rugosities of the huge precipice.

Having thrown a rapid glance around him, the engineer seated himself on a block of stone. Herbert offered him a few handfuls of shell-fish and sargassum, saying,—

'It is all that we have, Captain Harding.'

'Thanks, my boy,' replied Harding; 'it will do—for this morning at least.'

He ate the wretched food with appetite, and washed it down with a little fresh water, drawn from the river in an immense shell.

His companions looked at him without speaking. Then, feeling somewhat refreshed, Cyrus Harding crossed his arms, and said,—

'So, my friends, you do not know yet whether fate has thrown us on an island, or on a continent?'

'No, captain,' replied the boy.

'We shall know tomorrow,' said the engineer; 'till then, there is nothing to be done.'

'Yes,' replied Pencroft.

'What?'

'Fire,' said the sailor, who, also, had a fixed idea.

'We will make it, Pencroft,' replied Harding.

'While you were carrying me yesterday, did I not see in the west a mountain which commands the country?'

'Yes,' replied Spilett, 'a mountain which must be rather high—'

'Well,' replied the engineer, 'we will climb to the summit tomorrow, and then we shall see if this land is an island or a continent. Till then, I repeat, there is nothing to be done.'

'Yes, fire!' said the obstinate sailor again.

'But he will make us a fire!' replied Gideon Spilett, 'only have a little patience, Pencroft!'

The seaman looked at Spilett in a way which seemed to say, 'If it depended upon you to do it, we wouldn't taste roast meat very soon'; but he was silent.

Meanwhile Captain Harding had made no reply. He appeared to be very little troubled by the question of fire. For a few minutes he remained absorbed in thought; then again speaking,—

'My friends,' said he, 'our situation is, perhaps, deplorable; but, at any rate, it is very plain. Either we are on a continent, and then, at the expense of greater or less fatigue, we shall reach some inhabited place, or we are on an island. In the latter case, if the island is inhabited, we will try to get out of the scrape with the help of its inhabitants; if it is desert, we will try to get out of the scrape by ourselves.'

'Certainly, nothing could be plainer,' replied Pencroft.

'But, whether it is an island or a continent,' asked Gideon Spilett, 'whereabouts do you think, Cyrus, this storm has thrown us?'

'I cannot say exactly,' replied the engineer, 'but I presume it is some land in the Pacific. In fact, when we left Richmond, the wind was blowing from the northeast, and its very violence greatly proves that it could not have varied. If the direction has been maintained from the northeast to the southwest, we have traversed the States of North Carolina, of South Carolina, of Georgia, the Gulf of Mexico, Mexico, itself, in its narrow part, then a part of the Pacific Ocean. I cannot estimate the distance traversed by the balloon at less than six to seven thousand miles, and, even supposing that the wind had varied half a quarter, it must have brought us either to the archipelago of Mendava, either on the Pomotous, or even, if it had a greater strength than I suppose, to the land of New Zealand. If the last hypothesis is correct, it will be easy enough to get home again. English or Maoris, we shall always find some one to whom we can speak. If, on the contrary, this is the coast of a desert island in some tiny archipelago, perhaps we shall be able to reconnoiter it from the summit of that peak which overlooks the country, and then we shall see how best to establish ourselves here as if we are never to go away.'

'Never?' cried the reporter. 'You say 'Never,' my dear Cyrus?'

'Better to put things at the worst at first,' replied the engineer, 'and reserve the best for a surprise.'

'Well said,' remarked Pencroft. 'It is to be hoped, too, that this island, if it be one, is not situated just out of the course of ships; that would be really unlucky!'

'We shall not know what we have to rely on until we have first made the ascent of the mountain,' replied the engineer.

'But tomorrow, captain,' asked Herbert, 'shall you be in a state to bear the fatigue of the ascent?'

'I hope so,' replied the engineer, 'provided you and Pencroft, my boy, show yourselves quick and clever hunters.'

'Captain,' said the sailor, 'since you are speaking of game, if on my return, I was as certain of roasting it as I am of bringing it back—'

'Bring it back all the same, Pencroft,' replied Harding.

It was then agreed that the engineer and the reporter were to pass the day at the Chimneys, so as to examine the shore and the upper plateau. Neb, Herbert, and the sailor were to return to the forest, renew their store of wood, and lay violent hands on every creature, feathered or hairy, which might come within their reach.

They set out accordingly about ten o'clock in the morning, Herbert confident, Neb joyous, Pencroft murmuring aside,—

'If, on my return, I find a fire at the house, I shall believe that the thunder itself came to light it.' All three climbed the bank; and arrived at the angle made by the river, the sailor, stopping, said to his two companions,—

'Shall we begin by being hunters or wood-men?'

'Hunters,' replied Herbert. 'There is Top already in quest.'

'We will hunt, then,' said the sailor, 'and afterwards we can come back and collect our wood.'

This agreed to, Herbert, Neb, and Pencroft, after having torn three sticks from the trunk of a young fir, followed Top, who was bounding about among the long grass.

This time, the hunters, instead of following the course of the river, plunged straight into the heart of the forest. There were still the same trees, belonging, for the most part, to the pine family. In certain places, less crowded, growing in clumps, these pines exhibited considerable dimensions, and appeared to indicate, by their development, that the country was situated in a higher latitude than the engineer had supposed. Glades, bristling with stumps worn away by time, were covered with dry wood, which formed an inexhaustible store of fuel. Then, the glade passed, the underwood thickened again, and became almost impenetrable.

It was difficult enough to find the way among the groups of trees, without any beaten track. So the sailor from time to time broke off branches which might be easily recognized. But, perhaps, he was wrong not to follow the watercourse, as he and Herbert had done on their first excursion, for after walking an hour not a creature had shown itself. Top, running under the branches, only roused birds which could not be approached. Even the couroucous were invisible, and it was probable that the sailor would be obliged to return to the marshy part of the forest, in which he had so happily performed his grouse fishing.

'Well, Pencroft,' said Neb, in a slightly sarcastic tone, 'if this is all the game which you promised to bring back to my master, it won't need a large fire to roast it!'

'Have patience,' replied the sailor, 'it isn't the game which will be wanting on our return.'

'Have you not confidence in Captain Harding?'

'Yes.'

'But you don't believe that he will make fire?'

'I shall believe it when the wood is blazing in the fireplace.'

'It will blaze, since my master has said so.'

'We shall see!'

Meanwhile, the sun had not reached the highest point in its course above the horizon. The exploration, therefore, continued, and was usefully marked by a discovery which Herbert made of a tree whose fruit was edible. This was the stone-pine, which produces an excellent almond, very much esteemed in the temperate regions of America and Europe. These almonds were in a perfect state of maturity, and Herbert described them to his companions, who feasted on them.

'Come,' said Pencroft, 'sea-weed by way of bread, raw mussels for meat, and almonds for dessert, that's certainly a good dinner for those who have not a single match in their pocket!'

We mustn't complain,' said Herbert.

'I am not complaining, my boy,' replied Pencroft, 'only I repeat, that meat is a little too much economized in this sort of meal.'

'Top has found something!' cried Neb, who ran towards a thicket, in the midst of which the dog had disappeared, barking. With Top's barking were mingled curious gruntings.

The sailor and Herbert had followed Neb. If there was game there this was not the time to discuss how it was to be cooked, but rather, how they were to get hold of it.

The hunters had scarcely entered the bushes when they saw Top engaged in a struggle with an animal which he was holding by the ear. This quadruped was a sort of pig nearly two feet and a half long, of a blackish brown colour, lighter below, having hard scanty hair; its toes, then strongly fixed in the ground, seemed to be united by a membrane. Herbert recognized in this animal the capybara, that is to say, one of the largest members of the rodent order.

Meanwhile, the capybara did not struggle against the dog. It stupidly rolled its eyes, deeply buried in a thick bed of fat. Perhaps it saw men for the first time.

However, Neb having tightened his grasp on his stick, was just going to fell the pig, when the latter, tearing itself from Top's teeth, by which it was only held by the tip of its ear, uttered a vigorous grunt, rushed upon Herbert, almost overthrew him, and disappeared in the wood.

'The rascal!' cried Pencroft.

All three directly darted after Top, but at the moment when they joined him the animal had disappeared under the waters of a large pond shaded by venerable pines.

Neb, Herbert, and Pencroft stopped, motionless. Top plunged into the water, but the capybara, hidden at the bottom of the pond, did not appear.

'Let us wait,' said the boy, 'for he will soon come to the surface to breathe.'

'Won't he drown?' asked Neb.

'No,' replied Herbert, 'since he has webbed feet, and is almost an amphibious animal. But watch him.'

Top remained in the water. Pencroft and his two companions went to different parts of the bank, so as to cut off the retreat of the capybara, which the dog was looking for beneath the water.

Herbert was not mistaken. In a few minutes the animal appeared on the surface of the water. Top was upon it in a bound, and kept it from plunging again. An instant later the capybara, dragged to the bank, was killed by a blow from Neb's stick.

'Hurrah!' cried Pencroft, who was always ready with this cry of triumph.

'Give me but a good fire, and this pig shall be gnawed to the bones!'

Pencroft hoisted the capybara on his shoulders, and judging by the height of the sun that it was about two o'clock, he gave the signal to return.

Top's instinct was useful to the hunters, who, thanks to the intelligent animal, were enabled to discover the road by which they had come. Half an hour later they arrived at the river.

Pencroft soon made a raft of wood, as he had done before, though if there was no fire it would be a useless task, and the raft following the current, they returned towards the Chimneys.

But the sailor had not gone fifty paces when he stopped, and again uttering a tremendous hurrah, pointed towards the angle of the cliff,—

'Herbert! Neb! Look!' he shouted.

Smoke was escaping and curling up among the rocks.

Chapter 10

In a few minutes the three hunters were before a crackling fire. The captain and the reporter were there. Pencroft looked from one to the other, his capybara in his hand, without saying a word.

'Well, yes, my brave fellow,' cried the reporter.

'Fire, real fire, which will roast this splendid pig perfectly, and we will have a feast presently!'

'But who lighted it?' asked Pencroft.

'The sun!'

Gideon Spilett was quite right in his reply. It was the sun which had furnished the heat which so astonished Pencroft. The sailor could scarcely believe his eyes, and he was so amazed that he did not think of questioning the engineer.

'Had you a burning-glass, sir?' asked Herbert of Harding.

'No, my boy,' replied he, 'but I made one.'

And he showed the apparatus which served for a burning-glass. It was simply two glasses which he had taken from his own and the reporter's watches. Having filled them with water and rendered their edges adhesive by means of a little clay, he thus fabricated a regular burning-glass, which, concentrating the solar rays on some very dry moss, soon caused it to blaze.

The sailor considered the apparatus; then he gazed at the engineer without saying a word, only a look plainly expressed his opinion that if Cyrus Harding was not a magician, he was certainly no ordinary man. At last speech returned to him, and he cried,—

'Note that, Mr. Spilett, note that down on your paper!'

'It is noted,' replied the reporter.

Then, Neb helping him, the seaman arranged the spit, and the capybara, properly cleaned, was soon roasting like a suckling-pig before a clear, crackling fire.

The Chimneys had again become more habitable, not only because the passages were warmed by the fire, but because the partitions of wood and mud had been re-established.

It was evident that the engineer and his companions had employed their day well. Cyrus Harding had almost entirely recovered his strength, and had proved it by climbing to the upper plateau. From this point his eye, accustomed to estimate heights and distances, was fixed for a long time on the cone, the summit of which he wished to reach the next day. The mountain, situated about six miles to the northwest, appeared to him to measure 3,500 feet above the level of the sea. Consequently the gaze of an observer posted on its summit would extend over a radius of at least fifty miles. Therefore it was probable that Harding could easily solve the question of 'island or continent,' to which he attached so much importance.

They supped capitally. The flesh of the capybara was declared excellent. The sargassum and the almonds of the stone-pine completed the repast, during which the engineer spoke little. He was preoccupied with projects for the next day.

Once or twice Pencroft gave forth some ideas upon what it would be best to do; but Cyrus Harding, who was evidently of a methodical mind, only shook his head without uttering a word.

'Tomorrow,' he repeated, 'we shall know what we have to depend upon, and we will act accordingly.'

The meal ended, fresh armfuls of wood were thrown on the fire, and the inhabitants of the Chimneys, including the faithful Top, were soon buried in a deep sleep.

No incident disturbed this peaceful night, and the next day, the 29th of March, fresh and active they awoke, ready to undertake the excursion which must determine their fate.

All was ready for the start. The remains of the capybara would be enough to sustain Harding and his companions for at least twenty-four hours.

Besides, they hoped to find more food on the way. As the glasses had been returned to the watches of the engineer and reporter, Pencroft burned a little linen to serve as tinder. As to flint, that would not be wanting in these regions of Plutonic origin. It was half-past seven in the morning when the explorers, armed with sticks, left the Chimneys. Following Pencroft's advice, it appeared best to take the road already traversed through the forest, and to return by another route. It was also the most direct way to reach the mountain. They turned the south angle and followed the left bank of the river, which was abandoned at the point where it formed an elbow towards the southwest. The path, already trodden under the evergreen trees, was found, and at nine o'clock Cyrus Harding and his companions had reached the western border of the forest. The ground, till then, very little undulated, boggy at first, dry and sandy afterwards, had a gentle slope, which ascended from the shore towards the interior of the country. A few very timid animals were seen under the forest-trees. Top quickly started them, but his master soon called him back, for the time had not come to commence hunting; that would be attended to later. The engineer was not a man who would allow himself to be diverted from his fixed idea. It might even have been said that he did not observe the country at all, either in its configuration or in its natural productions, his great aim being to climb the mountain before him, and therefore straight towards it he went. At ten o'clock a halt of a few minutes was made. On leaving the forest, the mountain system of the country appeared before the explorers. The mountain was composed of two cones; the first, truncated at a height of about two thousand five hundred feet, was sustained by buttresses, which appeared to branch out like the talons of an immense claw set on the ground. Between these were narrow valleys, bristling with trees, the last clumps of which rose to the top of the lowest cone. There appeared to be less vegetation on that side of the mountain which was exposed to the northeast, and deep fissures could be seen which, no doubt, were watercourses.

On the first cone rested a second, slightly rounded, and placed a little on one side, like a great round hat cocked over the ear. A Scotchman would have said, 'His bonnet was a thocht ajee.' It appeared formed of bare earth, here and there pierced by reddish rocks.

They wished to reach the second cone, and proceeding along the ridge of the spurs seemed to be the best way by which to gain it.

'We are on volcanic ground,' Cyrus Harding had said, and his companions following him began to ascend by degrees on the back of a spur, which, by a winding and consequently more accessible path, joined the first plateau.

The ground had evidently been convulsed by subterranean force.

Here and there stray blocks, numerous debris of basalt and pumice-stone, were met with. In isolated groups rose fir-trees, which, some hundred feet lower, at the bottom of the narrow gorges, formed massive shades almost impenetrable to the sun's rays.

During the first part of the ascent, Herbert remarked on the footprints which indicated the recent passage of large animals.

'Perhaps these beasts will not let us pass by willingly,' said Pencroft.

'Well,' replied the reporter, who had already hunted the tiger in India, and the lion in Africa, 'we shall soon learn how successfully to encounter them. But in the meantime we must be upon our guard!'

They ascended but slowly.

The distance, increased by detours and obstacles which could not be surmounted directly, was long. Sometimes, too, the ground suddenly fell, and they found themselves on the edge of a deep chasm which they had to go round. Thus, in retracing their steps so as to find some practicable path, much time was employed and fatigue undergone for nothing. At twelve o'clock, when the small band of adventurers halted for breakfast at the foot of a large group of firs, near a little stream which fell in cascades, they found themselves still half way from the first plateau, which most probably they would not reach till nightfall. From this point the view of the sea was much extended, but on the right the high promontory prevented their seeing whether there was land beyond it. On the left, the sight extended several miles to the north; but, on the northwest, at the point occupied by the explorers, it was cut short by the ridge of a fantastically-shaped spur, which formed a powerful support of the central cone.

At one o'clock the ascent was continued. They slanted more towards the southwest and again entered among thick bushes. There under the shade of the trees fluttered several couples of gallinaceae belonging to the pheasant species. They were tragopans, ornamented by a pendant skin which hangs over their throats, and by two small, round horns, planted behind the eyes. Among these birds, which were about the size of a fowl, the female was uniformly brown, while the male was gorgeous in his red plumage, decorated with white spots. Gideon Spilett, with a stone cleverly and vigorously thrown, killed one of these tragopans, on which Pencroft, made hungry by the fresh air, had cast greedy eyes.

After leaving the region of bushes, the party, assisted by resting on each other's shoulders, climbed for about a hundred feet up a steep acclivity and reached a level place, with very few trees, where the soil appeared volcanic. It was necessary to ascend by zigzags to make the slope more easy, for it was very steep, and the footing being exceedingly precarious required the greatest caution. Neb and Herbert took the lead, Pencroft the rear, the captain and the reporter between them. The animals which frequented these heights—and there were numerous traces of them—must necessarily belong to those races of sure foot and supple spine, chamois or goat. Several were seen, but this was not the name Pencroft gave them, for all of a sudden—'Sheep!' he shouted.

All stopped about fifty feet from half-a-dozen animals of a large size, with strong horns bent back and flattened towards the point, with a woolly fleece, hidden under long silky hair of a tawny colour.

They were not ordinary sheep, but a species usually found in the mountainous regions of the temperate zone, to which Herbert gave the name of the musmon.

'Have they legs and chops?' asked the sailor.

'Yes,' replied Herbert.

'Well, then, they are sheep!' said Pencroft.

The animals, motionless among the blocks of basalt, gazed with an astonished eye, as if they saw human bipeds for the first time. Then their fears suddenly aroused, they disappeared, bounding over the rocks.

'Goodbye, till we meet again,' cried Pencroft, as he watched them, in such a comical tone that Cyrus Harding, Gideon Spilett, Herbert, and Neb could not help laughing.

The ascent was continued. Here and there were traces of lava. Sulphur springs sometimes stopped their way, and they had to go round them. In some places the sulphur had formed crystals among other substances, such as whitish cinders made of an infinity of little feldspar crystals.

In approaching the first plateau formed by the truncating of the lower cone, the difficulties of the ascent were very great. Towards four o'clock the extreme zone of the trees had been passed. There only remained here and there a few twisted, stunted pines, which must have had a hard life in resisting at this altitude the high winds from the open sea. Happily for the engineer and his companions the weather was beautiful, the atmosphere tranquil; for a high breeze at an elevation of three thousand feet would have hindered their proceedings. The purity of the sky at the zenith was felt through the transparent air. A perfect calm reigned around them. They could not see the sun, then hid by the vast screen of the upper cone, which masked the half-horizon of the west, and whose enormous shadow stretching to the shore increased as the radiant luminary sank in its diurnal course. Vapour—mist rather than clouds—began to appear in the east, and assume all the prismatic colours under the influence of the solar rays.

Five hundred feet only separated the explorers from the plateau, which they wished to reach so as to establish there an encampment for the night, but these five hundred feet were increased to more than two miles by the zigzags which they had to describe. The soil, as it were, slid under their feet.

The slope often presented such an angle that they slipped when the stones worn by the air did not give a sufficient support. Evening came on by degrees, and it was almost night when Cyrus Harding and his companions, much fatigued by an ascent of seven hours, arrived at the plateau of the first cone. It was then necessary to prepare an encampment, and to restore their strength by eating first and sleeping afterwards. This second stage of the mountain rose on a base of rocks, among which it would be easy to find a retreat. Fuel was not abundant. However, a fire could be made by means of the moss and dry brushwood, which covered certain parts of the plateau. While the sailor was preparing his hearth with stones which he put to this use, Neb and Herbert occupied themselves with getting a supply of fuel. They soon returned with a load of brushwood. The steel was struck, the burnt linen caught the sparks of flint, and, under Neb's breath, a crackling fire showed itself in a few minutes under the shelter of the rocks. Their object in lighting a fire was only to enable them to withstand the cold temperature of the night, as it was not employed in cooking the bird, which Neb kept for the next day. The remains of the capybara and some dozens of the stone-pine almonds formed their supper. It was not half-past six when all was finished.

Cyrus Harding then thought of exploring in the half-light the large circular layer which supported the upper cone of the mountain. Before taking any rest, he wished to know if it was possible to get round the base of the cone in the case of its sides being too steep and its summit being inaccessible. This question preoccupied him, for it was possible that from the way the hat inclined, that is to say, towards the north, the plateau was not practicable. Also, if the summit of the mountain could not be reached on one side, and if, on the other, they could not get round the base of the cone, it would be impossible to survey the western part of the country, and their object in making the ascent would in part be altogether unattained.

The engineer, accordingly, regardless of fatigue, leaving Pencroft and Neb to arrange the beds, and Gideon Spilett to note the incidents of the day, began to follow the edge of the plateau, going towards the north. Herbert accompanied him.

The night was beautiful and still, the darkness was not yet deep. Cyrus Harding and the boy walked near each other, without speaking. In some places the plateau opened before them, and they passed without hindrance. In others, obstructed by rocks, there was only a narrow path, in which two persons could not walk abreast. After a walk of twenty minutes, Cyrus Harding and Herbert were obliged to stop. From this point the slope of the two cones became one. No shoulder here separated the two parts of the mountain. The slope, being inclined almost seventy degrees, the path became impracticable.

But if the engineer and the boy were obliged to give up thoughts of following a circular direction, in return an opportunity was given for ascending the cone.

In fact, before them opened a deep hollow. It was the rugged mouth of the crater, by which the eruptive liquid matter had escaped at the periods when the volcano was still in activity. Hardened lava and crusted scoria formed a sort of natural staircase of large steps, which would greatly facilitate the ascent to the summit of the mountain.

Harding took all this in at a glance, and without hesitating, followed by the lad, he entered the enormous chasm in the midst of an increasing obscurity.

There was still a height of a thousand feet to overcome. Would the interior acclivities of the crater be practicable? It would soon be seen. The persevering engineer resolved to continue his ascent until he was stopped. Happily these acclivities wound up the interior of the volcano and favoured their ascent.

As to the volcano itself, it could not be doubted that it was completely extinct. No smoke escaped from its sides; not a flame could be seen in the dark hollows; not a roar, not a mutter, no trembling even issued from this black well, which perhaps reached far into the bowels of the earth. The atmosphere inside the crater was filled with no sulphurous vapour. It was more than the sleep of a volcano; it was its complete extinction. Cyrus Harding's attempt would succeed.

Little by little, Herbert and he climbing up the sides of the interior, saw the crater widen above their heads. The radius of this circular portion of the sky, framed by the edge of the cone, increased obviously. At each step, as it were, that the explorers made, fresh stars entered the field of their vision. The magnificent constellations of the southern sky shone resplendently. At the zenith glittered the splendid Antares in the Scorpion, and not far was Alpha Centauri, which is believed to be the nearest star to the terrestrial globe. Then, as the crater widened, appeared Fomalhaut of the Fish, the Southern Triangle, and lastly, nearly at the Antarctic Pole, the glittering Southern Cross, which replaces the Polar Star of the Northern Hemisphere.

It was nearly eight o'clock when Cyrus Harding and Herbert set foot on the highest ridge of the mountain at the summit of the cone.

It was then perfectly dark, and their gaze could not extend over a radius of two miles. Did the sea surround this unknown land, or was it connected in the west with some continent of the Pacific? It could not yet be made out. Towards the west, a cloudy belt, clearly visible at the horizon, increased the gloom, and the eye could not discover if the sky and water were blended together in the same circular line.

But at one point of the horizon a vague light suddenly appeared, which descended slowly in proportion as the cloud mounted to the zenith.

It was the slender crescent moon, already almost disappearing; but its light was sufficient to show clearly the horizontal line, then detached from the cloud, and the engineer could see its reflection trembling for an instant on a liquid surface. Cyrus Harding seized the lad's hand, and in a grave voice,—

'An island!' said he, at the moment when the lunar crescent disappeared beneath the waves.

Chapter 11

Half an hour later Cyrus Harding and Herbert had returned to the encampment. The engineer merely told his companions that the land upon which fate had thrown them was an island, and that the next day they would consult. Then each settled himself as well as he could to sleep, and in that rocky hole, at a height of two thousand five hundred feet above the level of the sea, through a peaceful night, the islanders enjoyed profound repose.

The next day, the 30th of March, after a hasty breakfast, which consisted solely of the roasted tragopan, the engineer wished to climb again to the summit of the volcano, so as more attentively to survey the island upon which he and his companions were imprisoned for life perhaps, should the island be situated at a great distance from any land, or if it was out of the course of vessels which visited the archipelagoes of the Pacific Ocean. This time his companions followed him in the new exploration. They also wished to see the island, on the productions of which they must depend for the supply of all their wants.

It was about seven o'clock in the morning when Cyrus Harding, Herbert, Pencroft, Gideon Spilett, and Neb quitted the encampment. No one appeared to be anxious about their situation. They had faith in themselves, doubtless, but it must be observed that the basis of this faith was not the same with Harding as with his companions. The engineer had confidence, because he felt capable of extorting from this wild country everything necessary for the life of himself and his companions; the latter feared nothing, just because Cyrus Harding was with them. Pencroft especially, since the incident of the relighted fire, would not have despaired for an instant, even if he was on a bare rock, if the engineer was with him on the rock.

'Pshaw,' said he, 'we left Richmond without permission from the authorities! It will be hard if we don't manage to get away some day or other from a place where certainly no one will detain us!'

Cyrus Harding followed the same road as the evening before. They went round the cone by the plateau which formed the shoulder, to the mouth of the enormous chasm. The weather was magnificent. The sun rose in a pure sky and flooded with his rays all the eastern side of the mountain.

The crater was reached. It was just what the engineer had made it out to be in the dark; that is to say, a vast funnel which extended, widening, to a height of a thousand feet above the plateau. Below the chasm, large thick streaks of lava wound over the sides of the mountain, and thus marked the course of the eruptive matter to the lower valleys which furrowed the northern part of the island.

The interior of the crater, whose inclination did not exceed thirty five to forty degrees, presented no difficulties nor obstacles to the ascent. Traces of very ancient lava were noticed, which probably had overflowed the summit of the cone, before this lateral chasm had opened a new way to it.

As to the volcanic chimney which established a communication between the subterranean layers and the crater, its depth could not be calculated with the eye, for it was lost in obscurity. But there was no doubt as to the complete extinction of the volcano.

Before eight o'clock Harding and his companions were assembled at the summit of the crater, on a conical mound which swelled the northern edge.

'The sea, the sea everywhere!' they cried, as if their lips could not restrain the words which made islanders of them.

The sea, indeed, formed an immense circular sheet of water all around them! Perhaps, on climbing again to the summit of the cone, Cyrus Harding had had a hope of discovering some coast, some island shore, which he had not been able to perceive in the dark the evening before. But nothing appeared on the farthest verge of the horizon, that is to say over a radius of more than fifty miles. No land in sight. Not a sail. Over all this immense space the ocean alone was visible—the island occupied the centre of a circumference which appeared to be infinite.

The engineer and his companions, mute and motionless, surveyed for some minutes every point of the ocean, examining it to its most extreme limits. Even Pencroft, who possessed a marvellous power of sight, saw nothing; and certainly if there had been land at the horizon, if it appeared only as an indistinct vapour, the sailor would undoubtedly have found it out, for nature had placed regular telescopes under his eyebrows.

From the ocean their gaze returned to the island which they commanded entirely, and the first question was put by Gideon Spilett in these terms:—

'About what size is this island?'

Truly, it did not appear large in the midst of the immense ocean.

Cyrus Harding reflected a few minutes; he attentively observed the perimeter of the island, taking into consideration the height at which he was placed; then,—

'My friends,' said he, 'I do not think I am mistaken in giving to the shore of the island a circumference of more than a hundred miles.'

'And consequently an area?'

'That is difficult to estimate,' replied the engineer, 'for it is so uneven.'

If Cyrus Harding was not mistaken in his calculation, the island had almost the extent of Malta or Zante, in the Mediterranean, but it was at the same time much more irregular and less rich in capes, promontories, points, bays, or creeks. Its strange form caught the eye, and when Gideon Spilett, on the engineer's advice, had drawn the outline, they found that it resembled some fantastic animal, a monstrous leviathan, which lay sleeping on the surface of the Pacific.

This was in fact the exact shape of the island, which it is of consequence to know, and a tolerably correct map of it was immediately drawn by the reporter.

The east part of the shore, where the castaways had landed, formed a wide bay, terminated by a sharp cape, which had been concealed by a high point from Pencroft on his first exploration. At the northeast two other capes closed the bay, and between them ran a narrow gulf, which looked like the half-open jaws of a formidable dog-fish.

From the northeast to the southwest the coast was rounded, like the flattened cranium of an animal, rising again, forming a sort of protuberance which did not give any particular shape to this part of the island, of which the centre was occupied by the volcano.

From this point the shore ran pretty regularly north and south, broken at two-thirds of its perimeter by a narrow creek, from which it ended in a long tail, similar to the caudal appendage of a gigantic alligator.

This tail formed a regular peninsula, which stretched more than thirty miles into the sea, reckoning from the cape southeast of the island, already mentioned; it curled round, making an open roadstead, which marked out the lower shore of this strangely-formed land.

At the narrowest part, that is to say between the Chimneys and the creek on the western shore, which corresponded to it in latitude, the island only measured ten miles; but its greatest length, from the jaws at the northeast to the extremity of the tail of the southwest, was not less than thirty miles.

As to the interior of the island, its general aspect was this, very woody throughout the southern part from the mountain to the shore, and arid and sandy in the northern part. Between the volcano and the east coast Cyrus Harding and his companions were surprised to see a lake, bordered with green trees, the existence of which they had not suspected. Seen from this height, the lake appeared to be on the same level as the ocean, but, on reflection, the engineer explained to his companions that the altitude of this little sheet of water must be about three hundred feet, because the plateau, which was its basin, was but a prolongation of the coast.

'Is it a freshwater lake?' asked Pencroft.

'Certainly,' replied the engineer, 'for it must be fed by the water which flows from the mountain.'

'I see a little river which runs into it,' said Herbert, pointing out a narrow stream, which evidently took its source somewhere in the west.

'Yes,' said Harding; 'and since this stream feeds the lake, most probably on the side near the sea there is an outlet by which the surplus water escapes. We shall see that on our return.'

This little winding watercourse and the river already mentioned constituted the water-system, at least such as it was displayed to the eyes of the explorers. However, it was possible that under the masses of trees which covered two-thirds of the island, forming an immense forest, other rivers ran towards the sea. It might even be inferred that such was the case, so rich did this region appear in the most magnificent specimens of the flora of the temperate zones. There was no indication of running water in the north, though perhaps there might be stagnant water among the marshes in the northeast; but that was all, in addition to the downs, sand, and aridity which contrasted so strongly with the luxuriant vegetation of the rest of the island.

The volcano did not occupy the central part; it rose, on the contrary, in the northwestern region, and seemed to mark the boundary of the two zones. At the southwest, at the south, and the southeast, the first part of the spurs were hidden under masses of verdure. At the north, on the contrary, one could follow their ramifications, which died away on the sandy plains. It was on this side that, at the time when the mountain was in a state of eruption, the discharge had worn away a passage, and a large heap of lava had spread to the narrow jaw which formed the northeastern gulf.

Cyrus Harding and his companions remained an hour at the top of the mountain. The island was displayed under their eyes, like a plan in relief with different tints, green for the forests, yellow for the sand, blue for the water. They viewed it in its tout-ensemble, nothing remained concealed but the ground hidden by verdure, the hollows of the valleys, and the interior of the volcanic chasms.

One important question remained to be solved, and the answer would have a great effect upon the future of the castaways.

Was the island inhabited?

It was the reporter who put this question, to which after the close examination they had just made, the answer seemed to be in the negative.

Nowhere could the work of a human hand be perceived. Not a group of huts, not a solitary cabin, not a fishery on the shore. No smoke curling in the air betrayed the presence of man. It is true, a distance of nearly thirty miles separated the observers from the extreme points, that is, of the tail which extended to the southwest, and it would have been difficult, even to Pencroft's eyes, to discover a habitation there. Neither could the curtain of verdure, which covered three-quarters of the island, be raised to see if it did not shelter some straggling village. But in general the islanders live on the shores of the narrow spaces which emerge above the waters of the Pacific, and this shore appeared to be an absolute desert.

Until a more complete exploration, it might be admitted that the island was uninhabited. But was it frequented, at least occasionally, by the natives of neighbouring islands? It was difficult to reply to this question. No land appeared within a radius of fifty miles. But fifty miles could be easily crossed, either by Malay proas or by the large Polynesian canoes. Everything depended on the position of the island, of its isolation in the Pacific, or of its proximity to archipelagoes. Would Cyrus Harding be able to find out their latitude and longitude without instruments? It would be difficult. Since he was in doubt, it was best to take precautions against a possible descent of neighbouring natives.

The exploration of the island was finished, its shape determined, its features made out, its extent calculated, the water and mountain systems ascertained. The disposition of the forests and plains had been marked in a general way on the reporter's plan. They had now only to descend the mountain slopes again, and explore the soil, in the triple point of view, of its mineral, vegetable, and animal resources.

But before giving his companions the signal for departure, Cyrus Harding said to them in a calm, grave voice,—

Here, my friends, is the small corner of land upon which the hand of the Almighty has thrown us. We are going to live here; a long time, perhaps. Perhaps, too, unexpected help will arrive, if some ship passes by chance. I say by chance, because this is an unimportant island; there is not even a port in which ships could anchor, and it is to be feared that it is situated out of the route usually followed, that is to say, too much to the south for the ships which frequent the archipelagoes of the Pacific, and too much to the north for those which go to Australia by doubling Cape Horn. I wish to hide nothing of our position from you—'

'And you are right, my dear Cyrus,' replied the reporter, with animation. 'You have to deal with men. They have confidence in you, and you can depend upon them. Is it not so, my friends?'

'I will obey you in everything, captain,' said Herbert, seizing the engineer's hand.

'My master always, and everywhere!' cried Neb.

'As for me,' said the sailor, 'if I ever grumble at work, my name's not Jack Pencroft, and if you like, captain, we will make a little America of this island! We will build towns, we will establish railways, start telegraphs, and one fine day, when it is quite changed, quite put in order and quite civilized, we will go and offer it to the government of the Union. Only, I ask one thing.'

'What is that?' said the reporter.

'It is, that we do not consider ourselves castaways, but colonists, who have come here to settle.' Harding could not help smiling, and the sailor's idea was adopted. He then thanked his companions, and added, that he would rely on their energy and on the aid of Heaven.

'Well, now let us set off to the Chimneys!' cried Pencroft.

'One minute, my friends,' said the engineer. 'It seems to me it would be a good thing to give a name to this island, as well as to, the capes, promontories, and watercourses, which we can see.

'Very good,' said the reporter. 'In the future, that will simplify the instructions which we shall have to give and follow.'

'Indeed,' said the sailor, 'already it is something to be able to say where one is going, and where one has come from. At least, it looks like somewhere.'

'The Chimneys, for example,' said Herbert.

'Exactly!' replied Pencroft. 'That name was the most convenient, and it came to me quite of myself. Shall we keep the name of the Chimneys for our first encampment, captain?'

'Yes, Pencroft, since you have so christened it.'

'Good! as for the others, that will he easy,' returned the sailor, who was in high spirits. 'Let us give them names, as the Robinsons did, whose story Herbert has often read to me; Providence Bay, Whale Point, Cape Disappointment!'

'Or, rather, the names of Captain Harding,' said Herbert, 'of Mr. Spilett, of Neb!—'

'My name!' cried Neb, showing his sparkling white teeth.

'Why not?' replied Pencroft. 'Port Neb, that would do very well! And Cape Gideon—'

'I should prefer borrowing names from our country,' said the reporter, 'which would remind us of America.'

'Yes, for the principal ones,' then said Cyrus Harding; 'for those of the bays and seas, I admit it willingly. We might give to that vast bay on the east the name of Union Bay, for example; to that large hollow on the south, Washington Bay; to the mountain upon which we are standing, that of Mount Franklin; to that lake which is extended under our eyes, that of Lake Grant; nothing could be better, my friends. These names will recall our country, and those of the great citizens who have honoured it; but for the rivers, gulfs, capes, and promontories, which we perceive from the top of this mountain, rather let us choose names which will recall their particular shape. They will impress themselves better on our memory, and at the same time will he more practical. The shape of the island is so strange that we shall not he troubled to imagine what it resembles. As to the streams which we do not know as yet, in different parts of the forest which we shall explore later, the creeks which afterwards will he discovered, we can christen them as we find them. What do you think, my friends?'

The engineer's proposal was unanimously agreed to by his companions. The island was spread out under their eyes like a map, and they had only to give names to all its angles and points. Gideon Spilett would write them down, and the geographical nomenclature of the island would be definitely adopted. First, they named the two bays and the mountain, Union Bay, Washington Bay, and Mount Franklin, as the engineer had suggested.

'Now,' said the reporter, 'to this peninsula at the southwest of the island, I propose to give the name of Serpentine Peninsula, and that of Reptile-end to the bent tail which terminates it, for it is just like a reptile's tail.'

'Adopted,' said the engineer.

'Now,' said Herbert, pointing to the other extremity of the island, 'let us call this gulf which is so singularly like a pair of open jaws, Shark Gulf.'

'Capital!' cried Pencroft, 'and we can complete the resemblance by naming the two parts of the jaws Mandible Cape.'

'But there are two capes,' observed the reporter.

'Well,' replied Pencroft, 'we can have North Mandible Cape and South Mandible Cape.'

'They are inscribed,' said Spilett.

'There is only the point at the southeastern extremity of the island to he named,' said Pencroft.

'That is, the extremity of Union Bay?' asked Herbert.

'Claw Cape,' cried Neb directly, who also wished to he godfather to some part of his domain.

In truth, Neb had found an excellent name, for this cape was very like the powerful claw of the fantastic animal which this singularly-shaped island represented.

Pencroft was delighted at the turn things had taken, and their imaginations soon gave to the river which furnished the settlers with drinking water and near which the balloon had thrown them, the name of the Mercy, in true gratitude to Providence. To the islet upon which the castaways had first landed, the name of Safety Island; to the plateau which crowned the high granite precipice above the Chimneys, and from whence the gaze could embrace the whole of the vast bay, the name of Prospect Heights.

Lastly, all the masses of impenetrable wood which covered the Serpentine Peninsula were named the forests of the Far West.

The nomenclature of the visible and known parts of the island was thus finished, and later, they would complete it as they made fresh discoveries.

As to the points of the compass, the engineer had roughly fixed them by the height and position of the sun, which placed Union Bay and Prospect Heights to the east. But the next day, by taking the exact hour of the rising and setting of the sun, and by marking its position between this rising and setting, he reckoned to fix the north of the island exactly, for, in consequence of its situation in the Southern Hemisphere, the sun, at the precise moment of its culmination, passed in the north and not in the south, as, in its apparent movement, it seems to do, to those places situated in the Northern Hemisphere.

Everything was finished, and the settlers had only to descend Mount

Franklin to return to the Chimneys, when Pencroft cried out,—

'Well! we are preciously stupid!'

'Why?' asked Gideon Spilett, who had closed his notebook and risen to depart.

'Why! our island! we have forgotten to christen it!'

Herbert was going to propose to give it the engineer's name and all his companions would have applauded him, when Cyrus Harding said simply,—

'Let us give it the name of a great citizen, my friend; of him who now struggles to defend the unity of the American Republic! Let us call it Lincoln Island!'

The engineer's proposal was replied to by three hurrahs.

And that evening, before sleeping, the new colonists talked of their absent country; they spoke of the terrible war which stained it with blood; they could not doubt that the South would soon be subdued, and that the cause of the North, the cause of justice, would triumph, thanks to Grant, thanks to Lincoln!

Now this happened the 30th of March, 1865. They little knew that sixteen days afterwards a frightful crime would be committed in Washington, and that on Good Friday Abraham Lincoln would fall by the hand of a fanatic.

Chapter 12

They now began the descent of the mountain. Climbing down the crater, they went round the cone and reached their encampment of the previous night. Pencroft thought it must be breakfast-time, and the watches of the reporter and engineer were therefore consulted to find out the hour.

That of Gideon Spilett had been preserved from the sea-water, as he had been thrown at once on the sand out of reach of the waves. It was an instrument of excellent quality, a perfect pocket chronometer, which the reporter had not forgotten to wind up carefully every day.

As to the engineer's watch, it, of course, had stopped during the time which he had passed on the downs.

The engineer now wound it up, and ascertaining by the height of the sun that it must be about nine o'clock in the morning, he put his watch at that hour.

'No, my dear Spilett, wait. You have kept the Richmond time, have you not?'

'Yes, Cyrus.'

'Consequently, your watch is set by the meridian of that town, which is almost that of Washington?'

'Undoubtedly.'

'Very well, keep it thus. Content yourself with winding it up very, exactly, but do not touch the hands. This may be of use to us.

'What will be the good of that?' thought the sailor.

They ate, and so heartily, that the store of game and almonds was totally exhausted. But Pencroft was not at all uneasy, they would supply themselves on the way. Top, whose share had been very much to his taste, would know how to find some fresh game among the brushwood. Moreover, the sailor thought of simply asking the engineer to manufacture some powder and one or two fowling-pieces; he supposed there would be no difficulty in that.

On leaving the plateau, the captain proposed to his companions to return to the Chimneys by a new way. He wished to reconnoiter Lake Grant, so magnificently framed in trees. They therefore followed the crest of one of the spurs, between which the creek that supplied the lake probably had its source. In talking, the settlers already employed the names which they had just chosen, which singularly facilitated the exchange of their ideas. Herbert and Pencroft—the one young and the other very boyish—were enchanted, and while walking, the sailor said,

'Hey, Herbert! how capital it sounds! It will be impossible to lose ourselves, my boy, since, whether we follow the way to Lake Grant, or whether we join the Mercy through the woods of the Far West, we shall be certain to arrive at Prospect Heights, and, consequently, at Union Bay!'

It had been agreed, that without forming a compact band, the settlers should not stray away from each other. It was very certain that the thick forests of the island were inhabited by dangerous animals, and it was prudent to be on their guard. In general, Pencroft, Herbert, and Neb walked first, preceded by Top, who poked his nose into every bush. The reporter and the engineer went together, Gideon Spilett ready to note every incident, the engineer silent for the most part, and only stepping aside to pick up one thing or another, a mineral or vegetable substance, which he put into his pocket, without making any remark.

'What can he be picking up?' muttered Pencroft. 'I have looked in vain for anything that's worth the trouble of stooping for.'

Towards ten o'clock the little band descended the last declivities of Mount Franklin. As yet the ground was scantily strewn with bushes and trees. They were walking over yellowish calcinated earth, forming a plain of nearly a mile long, which extended to the edge of the wood. Great blocks of that basalt, which, according to Bischof, takes three hundred and fifty millions of years to cool, strewed the plain, very confused in some places. However, there were here no traces of lava, which was spread more particularly over the northern slopes.

Cyrus Harding expected to reach, without incident, the course of the creek, which he supposed flowed under the trees at the border of the plain, when he saw Herbert running hastily back, while Neb and the sailor were hiding behind the rocks.

'What's the matter, my boy?' asked Spilett.

'Smoke,' replied Herbert. 'We have seen smoke among the rocks, a hundred paces from us.'

'Men in this place?' cried the reporter.

'We must avoid showing ourselves before knowing with whom we have to deal,' replied Cyrus Harding. 'I trust that there are no natives on this island; I dread them more than anything else. Where is Top?'

'Top is on before.'

'And he doesn't bark?'

'No.'

'That is strange. However, we must try to call him back.'

In a few moments, the engineer, Gideon Spilett, and Herbert had rejoined their two companions, and like them, they kept out of sight behind the heaps of basalt.

From thence they clearly saw smoke of a yellowish colour rising in the air.

Top was recalled by a slight whistle from his master, and the latter, signing to his companions to wait for him, glided away among the rocks. The colonists, motionless, anxiously awaited the result of this exploration, when a shout from the engineer made them hasten forward. They soon joined him, and were at once struck with a disagreeable odour which impregnated the atmosphere.

The odor, easily recognized, was enough for the engineer to guess what the smoke was which at first, not without cause, had startled him.

'This fue,' said he, 'or rather, this smoke is produced by nature alone. There is a sulphur spring there, which will cure all our sore throats.'

'Captain!' cried Pencroft. 'What a pity that I haven't got a cold!'

The settlers then directed their steps towards the place from which the smoke escaped. They there saw a sulphur spring which flowed abundantly between the rocks, and its waters discharged a strong sulphuric acid odor, after having absorbed the oxygen of the air.

Cyrus Harding, dipping in his hand, felt the water oily to the touch. He tasted it and found it rather sweet. As to its temperature, that he estimated at ninety-five degrees Fahrenheit. Herbert having asked on what he based this calculation,—

'Its quite simple, my boy,' said he, 'for, in plunging my hand into the water, I felt no sensation either of heat or cold. Therefore it has the same temperature as the human body, which is about ninety-five degrees.'

The sulphur spring not being of any actual use to the settlers, they proceeded towards the thick border of the forest, which began some hundred paces off.

There, as they had conjectured, the waters of the stream flowed clear and limpid between high banks of red earth, the colour of which betrayed the presence of oxide of iron. From this colour, the name of Red Creek was immediately given to the watercourse.

It was only a large stream, deep and clear, formed of the mountain water, which, half river, half torrent, here rippling peacefully over the sand, there falling against the rocks or dashing down in a cascade, ran towards the lake, over a distance of a mile and a half, its breadth varying from thirty to forty feet. Its waters were sweet, and it was supposed that those of the lake were so also. A fortunate circumstance, in the event of their finding on its borders a more suitable dwelling than the Chimneys.

As to the trees, which some hundred feet downwards shaded the banks of the creek, they belonged, for the most part, to the species which abound in the temperate zone of America and Tasmania, and no longer to those coniferae observed in that portion of the island already explored to some miles from Prospect Heights. At this time of the year, the commencement of the month of April, which represents the month of October, in this hemisphere, that is, the beginning of autumn, they were still in full leaf. They consisted principally of casuarinas and eucalypti, some of which next year would yield a sweet manna, similar to the manna of the East. Clumps of Australian cedars rose on the sloping banks, which were also covered with the high grass called 'tussac' in New Holland; but the cocoanut, so abundant in the archipelagoes of the Pacific, seemed to be wanting in the island, the latitude, doubtless, being too low.

'What a pity!' said Herbert, 'such a useful tree, and which has such beautiful nuts!'

As to the birds, they swarmed among the scanty branches of the eucalypti and casuarinas, which did not hinder the display of their wings. Black, white, or gray cockatoos, paroquets, with plumage of all colours, kingfishers of a sparkling green and crowned with red, blue lories, and various other birds appeared on all sides, as through a prism, fluttering about and producing a deafening clamour. Suddenly, a strange concert of discordant voices resounded in the midst of a thicket. The settlers heard successively the song of birds, the cry of quadrupeds, and a sort of clacking which they might have believed to have escaped from the lips of a native. Neb and Herbert rushed towards the bush, forgetting even the most elementary principles of prudence. Happily, they found there, neither a formidable wild beast nor a dangerous native, but merely half a dozen mocking and singing birds, known as mountain pheasants. A few skilful blows from a stick soon put an end to their concert, and procured excellent food for the evening's dinner.

Herbert also discovered some magnificent pigeons with bronzed wings, some superbly crested, others draped in green, like their congeners at Port- Macquarie; but it was impossible to reach them, or the crows and magpies which flew away in flocks.

A charge of small shot would have made great slaughter among these birds, but the hunters were still limited to sticks and stones, and these primitive weapons proved very insufficient.

Their insufficiency was still more clearly shown when a troop of quadrupeds, jumping, bounding, making leaps of thirty feet, regular flying mammiferae, fled over the thickets, so quickly and at such a height, that one would have thought that they passed from one tree to another like squirrels.

'Kangaroos!' cried Herbert.

'Are they good to eat?' asked Pencroft.

'Stewed,' replied the reporter, 'their flesh is equal to the best venison!—'

Gideon Spilett had not finished this exciting sentence when the sailor, followed by Neb and Herbert, darted on the kangaroos tracks. Cyrus Harding called them back in vain. But it was in vain too for the hunters to pursue such agile game, which went bounding away like balls. After a chase of five minutes, they lost their breath, and at the same time all sight of the creatures, which disappeared in the wood. Top was not more successful than his masters.

'Captain,' said Pencroft, when the engineer and the reporter had rejoined them, 'Captain, you see quite well we can't get on unless we make a few guns. Will that be possible?'

'Perhaps,' replied the engineer, 'but we will begin by first manufacturing some bows and arrows, and I don't doubt that you will become as clever in the use of them as the Australian hunters.'

'Bows and arrows!' said Pencroft scornfully. 'That's all very well for children!'

'Don't be proud, friend Pencroft,' replied the reporter. 'Bows and arrows were sufficient for centuries to stain the earth with blood. Powder is but a thing of yesterday, and war is as old as the human race—unhappily.'

'Faith, that's true, Mr. Spilett,' replied the sailor, 'and I always speak too quickly. You must excuse me!'

Meanwhile, Herbert constant to his favourite science, Natural History, reverted to the kangaroos, saying,—

'Besides, we had to deal just now with the species which is most difficult to catch. They were giants with long gray fur; but if I am not mistaken, there exist black and red kangaroos, rock kangaroos, and rat kangaroos, which are more easy to get hold of. It is reckoned that there are about a dozen species.'

'Herbert,' replied the sailor sententiously, 'there is only one species of kangaroos to me, that is 'kangaroo on the spit,' and it's just the one we haven't got this evening!'

They could not help laughing at Master Pencroft's new classification. The honest sailor did not hide his regret at being reduced for dinner to the singing pheasants, but fortune once more showed itself obliging to him.

In fact, Top, who felt that his interest was concerned went and ferreted everywhere with an instinct doubled by a ferocious appetite. It was even probable that if some piece of game did fall into his clutches, none would be left for the hunters, if Top was hunting on his own account; but Neb watched him and he did well.

Towards three o'clock the dog disappeared in the brushwood and gruntings showed that he was engaged in a struggle with some animal. Neb rushed after him, and soon saw Top eagerly devouring a quadruped, which ten seconds later would have been past recognizing in Top's stomach. But fortunately the dog had fallen upon a brood, and besides the victim he was devouring, two other rodents—the animals in question belonged to that order—lay strangled on the turf.

Neb reappeared triumphantly holding one of the rodents in each hand. Their size exceeded that of a rabbit, their hair was yellow, mingled with green spots, and they had the merest rudiments of tails.

The citizens of the Union were at no loss for the right name of these rodents. They were maras, a sort of agouti, a little larger than their congeners of tropical countries, regular American rabbits, with long ears, jaws armed on each side with five molars, which distinguish the agouti.

'Hurrah!' cried Pencroft, 'the roast has arrived! and now we can go home.'

The walk, interrupted for an instant, was resumed. The limpid waters of the Red Creek flowed under an arch of casuannas, banksias, and gigantic gum-trees. Superb lilacs rose to a height of twenty feet. Other arborescent species, unknown to the young naturalist, bent over the stream, which could be heard murmuring beneath the bowers of verdure.

Meanwhile the stream grew much wider, and Cyrus Harding supposed that they would soon reach its mouth. In fact, on emerging from beneath a thick clump of beautiful trees, it suddenly appeared before their eyes.

The explorers had arrived on the western shore of Lake Grant. The place was well worth looking at. This extent of water, of a circumference of nearly seven miles and an area of two hundred and fifty acres, reposed in a border of diversified trees. Towards the east, through a curtain of verdure, picturesquely raised in some places, sparkled an horizon of sea. The lake was curved at the north, which contrasted with the sharp outline of its lower part. Numerous aquatic birds frequented the shores of this little Ontario, in which the thousand isles of its American namesake were represented by a rock which emerged from its surface, some hundred feet from the southern shore. There lived in harmony several couples of kingfishers perched on a stone, grave, motionless, watching for fish, then darting down, they plunged in with a sharp cry, and reappeared with their prey in their beaks. On the shores and on the islets, strutted wild ducks, pelicans, water-hens, red-beaks, philedons, furnished with a tongue like a brush, and one or two specimens of the splendid menura, the tail of which expands gracefully like a lyre.

As to the water of the lake, it was sweet, limpid, rather dark, and from certain bubblings, and the concentric circles which crossed each other on the surface, it could not be doubted that it abounded in fish.

'This lake is really beautiful!' said Gideon Spilett. 'We could live on its borders!'

'We will live there!' replied Harding.

The settlers, wishing to return to the Chimneys by the shortest way, descended towards the angle formed on the south by the junction of the lake's bank. It was not without difficulty that they broke a path through the thickets and brushwood which had never been put aside by the hand of mm, and they thus went towards the shore, so as to arrive at the north of Prospect Heights. Two miles were cleared in this direction, and then, after they had passed the last curtain of trees, appeared the plateau, carpeted with thick turf, and beyond that the infinite sea.

To return to the Chimneys, it was enough to cross the plateau obliquely for the space of a mile, and then to descend to the elbow formed by the first detour of the Mercy. But the engineer desired to know how and where the overplus of the water from the lake escaped, and the exploration was prolonged under the trees for a mile and a half towards the north. It was most probable that an overfall existed somewhere, and doubtless through a cleft in the granite. This lake was only, in short, an immense centre basin, which was filled by degrees by the creek, and its waters must necessarily pass to the sea by some fall. If it was so, the engineer thought that it might perhaps be possible to utilize this fall and borrow its power, actually lost without profit to any one. They continued then to follow the shores of Lake Grant by climbing the plateau; but, after having gone a mile in this direction, Cyrus Harding had not been able to discover the overfall, which, however, must exist somewhere.

It was then half-past four. In order to prepare for dinner it was necessary that the settlers should return to their dwelling. The little band retraced their steps, therefore, and by the left bank of the Mercy, Cyrus Harding and his companions arrived at the Chimneys.

The fire was lighted, and Neb and Pencroft, on whom the functions of cooks naturally devolved, to the one in his quality of Negro, to the other in that of sailor, quickly prepared some broiled agouti, to which they did great justice.

The repast at length terminated; at the moment when each one was about to give himself up to sleep, Cyrus Harding drew from his pocket little specimens of different sorts of minerals, and just said,—

'My friends, this is iron mineral, this a pyrite, this is clay, this is lime, and this is coal. Nature gives us these things. It is our business to make a right use of them. Tomorrow we will commence operations.'

Chapter 13

'Well, captain, where are we going to begin?' asked Pencroft next morning of the engineer.

'At the beginning,' replied Cyrus Harding.

And in fact, the settlers were compelled to begin 'at the very beginning.' They did not possess even the tools necessary for making tools, and they were not even in the condition of nature, who, 'having time, husbands her strength.' They had no time, since they had to provide for the immediate wants of their existence, and though, profiting by acquired experience, they had nothing to invent, still they had everything to make; their iron and their steel were as yet only in the state of minerals, their earthenware in the state of clay, their linen and their clothes in the state of textile material.

It must be said, however, that the settlers were men' in the complete and higher sense of the word. The engineer Harding could not have been seconded by more intelligent companions, nor with more devotion and zeal. He had tried them. He knew their abilities.

Gideon Spilett, a talented reporter, having learned everything so as to be able to speak of everything, would contribute largely with his head and hands to the colonization of the island. He would not draw back from any task: a determined sportsman, he would make a business of what till then had only been a pleasure to him.

Herbert, a gallant boy, already remarkably well informed in the natural sciences, would render greater service to the common cause.

Neb was devotion personified. Clever, intelligent, indefatigable, robust, with iron health, he knew a little about the work of the forge, and could not fail to be very useful in the colony.

As to Pencroft, he had sailed over every sea, a carpenter in the dockyards in Brooklyn, assistant tailor in the vessels of the state, gardener, cultivator, during his holidays, etc., and like all seamen, fit for anything, he knew how to do everything.

It would have been difficult to unite five men, better fitted to struggle against fate, more certain to triumph over it.

'At the beginning,' Cyrus Harding had said. Now this beginning of which the engineer spoke was the construction of an apparatus which would serve to transform the natural substances. The part which heat plays in these transformations is known. Now fuel, wood or coal, was ready for immediate use, an oven must be built to use it.

'What is this oven for?' asked Pencroft.

'To make the pottery which we have need of,' replied Harding.

'And of what shall we make the oven?'

'With bricks.'

'And the bricks?'

'With clay. Let us start, my friends. To save trouble, we will establish our manufactory at the place of production. Neb will bring provisions, and there will be no lack of fire to cook the food.'

'No,' replied the reporter; 'but if there is a lack of food for want of instruments for the chase?'

'Ah, if we only had a knife!' cried the sailor.

'Well?' asked Cyrus Harding.

'Well! I would soon make a bow and arrows, and then there could be plenty of game in the larder!'

'Yes, a knife, a sharp blade.' said the engineer, as if he was speaking to himself.

At this moment his eyes fell upon Top, who was running about on the shore. Suddenly Harding's face became animated.

'Top, here,' said he.

The dog came at his master's call. The latter took Top's head between his hands, and unfastening the collar which the animal wore round his neck, he broke it in two, saying,—

'There are two knives, Pencroft!'

Two hurrahs from the sailor was the reply. Top's collar was made of a thin piece of tempered steel. They had only to sharpen it on a piece of sandstone, then to raise the edge on a finer stone. Now sandstone was abundant on the beach, and two hours after the stock of tools in the colony consisted of two sharp blades, which were easily fixed in solid handles.

The production of these their first tools was hailed as a triumph. It was indeed a valuable result of their labour, and a very opportune one. They set out.

Cyrus Harding proposed that they should return to the western shore of the lake, where the day before he had noticed the clayey ground of which he possessed a specimen. They therefore followed the bank of the Mercy, traversed Prospect Heights, and alter a walk of five miles or more they reached a glade, situated two hundred feet from Lake Grant.

On the way Herbert had discovered a tree, the branches of which the Indians of South America employ for making their bows. It was the crejimba, of the palm family, which does not bear edible fruit. Long straight branches were cut, the leaves stripped off; it was shaped, stronger in the middle, more slender at the extremities, and nothing remained to be done but to find a plant fit to make the bow-string. This was the 'hibiscus heterophyllus,' which furnishes fibres of such remarkable tenacity that they have been compared to the tendons of animals. Pencroft thus obtained bows of tolerable strength, for which he only wanted arrows. These were easily made with straight stiff branches, without knots, but the points with which they must be armed, that is to say, a substance to serve in lieu of iron, could not be met with so easily. But Pencroft said, that having done his part of the work, chance would do the rest.

The settlers arrived on the ground which had been discovered the day before. Being composed of the sort of clay which is used for making bricks and tiles, it was very useful for the work in question. There was no great difficulty in it. It was enough to scour the clay with sand, then to mould the bricks and bake them by the heat of a wood fire.

Generally bricks are formed in moulds, but the engineer contented himself with making them by hand. All that day and the day following were employed in this work. The clay, soaked in water, was mixed by the feet and hands of the manipulators, and then divided into pieces of equal size. A practised workman can make, without a machine, about ten thousand bricks in twelve hours; but in their two days work the five brickmakers on Lincoln Island had not made more than three thousand, which were ranged near each other, until the time when their complete desiccation would permit them to be used in building the oven, that is to say, in three or four days.

It was on the 2nd of April that Harding had employed himself in fixing the orientation of the island, or, in other words, the precise spot where the sun rose. The day before he had noted exactly the hour when the sun disappeared beneath the horizon, making allowance for the refraction. This morning he noted, no less exactly, the hour at which it reappeared. Between this setting and rising twelve hours, twenty-four minutes passed. Then, six hours, twelve minutes after its rising, the sun on this day would exactly pass the meridian and the point of the sky which it occupied at this moment would be the north. At the said hour, Cyrus marked this point, and putting in a line with the sun two trees which would serve him for marks, he thus obtained an invariable meridian for his ulterior operations.

The settlers employed the two days before the oven was built in collecting fuel. Branches were cut all round the glade, and they picked up all the fallen wood under the trees. They were also able to hunt with greater success, since Pencroft now possessed some dozen arrows armed with sharp points. It was Top who had famished these points, by bringing in a porcupine, rather inferior eating, but of great value, thanks to the quills with which it bristled. These quills were fixed firmly at the ends of the arrows, the flight of which was made more certain by some cockatoos' feathers. The reporter and Herbert soon became very skilful archers. Game of all sorts in consequence abounded at the Chimneys, capybaras, pigeons, agouties, grouse, etc. The greater part of these animals were killed in the part of the forest on the left bank of the Mercy, to which they gave the name of Jacamar Wood, in remembrance of the bird which Pencroft and Herbert had pursued when on their first exploration.

This game was eaten fresh, but they preserved some capybara hams, by smoking them above a fire of green wood, after having perfumed them with sweet-smelling leaves. However, this food, although very strengthening, was always roast upon roast, and the party would have been delighted to hear some soup bubbling on the hearth, but they must wait till a pot could be made, and, consequently, till the oven was built.

During these excursions, which were not extended far from the brick-field, the hunters could discern the recent passage of animals of a large size, armed with powerful claws, but they could not recognize the species. Cyrus Harding advised them to be very careful, as the forest probably enclosed many dangerous beasts.

And he did right. Indeed, Gideon Spilett and Herbert one day saw an animal which resembled a jaguar. Happily the creature did not attack them, or they might not have escaped without a severe wound. As soon as he could get a regular weapon, that is to say, one of the guns which Pencroft begged for, Gideon Spilett resolved to make desperate war against the ferocious beasts, and exterminate them from the island.

The Chimneys during these few days was not made more comfortable, for the engineer hoped to discover, or build if necessary, a more convenient dwelling. They contented themselves with spreading moss and dry leaves on the sand of the passages, and on these primitive couches the tired workers slept soundly.

They also reckoned the days they had passed on Lincoln Island, and from that time kept a regular account. The 5th of April, which was Wednesday, was twelve days from the time when the wind threw the castaways on this shore.

On the 6th of April, at daybreak, the engineer and his companions were collected in the glade, at the place where they were going to perform the operation of baking the bricks. Naturally this had to be in the open air, and not in a kiln, or rather, the agglomeration of bricks made an enormous kiln, which would bake itself. The fuel, made of well-prepared faggots, was laid on the ground and surrounded with several rows of dried bricks, which soon formed an enormous cube, to the exterior of which they contrived air- holes. The work lasted all day, and it was not till the evening that they set fire to the faggots. No one slept that night, all watching carefully to keep up the fire.

The operation lasted forty-eight hours, and succeeded perfectly. It then became necessary to leave the smoking mass to cool, and during this time Neb and Pencroft, guided by Cyrus Harding, brought, on a hurdle made of interlaced branches, loads of carbonate of lime and common stones, which were very abundant, to the north of the lake. These stones, when decomposed by heat, made a very strong quicklime, greatly increased by slacking, at least as pure as if it had been produced by the calcination of chalk or marble. Mixed with sand the lime made excellent mortar.

The result of these different works was, that, on the 9th of April, the engineer had at his disposal a quantity of prepared lime and some thousands of bricks.

Without losing an instant, therefore, they began the construction of a kiln to bake the pottery, which was indispensable for their domestic use. They succeeded without much difficulty. Five days after, the kiln was supplied with coal, which the engineer had discovered lying open to the sky towards the mouth of the Red Creek, and the first smoke escaped from a chimney twenty feet high. The glade was transformed into a manufactory, and Pencroft was not far wrong in believing that from this kiln would issue all the products of modern industry.

In the meantime what the settlers first manufactured was a common pottery in which to cook their food. The chief material was clay, to which Harding added a little lime and quartz. This paste made regular 'pipe-clay,' with which they manufactured bowls, cups moulded on stones of a proper size, great jars and pots to hold water, etc. The shape of these objects was clumsy and defective, but after they had been baked in a high temperature, the kitchen of the Chimneys was provided with a number of utensils, as precious to the settlers as the most beautifully enamelled china. We must mention here that Pencroft, desirous to know if the clay thus prepared was worthy of its name of pipe-clay, made some large pipes, which he thought charming, but for which, alas! he had no tobacco, and that was a great privation to Pencroft. 'But tobacco will come, like everything else!' he repeated, in a burst of absolute confidence.

This work lasted till the 15th of April, and the time was well employed. The settlers, having become potters, made nothing but pottery. When it suited Cyrus Harding to change them into smiths, they would become smiths. But the next day being Sunday, and also Easter Sunday, all agreed to sanctify the day by rest. These Americans were religious men, scrupulous observers of the precepts of the Bible, and their situation could not but develop sentiments of confidence towards the Author of all things.

On the evening of the 15th of April they returned to the Chimneys, carrying with them the pottery, the furnace being extinguished until they could put it to a new use. Their return was marked by a fortunate incident; the engineer discovered a substance which replaced tinder. It is known that a spongy, velvety flesh is procured from a certain mushroom of the genus polyporous. Properly prepared, it is extremely inflammable, especially when it has been previously saturated with gunpowder, or boiled in a solution of nitrate or chlorate of potash. But, till then, they had not found any of these polypores or even any of the morels which could replace them. On this day, the engineer, seeing a plant belonging to the wormwood genus, the principal species of which are absinthe, balm-mint, tarragon, etc., gathered several tufts, and, presenting them to the sailor, said,—

'Here, Pencroft, this will please you.'

Pencroft looked attentively at the plant, covered with long silky hair, the leaves being clothed with soft down.

'What's that, captain?' asked Pencroft. 'Is it tobacco?'

'No,' replied Harding, 'it is wormwood; Chinese wormwood to the learned, but to us it will be tinder.'

When the wormwood was properly dried it provided them with a very inflammable substance, especially afterwards when the engineer had impregnated it with nitrate of potash, of which the island possessed several beds, and which is in truth saltpetre.

The colonists had a good supper that evening. Neb prepared some agouti soup, a smoked capybara ham, to which was added the boiled tubercules of the 'caladium macrorhizum,' an herbaceous plant of the arum family. They had an excellent taste, and were very nutritious, being something similar to the substance which is sold in England under the name of 'Portland sago'; they were also a good substitute for bread, which the settlers in Lincoln Island did not yet possess.

When supper was finished, before sleeping, Harding and his companions went to take the air on the beach. It was eight o'clock in the evening; the night was magnificent. The moon, which had been full five days before, had not yet risen, but the horizon was already silvered by those soft, pale shades which might be called the dawn of the moon. At the southern zenith glittered the circumpolar constellations, and above all the Southern Cross, which some days before the engineer had greeted on the summit of Mount Franklin.

Cyrus Harding gazed for some time at this splendid constellation, which has at its summit and at its base two stars of the first magnitude, at its left arm a star of the second, and at its right arm a star of the third magnitude.

Then, after some minutes thought—

'Herbert,' he asked of the lad, 'is not this the 15th of April?'

'Yes, captain,' replied Herbert.

'Well, if I am not mistaken, tomorrow will be one of the four days in the year in which the real time is identical with average time; that is to say, my boy, that tomorrow, to within some seconds, the sun will pass the meridian just at midday by the clocks. If the weather is fine I think that I shall obtain the longitude of the island with an approximation of some degrees.'

'Without instruments, without sextant?' asked Gideon Spilett.

'Yes,' replied the engineer. 'Also, since the night is clear, I will try, this very evening, to obtain our latitude by calculating the height of the Southern Cross, that is, from the southern pole above the horizon. You understand, my friends, that before undertaking the work of installation in earnest it is not enough to have found out that this land is an island; we must, as nearly as possible, know at what distance it is situated, either from the American continent or Australia, or from the principal archipelagoes of the Pacific.'

'In fact,' said the reporter, 'instead of building a house it would be more important to build a boat, if by chance we are not more than a hundred miles from an inhabited coast.'

'That is why,' returned Harding, 'I am going to try this evening to calculate the latitude of Lincoln Island, and tomorrow, at midday, I will try to calculate the longitude.'

If the engineer had possessed a sextant, an apparatus with which the angular distance of objects can be measured with great precision, there would have been no difficulty in the operation. This evening by the height of the pole, the next day by the passing of the sun at the meridian, he would obtain the position of the island. But as they had not one he would have to supply the deficiency.

Harding then entered the Chimneys. By the light of the fire he cut two little flat rulers, which he joined together at one end so as to form a pair of compasses, whose legs could separate or come together. The fastening was fixed with a strong acacia thorn which was found in the wood pile. This instrument finished, the engineer returned to the beach, but as it was necessary to take the height of the pole from above a clear horizon, that is, a sea horizon, and as Claw Cape hid the southern horizon, he was obliged to look for a more suitable station. The best would evidently have been the shore exposed directly to the south; but the Mercy would have to be crossed, and that was a difficulty. Harding resolved, in consequence, to make his observation from Prospect Heights, taking into consideration its height above the level of the sea—a height which he intended to calculate next day by a simple process of elementary geometry.

The settlers, therefore, went to the plateau, ascending the left bank of the Mercy, and placed themselves on the edge which looked northwest and southeast, that is, above the curiously-shaped rocks which bordered the river.

This part of the plateau commanded the heights of the left bank, which sloped away to the extremity of Claw Cape, and to the southern side of the island. No obstacle intercepted their gaze, which swept the horizon in a semicircle from the cape to Reptile End. To the south the horizon, lighted by the first rays of the moon, was very clearly defined against the sky.

At this moment the Southern Cross presented itself to the observer in an inverted position, the star Alpha marking its base, which is nearer to the southern pole.

This constellation is not situated as near to the antarctic pole as the

Polar Star is to the arctic pole. The star Alpha is about twenty-seven degrees from it, but Cyrus Harding knew this and made allowance for it in his calculation. He took care also to observe the moment when it passed the meridian below the pole, which would simplify the operation.

Cyrus Harding pointed one leg of the compasses to the horizon, the other to Alpha, and the space between the two legs gave him the angular distance which separated Alpha from the horizon. In order to fix the angle obtained, he fastened with thorns the two pieces of wood on a third placed transversely, so that their separation should be properly maintained.

That done, there was only the angle to calculate by bringing back the observation to the level of the sea, taking into consideration the depression of the horizon, which would necessitate measuring the height of the cliff. The value of this angle would give the height of Alpha, and consequently that of the pole above the horizon, that is to say, the latitude of the island, since the latitude of a point of the globe is always equal to the height of the pole above the horizon of this point.

The calculations were left for the next day, and at ten o'clock every one was sleeping soundly.

Chapter 14

The next day, the 16th of April, and Easter Sunday, the settlers issued from the Chimneys at daybreak, and proceeded to wash their linen. The engineer intended to manufacture soap as soon as he could procure the necessary materials—soda or potash, fat or oil. The important question of renewing their wardrobe would be treated of in the proper time and place. At any rate their clothes would last at least six months longer, for they were strong, and could resist the wear of manual labour. But all would depend on the situation of the island with regard to inhabited land. This would be settled today if the weather permitted.

The sun rising above a clear horizon, announced a magnificent day, one of those beautiful autumn days which are like the last farewells of the warm season.

It was now necessary to complete the observations of the evening before by measuring the height of the cliff above the level of the sea.

'Shall you not need an instrument similar to the one which you used yesterday?' said Herbert to the engineer.

'No, my boy,' replied the latter, 'we are going to proceed differently, but in as precise a way.'

Herbert, wishing to learn everything he could, followed the engineer to the beach. Pencroft, Neb, and the reporter remained behind and occupied themselves in different ways.

Cyrus Harding had provided himself with a straight stick, twelve feet long, which he had measured as exactly as possible by comparing it with his own height, which he knew to a hair. Herbert carried a plumbline which Harding had given him, that is to say, a simple stone fastened to the end of a flexible fibre. Having reached a spot about twenty feet from the edge of the beach, and nearly five hundred feet from the cliff, which rose perpendicularly, Harding thrust the pole two feet into the sand, and wedging it up carefully, he managed, by means of the plumbline, to erect it perpendicularly with the plane of the horizon.

That done, he retired the necessary distance, when, lying on the sand, his eye glanced at the same time at the top of the pole and the crest of the cliff. He carefully marked the place with a little stick.

Then addressing Herbert—'Do you know the first principles of geometry?' he asked.

'Slightly, captain,' replied Herbert, who did not wish to put himself forward.

'You remember what are the properties of two similar triangles?'

'Yes,' replied Herbert; 'their homologous sides are proportional.'

'Well, my boy, I have just constructed two similar right-angled triangles; the first, the smallest, has for its sides the perpendicular pole, the distance which separates the little stick from the foot of the pole and my visual ray for hypothenuse; the second has for its sides the perpendicular cliff, the height of which we wish to measure, the distance which separates the little stick from the bottom of the cliff, and my visual ray also forms its hypothenuse, which proves to be prolongation of that of the first triangle.'

'Ah, captain, I understand!' cried Herbert. 'As the distance from the stick to the pole is to the distance from the stick to the base of the cliff, so is the height of the pole to the height of the cliff.'

'Just so, Herbert,' replied the engineer; 'and when we have measured the two first distances, knowing the height of the pole, we shall only have a sum in proportion to do, which will give us the height of the cliff, and will save us the trouble of measuring it directly.'

The two horizontal distances were found out by means of the pole, whose length above the sand was exactly ten feet.

The first distance was fifteen feet between the stick and the place where the pole was thrust into the sand.

The second distance between the stick and the bottom of the cliff was five hundred feet.

These measurements finished, Cyrus Harding and the lad returned to the Chimneys.

The engineer then took a flat stone which he had brought back from one of his previous excursions, a sort of slate, on which it was easy to trace figures with a sharp shell. He then proved the following proportions:—

15:500::10:x

500 x 10= 5000

5000 /15=333.3

From which it was proved that the granite cliff measured 333 feet in height.

Cyrus Harding then took the instrument which he had made the evening before, the space between its two legs giving the angular distance between the star Alpha and the horizon. He measured, very exactly, the opening of this angle on a circumference which he divided into 360 equal parts. Now, this angle by adding to it the twenty-seven degrees which separated Alpha from the antarctic pole, and by reducing to the level of the sea the height of the cliff on which the observation had been made, was found to be fifty- three degrees. These fifty-three degrees being subtracted from ninety degrees—the distance from the pole to the equator—there remained thirty- seven degrees. Cyrus Harding concluded, therefore, that Lincoln Island was situated on the thirty-seventh degree of the southern latitude, or taking into consideration through the imperfection of the performance, an error of five degrees, that it must be situated between the thirty-fifth and the fortieth parallel.

There was only the longitude to be obtained, and the position of the island would be determined, The engineer hoped to attempt this the same day, at twelve o'clock, at which moment the sun would pass the meridian.

It was decided that Sunday should be spent in a walk, or rather an exploring expedition, to that side of the island between the north of the lake and Shark Gulf, and if there was time they would push their discoveries to the northern side of Cape South Mandible. They would breakfast on the downs, and not return till evening.

At half-past eight the little band was following the edge of the channel. On the other side, on Safety Islet, numerous birds were gravely strutting. They were divers, easily recognized by their cry, which much resembles the braying of a donkey. Pencroft only considered them in an eatable point of view, and learnt with some satisfaction that their flesh, though blackish, is not bad food.

Great amphibious creatures could also be seen crawling on the sand;

seals, doubtless, who appeared to have chosen the islet for a place of refuge. It was impossible to think of those animals in an alimentary point of view, for their oily flesh is detestable; however, Cyrus Harding observed them attentively, and without making known his idea, he announced to his companions that very soon they would pay a visit to the islet. The beach was strewn with innumerable shells, some of which would have rejoiced the heart of a conchologist; there were, among others, the phasianella, the terebratual, etc. But what would be of more use, was the discovery, by Neb, at low tide, of a large oysterbed among the rocks, nearly five miles from the Chimneys.

'Neb will not have lost his day,' cried Pencroft, looking at the spacious oysterbed.

'It is really a fortunate discovery,' said the reporter, 'and as it is said that each oyster produces yearly from fifty to sixty thousand eggs, we shall have an inexhaustible supply there.'

'Only I believe that the oyster is not very nourishing,' said Herbert.

'No,' replied Harding. 'The oyster contains very little nitrogen, and if a man lived exclusively on them, he would have to eat not less than fifteen to sixteen dozen a day.'

'Capital!' replied Pencroft. 'We might swallow dozens and dozens without exhausting the bed. Shall we take some for breakfast?'

And without waiting for a reply to this proposal, knowing that it would be approved of, the sailor and Neb detached a quantity of the molluscs. They put them in a sort of net of hibiscus fibre, which Neb had manufactured, and which already contained food; they then continued to climb the coast between the downs and the sea.

From time to time Harding consulted his watch, so as to be prepared in time for the solar observation, which had to be made exactly at midday.

All that part of the island was very barren as far as the point which closed Union Bay, and which had received the name of Cape South Mandible. Nothing could be seen there but sand and shells, mingled with debris of lava. A few sea-birds frequented this desolate coast, gulls, great albatrosses, as well as wild duck, for which Pencroft had a great fancy. He tried to knock some over with an arrow, but without result, for they seldom perched, and he could not hit them on the wing.

This led the sailor to repeat to the engineer,—

'You see, captain, so long as we have not one or two fowling-pieces, we shall never get anything!'

'Doubtless, Pencroft,' replied the reporter, 'but it depends on you. Procure us some iron for the barrels, steel for the hammers, saltpetre, coal and sulphur for powder, mercury and nitric acid for the fulminate, and lead for the shot, and the captain will make us first-rate guns.'

'Oh!' replied the engineer, 'we might, no doubt, find all these substances on the island, but a gun is a delicate instrument, and needs very particular tools. However, we shall see later!'

'Why,' cried Pencroft, 'were we obliged to throw overboard all the weapons we had with us in the car, all our implements, even our pocket-knives?'

'But if we had not thrown them away, Pencroft, the balloon would have thrown us to the bottom of the sea!' said Herbert.

'What you say is true, my boy,' replied the sailor.

Then passing to another idea,—'Think,' said he, 'how astounded Jonathan Forster and his companions must have been when, next morning, they found the place empty, and the machine flown away!'

'I am utterly indifferent about knowing what they may have thought,' said the reporter.

'It was all my idea, that!' said Pencroft, with a satisfied air.

'A splendid idea, Pencroft!' replied Gideon Spilett, laughing, 'and which has placed us where we are.'

'I would rather be here than in the hands of the Southerners,' cried the sailor, 'especially since the captain has been kind enough to come and join us again.'

'So would I, truly!' replied the reporter. 'Besides, what do we want? Nothing.'

'If that is not—everything!' replied Pencroft, laughing and shrugging his shoulders. 'But, some day or other, we shall find means of going away!'

'Sooner, perhaps, than you imagine, my friends,' remarked the engineer, 'if Lincoln Island is but a medium distance from an inhabited island, or from a continent. We shall know in an hour. I have not a map of the Pacific, but my memory has preserved a very clear recollection of its southern part. The latitude which I obtained yesterday placed New Zealand to the west of Lincoln Island, and the coast of Chile to the east. But between these two countries, there is a distance of at least six thousand miles. It has, therefore, to be determined what point in this great space the island occupies, and this the longitude will give us presently, with a sufficient approximation, I hope.'

'Is not the archipelago of the Pomoutous the nearest point to us in latitude?' asked Herbert.

'Yes,' replied the engineer, 'but the distance which separates us from it is more than twelve hundred miles.'

'And that way?' asked Neb, who followed the conversation with extreme interest, pointing to the south.

'That way, nothing,' replied Pencroft.

'Nothing, indeed,' added the engineer.

'Well, Cyrus,' asked the reporter, 'if Lincoln Island is not more than two or three thousand miles from New Zealand or Chile?'

'Well,' replied the engineer, 'instead of building a house we will build a boat, and Master Pencroft shall be put in command—'

'Well then,' cried the sailor, 'I am quite ready to be captain—as soon as you can make a craft that's able to keep at sea!'

'We shall do it, if it is necessary,' replied Cyrus Harding.

But while these men, who really hesitated at nothing, were talking, the hour approached at which the observation was to be made. What Cyrus Harding was to do to ascertain the passage of the sun at the meridian of the island, without an instrument of any sort, Herbert could not guess.

The observers were then about six miles from the Chimneys, not far from that part of the downs in which the engineer had been found after his enigmatical preservation. They halted at this place and prepared for breakfast, for it was half-past eleven. Herbert went for some fresh water from a stream which ran near, and brought it back in a jug, which Neb had provided.

During these preparations Harding arranged everything for his astronomical observation. He chose a clear place on the shore, which the ebbing tide had left perfectly level. This bed of fine sand was as smooth as ice, not a grain out of place. It was of little importance whether it was horizontal or not, and it did not matter much whether the stick six feet high, which was planted there, rose perpendicularly. On the contrary, the engineer inclined it towards the south, that is to say, in the direction of the coast opposite to the sun, for it must not be forgotten that the settlers in Lincoln Island, as the island was situated in the Southern Hemisphere, saw the radiant planet describe its diurnal arc above the northern, and not above the southern horizon.

Herbert now understood how the engineer was going to proceed to ascertain the culmination of the sun, that is to say its passing the meridian of the island or, in other words, determine due south. It was by means of the shadow cast on the sand by the stick, a way which, for want of an instrument, would give him a suitable approach to the result which he wished to obtain.

In fact, the moment when this shadow would reach its minimum of length would be exactly twelve o'clock, and it would be enough to watch the extremity of the shadow, so as to ascertain the instant when, alter having successively diminished, it began to lengthen. By inclining his stick to the side opposite to the sun, Cyrus Harding made the shadow longer, and consequently its modifications would be more easily ascertained. In fact, the longer the needle of a dial is, the more easily can the movement of its point be followed. The shadow of the stick was nothing but the needle of a dial. The moment had come, and Cyrus Harding knelt on the sand, and with little wooden pegs, which he stuck into the sand, he began to mark the successive diminutions of the stick's shadow. His companions, bending over him, watched the operation with extreme interest. The reporter held his chronometer in his hand, ready to tell the hour which it marked when the shadow would be at its shortest. Moreover, as Cyrus Harding was working on the 16th of April, the day on which the true and the average time are identical, the hour given by Gideon Spilett would be the true hour then at Washington, which would simplify the calculation. Meanwhile as the sun slowly advanced, the shadow slowly diminished, and when it appeared to Cyrus Harding that it was beginning to increase, he asked, 'What o'clock is it?'

'One minute past five,' replied Gideon Spilett directly. They had now only to calculate the operation. Nothing could be easier. It could be seen that there existed, in round numbers, a difference of five hours between the meridian of Washington and that of Lincoln Island, that is to say, it was midday in Lincoln Island when it was already five o'clock in the evening in Washington. Now the sun, in its apparent movement round the earth, traverses one degree in four minutes, or fifteen degrees an hour. Fifteen degrees multiplied by five hours give seventy-five degrees.

Then, since Washington is 770° 3' 11" as much as to say seventy-seven degrees counted from the meridian of Greenwich which the Americans take for their starting-point for longitudes concurrently with the English—it followed that the island must be situated seventy-seven and seventy-five degrees west of the meridian of Greenwich, that is to say, on the hundred and fifty-second degree of west longitude.

Cyrus Harding announced this result to his companions, and taking into consideration errors of observation, as he had done for the latitude, he believed he could positively affirm that the position of Lincoln Island was between the thirty-fifth and the thirty-seventh parallel, and between the hundred and fiftieth and the hundred and fifty-fifth meridian to the west of the meridian of Greenwich.

The possible fault which he attributed to errors in the observation was, it may be seen, of five degrees on both sides, which, at sixty miles to a degree, would give an error of three hundred miles in latitude and longitude for the exact position.

But this error would not influence the determination which it was necessary to take. It was very evident that Lincoln Island was at such a distance from every country or island that it would be too hazardous to attempt to reach one in a frail boat.

In fact, this calculation placed it at least twelve hundred miles from Tahiti and the islands of the archipelago of the Pomoutous, more than eighteen hundred miles from New Zealand, and more than four thousand five hundred miles from the American coast!

And when Cyrus Harding consulted his memory, he could not remember in any way that such an island occupied, in that part of the Pacific, the situation assigned to Lincoln Island.

Chapter 15

The next day, the 17th of April, the sailor's first words were addressed to Gideon Spilett.

'Well, sir,' he asked, 'what shall we do today?'

'What the captain pleases,' replied the reporter.

Till then the engineer's companions had been brickmakers and potters, now they were to become metallurgists.

The day before, after breakfast, they had explored as far as the point of Mandible Cape, seven miles distant from the Chimneys. There, the long series of downs ended, and the soil had a volcanic appearance. There were no longer high cliffs as at Prospect Heights, but a strange and capricious border which surrounded the narrow gulf between the two capes, formed of mineral matter, thrown up by the volcano. Arrived at this point the settlers retraced their steps, and at nightfall entered the Chimneys; but they did not sleep before the question of knowing whether they could think of leaving Lincoln Island or not was definitely settled.

The twelve hundred miles which separated the island from the Pomoutous Island was a considerable distance. A boat could not cross it, especially at the approach of the bad season. Pencroft had expressly declared this. Now, to construct a simple boat even with the necessary tools, was a difficult work, and the colonists not having tools they must begin by making hammers, axes, adzes, saws, augers, planes, etc., which would take some time. It was decided, therefore, that they would winter at Lincoln Island, and that they would look for a more comfortable dwelling than the Chimneys, in which to pass the winter months.

Before anything else could be done it was necessary to make the iron ore, of which the engineer had observed some traces in the northwest part of the island, fit for use by converting it either into iron or into steel.

Metals are not generally found in the ground in a pure state. For the most part they are combined with oxygen or sulphur. Such was the case with the two specimens which Cyrus Harding had brought back, one of magnetic iron, not carbonated, the other a pyrite, also called sulphuret of iron. It was, therefore the first, the oxide of iron, which they must reduce with coal, that is to say, get rid of the oxygen, to obtain it in a pure state. This reduction is made by subjecting the ore with coal to a high temperature, either by the rapid and easy Catalan method, which has the advantage of transforming the ore into iron in a single operation, or by the blast furnace, which first smelts the ore, then changes it into iron, by carrying away the three to four per cent of coal, which is combined with it.

Now Cyrus Harding wanted iron, and he wished to obtain it as soon as possible. The ore which he had picked up was in itself very pure and rich. It was the oxydulous iron, which is found in confused masses of a deep gray colour; it gives a black dust, crystallized in the form of the regular octahedron. Native lodestones consist of this ore, and iron of the first quality is made in Europe from that with which Sweden and Norway are so abundantly supplied. Not far from this vein was the vein of coal already made use of by the settlers. The ingredients for the manufacture being close together would greatly facilitate the treatment of the ore. This is the cause of the wealth of the mines in Great Britain, where the coal aids the manufacture of the metal extracted from the same soil at the same time as itself.

'Then, captain,' said Pencroft, 'we are going to work iron ore?'

'Yes, my friend,' replied the engineer, 'and for that—something which will please you—we must begin by having a seal hunt on the islet.'

'A seal hunt!' cried the sailor, turning towards Gideon Spilett. 'Are seals needed to make iron?'

'Since Cyrus has said so!' replied the reporter.

But the engineer had already left the Chimneys, and Pencroft prepared for the seal hunt, without having received any other explanation.

Cyrus Harding, Herbert, Gideon Spilett, Neb, and the sailor were soon collected on the shore, at a place where the channel left a ford passable at low tide. The hunters could therefore traverse it without getting wet higher than the knee.

Harding then put his foot on the islet for the first, and his companions for the second time.

On their landing some hundreds of penguins looked fearlessly at them. The hunters, armed with sticks, could have killed them easily, but they were not guilty of such useless massacre, as it was important not to frighten the seals, who were lying on the sand several cable lengths off. They also respected certain innocent-looking birds, whose wings were reduced to the state of stumps, spread out like fins, ornamented with feathers of a scaly appearance. The settlers, therefore, prudently advanced towards the north point, walking over ground riddled with little holes, which formed nests for the sea-birds. Towards the extremity of the islet appeared great black heads floating just above the water, having exactly the appearance of rocks in motion.

These were the seals which were to be captured. It was necessary, however, first to allow them to land, for with their close, short hair, and their fusiform conformation, being excellent swimmers, it is difficult to catch them in the sea, while on land their short, webbed feet prevent their having more than a slow, waddling movement.

Pencroft knew the habits of these creatures, and he advised waiting till they were stretched on the sand, when the sun, before long, would send them to sleep. They must then manage to cut off their retreat and knock them on the head.

The hunters, having concealed themselves behind the rocks, waited silently.

An hour passed before the seals came to play on the sand. They could count half a dozen. Pencroft and Herbert then went round the point of the islet, so as to take them in the rear, and cut off their retreat. During this time Cyrus Harding, Spilett, and Neb, crawling behind the rocks, glided towards the future scene of combat.

All at once the tall figure of the sailor appeared. Pencroft shouted. The engineer and his two companions threw themselves between the sea and the seals. Two of the animals soon lay dead on the sand, but the rest regained the sea in safety.

'Here are the seals required, captain!' said the sailor, advancing towards the engineer.

'Capital,' replied Harding. 'We will make bellows of them!'

'Bellows!' cried Pencroft. 'Well! these are lucky seals!'

It was, in fact, a blowing-machine, necessary for the treatment of the ore that the engineer wished to manufacture with the skins of the amphibious creatures. They were of a medium size, for their length did not exceed six feet. They resembled a dog about the head.

As it was useless to burden themselves with the weight of both the animals, Neb and Pencroft resolved to skin them on the spot, while Cyrus Harding and the reporter continued to explore the islet.

The sailor and the Negro cleverly performed the operation, and three hours afterwards Cyrus Harding had at his disposal two seals' skins, which he intended to use in this state, without subjecting them to any tanning process.

The settlers waited till the tide was again low, and crossing the channel they entered the Chimneys.

The skins had then to be stretched on a frame of wood and sewn by means of fibres so as to preserve the air without allowing too much to escape. Cyrus Harding had nothing but the two steel blades from Top's collar, and yet he was so clever, and his companions aided him with so much intelligence, that three days afterwards the little colony's stock of tools was augmented by a blowing-machine, destined to inject the air into the midst of the ore when it should be subjected to heat—an indispensable condition to the success of the operation.

On the morning of the 20th of April began the 'metallic period,' as the reporter called it in his notes. The engineer had decided, as has been said, to operate near the veins both of coal and ore. Now, according to his observations, these veins were situated at the foot of the northeast spurs of Mount Franklin, that is to say, a distance of six miles from their home. It was impossible, therefore, to return every day to the Chimneys, and it was agreed that the little colony should camp under a hut of branches, so that the important operation could be followed night and day.

This settled, they set out in the morning. Neb and Pencroft dragged the bellows on a hurdle; also a quantity of vegetables and animals, which they besides could renew on the way.

The road led through Jacamar Wood, which they traversed obliquely from southeast to northwest, and in the thickest part. It was necessary to beat a path, which would in the future form the most direct road to Prospect Heights and Mount Franklin. The trees, belonging to the species already discovered, were magnificent. Herbert found some new ones, among others some which Pencroft called 'sham leeks'; for, in spite of their size, they were of the same liliaceous family as the onion, chive, shallot, or asparagus. These trees produce ligneous roots which, when cooked, are excellent; from them, by fermentation, a very agreeable liquor is made. They therefore made a good store of the roots.

The journey through the wood was long; it lasted the whole day, and so allowed plenty of time for examining the flora and fauna. Top, who took special charge of the fauna, ran through the grass and brushwood, putting up all sorts of game. Herbert and Gideon Spilett killed two kangaroos with bows and arrows, and also an animal which strongly resembled both a hedgehog and an ant-eater. It was like the first because it rolled itself into a ball, and bristled with spines, and the second because it had sharp claws, a long slender snout which terminated in a bird's beak, and an extendible tongue, covered with little thorns which served to hold the insects.

'And when it is in the pot,' asked Pencroft naturally, 'what will it be like?'

'An excellent piece of beef,' replied Herbert.

'We will not ask more from it,' replied the sailor,

During this excursion they saw several wild boars, which however, did not offer to attack the little band, and it appeared as if they would not meet with any dangerous beasts; when, in a thick part of the wood, the reporter thought he saw, some paces from him, among the lower branches of a tree, an animal which he took for a bear, and which he very tranquilly began to draw. Happily for Gideon Spilett, the animal in question did not belong to the redoubtable family of the plantigrades. It was only a koala, better known under the name of the sloth, being about the size of a large dog, and having stiff hair of a dirty colour, the paws armed with strong claws, which enabled it to climb trees and feed on the leaves. Having identified the animal, which they did not disturb, Gideon Spilett erased 'bear' from the title of his sketch, putting koala in its place, and the journey was resumed.

At five o'clock in the evening, Cyrus Harding gave the signal to halt. They were now outside the forest, at the beginning of the powerful spurs which supported Mount Franklin towards the west. At a distance of some hundred feet flowed the Red Creek, and consequently plenty of fresh water was within their reach.

The camp was soon organized. In less than an hour, on the edge of the forest, among the trees, a hut of branches interlaced with creepers, and pasted over with clay, offered a tolerable shelter. Their geological researches were put off till the next day. Supper was prepared, a good fire blazed before the hut, the roast turned, and at eight o'clock, while one of the settlers watched to keep up the fire, in case any wild beasts should prowl in the neighbourhood, the others slept soundly.

The next day, the 21st of April, Cyrus Harding accompanied by Herbert, went to look for the soil of ancient formation, on which he had already discovered a specimen of ore. They found the vein above ground, near the source of the creek, at the foot of one of the northeastern spurs. This ore, very rich in iron, enclosed in its fusible veinstone, was perfectly suited to the mode of reduction which the engineer intended to employ; that is, the Catalan method, but simplified, as it is used in Corsica. In fact, the Catalan method, properly so called, requires the construction of kilns and crucibles, in which the ore and the coal, placed in alternate layers, are transformed and reduced, But Cyrus Harding intended to economize these constructions, and wished simply to form, with the ore and the coal, a cubic mass, to the centre of which he would direct the wind from his bellows. Doubtless, it was the proceeding employed by Tubalcain, and the first metallurgists of the inhabited world. Now that which had succeeded with the grandson of Adam, and which still yielded good results in countries which in ore and fuel, could not but succeed with the settlers in Lincoln Island.

The coal, as well as the ore, was collected without trouble on the surface of the ground. They first broke the ore into little pieces, and cleansed them with the hand from the impurities which soiled their surface. Then coal and ore were arranged in heaps and in successive layers, as the charcoal-burner does with the wood which he wishes to carbonize. In this way, under the influence of the air projected by the blowing-machine, the coal would be transformed into carbonic acid, then into oxide of carbon, its use being to reduce the oxide of iron, that is to say, to rid it of the oxygen.

Thus the engineer proceeded. The bellows of sealskin, furnished at its extremity with a nozzle of clay, which had been previously fabricated in the pottery kiln, was established near the heap of ore. Using the mechanism which consisted of a frame, cords of fibre and counterpoise, he threw into the mass an abundance of air, which by raising the temperature also concurred with the chemical transformation to produce in time pure iron.

The operation was difficult. All the patience, all the ingenuity of the settlers was needed; but at last it succeeded, and the result was a lump of iron, reduced to a spongy state, which it was necessary to shingle and faggot, that is to say, to forge so as to expel from it the liquefied veinstone. These amateur smiths had, of course, no hammer; but they were in no worse a situation than the first metallurgist, and therefore did what, no doubt, he had to do.

A handle was fixed to the first lump, and was used as a hammer to forge the second on a granite anvil, and thus they obtained a coarse but useful metal. At length, after many trials and much fatigue, on the 25th of April several bars of iron were forged, and transformed into tools, crowbars, pincers, pickaxes, spades, etc., which Pencroft and Neb declared to be real jewels. But the metal was not yet in its most serviceable state, that is, of steel. Now steel is a combination of iron and coal, which is extracted, either from the liquid ore, by taking from it the excess of coal, or from the iron by adding to it the coal which was wanting. The first, obtained by the decarburation of the metal, gives natural or puddled steel; the second, produced by the carburation of the iron, gives steel of cementation.

It was the last which Cyrus Harding intended to forge, as he possessed iron in a pure state. He succeeded by heating the metal with powdered coal in a crucible which had previously been manufactured from clay suitable for the purpose.

He then worked this steel, which is malleable both when hot or cold, with the hammer. Neb and Pencroft, cleverly directed, made hatchets, which, heated red-hot, and plunged suddenly into cold water, acquired an excellent temper.

Other instruments, of course roughly fashioned, were also manufactured; blades for planes, axes, hatchets, pieces of steel to be transformed into saws, chisels; then iron for spades, pickaxes, hammers, nails, etc. At last, on the 5th of May, the metallic period ended, the smiths returned to the Chimneys, and new work would soon authorize them to take a fresh title.

Chapter 16

It was the 6th of May, a day which corresponds to the 6th of November in the countries of the Northern Hemisphere. The sky had been obscured for some days, and it was of importance to make preparations for the winter. However, the temperature was not as yet much lower, and a centigrade thermometer, transported to Lincoln Island, would still have marked an average of ten to twelve degrees above zero. This was not surprising, since Lincoln Island, probably situated between the thirty-fifth and fortieth parallel, would be subject, in the Southern Hemisphere, to the same climate as Sicily or Greece in the Northern Hemisphere. But as Greece and Sicily have severe cold, producing snow and ice, so doubtless would Lincoln Island in the severest part of the winter and it was advisable to provide against it.

In any case if cold did not yet threaten them, the rainy season would begin, and on this lonely island, exposed to all the fury of the elements, in mid-ocean, bad weather would be frequent, and probably terrible. The question of a more comfortable dwelling than the Chimneys must therefore be seriously considered and promptly resolved on.

Pencroft, naturally, had some predilection for the retreat which he had discovered, but he well understood that another must be found. The Chimneys had been already visited by the sea, under circumstances which are known, and it would not do to be exposed again to a similar accident.

'Besides,' added Cyrus Harding, who this day was talking of these things with his companions, 'we have some precautions to take.'

'Why? The island is not inhabited,' said the reporter.

'That is probable,' replied the engineer, 'although we have not yet explored the interior; but if no human beings are found, I fear that dangerous animals may abound. It is necessary to guard against a possible attack, so that we shall not be obliged to watch every night, or to keep up a fire. And then, my friends, we must foresee everything. We are here in a part of the Pacific often frequented by Malay pirates—'

'What!' said Herbert, 'at such a distance from land?'

'Yes, my boy,' replied the engineer. 'These pirates are bold sailors as well as formidable enemies, and we must take measures accordingly.'

'Well,' replied Pencroft, 'we will fortify ourselves against savages with two legs as well as against savages with four. But, captain, will it not be best to explore every part of the island before undertaking anything else?'

'That would be best,' added Gideon Spilett.

'Who knows if we might not find on the opposite side one of the caverns which we have searched for in vain here?'

'That is true,' replied the engineer, 'but you forget, my friends, that it will be necessary to establish ourselves in the neighbourhood of a watercourse, and that, from the summit of Mount Franklin, we could not see towards the west, either stream or river. Here, on the contrary, we are placed between the Mercy and Lake Grant, an advantage which must not be neglected. And, besides, this side, looking towards the east, is not exposed as the other is to the trade-winds, which in this hemisphere blow from the northwest.'

'Then, captain,' replied the sailor, 'let us build a house on the edge of the lake. Neither bricks nor tools are wanting now. After having been brickmakers, potters, smelters, and smiths, we shall surely know how to be masons!'

'Yes, my friend; but before coming to any decision we must consider the matter thoroughly. A natural dwelling would spare us much work, and would be a surer retreat, for it would be as well defended against enemies from the interior as those from outside.'

'That is true, Cyrus,' replied the reporter, 'but we have already examined all that mass of granite, and there is not a hole, not a cranny!'

'No, not one!' added Pencroft. 'Ah, if we were able to dig out a dwelling in that cliff, at a good height, so as to be out of the reach of harm, that would be capital! I can see that on the front which looks seaward, five or six rooms—'

'With windows to light them!' said Herbert, laughing.

'And a staircase to climb up to them!' added Neb.

'You are laughing,' cried the sailor, 'and why? What is there impossible in what I propose? Haven't we got pickaxes and spades? Won't Captain Harding be able to make powder to blow up the mine? Isn't it true, captain, that you will make powder the very day we want it?'

Cyrus Harding listened to the enthusiastic Pencroft developing his fanciful projects. To attack this mass of granite, even by a mine, was Herculean work, and it was really vexing that nature could not help them at their need. But the engineer did not reply to the sailor except by proposing to examine the cliff more attentively, from the mouth of the river to the angle which terminated it on the north.

They went out, therefore, and the exploration was made with extreme care, over an extent of nearly two miles. But in no place in the bare, straight cliff, could any cavity be found. The nests of the rock pigeons which fluttered at its summit were only, in reality, holes bored at the very top, and on the irregular edge of the granite.

It was a provoking circumstance, and as to attacking this cliff, either with pickaxe or with powder, so as to effect a sufficient excavation, it was not to be thought of. It so happened that, on all this part of the shore, Pencroft had discovered the only habitable shelter, that is to say, the Chimneys, which now had to be abandoned.

The exploration ended, the colonists found themselves at the north angle of the cliff, where it terminated in long slopes which died away on the shore. From this place, to its extreme limit in the west, it only formed a sort of declivity, a thick mass of stones, earth, and sand, bound together by plants, bushes, and grass inclined at an angle of only forty-five degrees. Clumps of trees grew on these slopes, which were also carpeted with thick grass. But the vegetation did not extend far, and a long, sandy plain, which began at the foot of these slopes, reached to the beach.

Cyrus Harding thought, not without reason, that the overplus of the lake must overflow on this side. The excess of water furnished by the Red Creek must also escape by some channel or other. Now the engineer had not yet found this channel on any part of the shore already explored, that is to say, from the mouth of the stream on the west of Prospect Heights.

The engineer now proposed to his companions to climb the slope, and to return to the Chimneys by the heights, while exploring the northern and eastern shores of the lake. The proposal was accepted, and in a few minutes Herbert and Neb were on the upper plateau. Cyrus Harding, Gideon Spilett, and Pencroft followed with more sedate steps.

The beautiful sheet of water glittered through the trees under the rays of the sun. In this direction the country was charming. The eye feasted on the groups of trees. Some old trunks, bent with age, showed black against the verdant grass which covered the ground. Crowds of brilliant cockatoos screamed among the branches, moving prisms, hopping from one bough to another.

The settlers instead of going directly to the north bank of the lake, made a circuit round the edge of the plateau, so as to join the mouth of the creek on its left bank. It was a detour of more than a mile and a half. Walking was easy, for the trees widely spread, left a considerable space between them. The fertile zone evidently stopped at this point, and vegetation would be less vigorous in the part between the course of the Creek and the Mercy.

Cyrus Harding and his companions walked over this new ground with great care. Bows, arrows, and sticks with sharp iron points were their only weapons. However, no wild beast showed itself, and it was probable that these animals frequented rather the thick forests in the south; but the settlers had the disagreeable surprise of seeing Top stop before a snake of great size, measuring from fourteen to fifteen feet in length. Neb killed it by a blow from his stick. Cyrus Harding examined the reptile, and declared it not venomous, for it belonged to that species of diamond serpents which the natives of New South Wales rear. But it was possible that others existed whose bite was mortal such as the deaf vipers with forked tails, which rise up under the feet, or those winged snakes, furnished with two ears, which enable them to proceed with great rapidity. Top, the first moment of surprise over, began a reptile chase with such eagerness, that they feared for his safety. His master called him back directly.

The mouth of the Red Creek, at the place where it entered into the lake, was soon reached. The explorers recognized on the opposite shore the point which they had visited on their descent from Mount Franklin. Cyrus Harding ascertained that the flow of water into it from the creek was considerable. Nature must therefore have provided some place for the escape of the overplus. This doubtless formed a fall, which, if it could be discovered, would be of great use.

The colonists, walking apart, but not straying far from each other, began to skirt the edge of the lake, which was very steep. The water appeared to be full of fish, and Pencroft resolved to make some fishing-rods, so as to try and catch some.

The northeast point was first to be doubled. It might have been supposed that the discharge of water was at this place, for the extremity of the lake was almost on a level with the edge of the plateau. But no signs of this were discovered, and the colonists continued to explore the bank, which, after a slight bend, descended parallel to the shore.

On this side the banks were less woody, but clumps of trees, here and there, added to the picturesqueness of the country. Lake Grant was viewed from thence in all its extent, and no breath disturbed the surface of its waters. Top, in beating the bushes, put up flocks of birds of different kinds, which Gideon Spilett and Herbert saluted with arrows. Orie was hit by the lad, and fell into some marshy grass. Top rushed forward, and brought a beautiful swimming bird, of a slate colour, short beak, very developed frontal plate, and wings edged with white. It was a 'coot,' the size of a large partridge, belonging to the group of macrodactyls which form the transition between the order of wading birds and that of palmipeds. Sorry game, in truth, and its flavour is far from pleasant. But Top was not so particular in these things as his masters, and it was agreed that the coot should be for his supper.

The settlers were now following the eastern bank of the lake, and they would not be long in reaching the part which they already knew. The engineer was much surprised at not seeing any indication of the discharge of water. The reporter and the sailor talked with him, and he could not conceal his astonishment.

At this moment Top, who had been very quiet till then, gave signs of agitation. The intelligent animal went backwards and forwards on the shore, stopped suddenly, and looked at the water, one paw raised, as if he was pointing at some invisible game; then he barked furiously, and was suddenly silent.

Neither Cyrus Harding nor his companions had at first paid any attention to Top's behaviour; but the dog's barking soon became so frequent that the engineer noticed it.

'What is there, Top?' he asked.

The dog bounded towards his master, seeming to be very uneasy, and then rushed again towards the bank. Then, all at once, he plunged into the lake.

'Here, Top!' cried Cyrus Harding, who did not like his dog to venture into the treacherous water.

'What's happening down there?' asked Pencroft, examining the surface of the lake.

'Top smells some amphibious creature,' replied Herbert.

'An alligator, perhaps,' said the reporter.

'I do not think so,' replied Harding. 'Alligators are only met with in regions less elevated in latitude.'

Meanwhile Top had returned at his master's call, and had regained the shore: but he could not stay quiet; he plunged in among the tall grass, and guided by instinct, he appeared to follow some invisible being which was slipping along under the surface of the water. However the water was calm; not a ripple disturbed its surface. Several times the settlers stopped on the bank, and observed it attentively. Nothing appeared. There was some mystery there.

The engineer was puzzled.

'Let us pursue this exploration to the end,' said he.

Half an hour after they had all arrived at the southeast angle of the lake, on Prospect Heights. At this point the examination of the banks of the lake was considered finished, and yet the engineer had not been able to discover how and where the waters were discharged. 'There is no doubt this overflow exists,' he repeated, and since it is not visible it must go through the granite cliff at the west!'

'But what importance do you attach to knowing that, my dear Cyrus?' asked Gideon Spilett.

'Considerable importance,' replied the engineer; 'for if it flows through the cliff there is probably some cavity, which it would be easy to render habitable after turning away the water.'

'But is it not possible, captain, that the water flows away at the bottom of the lake,' said Herbert, 'and that it reaches the sea by some subterranean passage?'

'That might be,' replied the engineer, 'and should it be so we shall be obliged to build our house ourselves, since nature has not done it for us.'

The colonists were about to begin to traverse the plateau to return to the Chimneys, when Top gave new signs of agitation. He barked with fury, and before his master could restrain him, he had plunged a second time into the lake.

All ran towards the bank. The dog was already more than twenty feet off, and Cyrus was calling him back, when an enormous head emerged from the water, which did not appear to be deep in that place.

Herbert recognized directly the species of amphibian to which the tapering head, with large eyes, and adorned with long silky moustaches, belonged.

'A lamantin!' he cried.

It was not a lamantin, but one of that species of the order of cetaceans, which bear the name of the 'dugong,' for its nostrils were open at the upper part of its snout. The enormous animal rushed on the dog, who tried to escape by returning towards the shore. His master could do nothing to save him, and before Gideon Spilett or Herbert thought of bending their bows, Top, seized by the dugong, had disappeared beneath the water.

Neb, his iron-tipped spear in his hand, wished to go to Top's help, and attack the dangerous animal in its own element.

'No, Neb,' said the engineer, restraining his courageous servant.

Meanwhile, a struggle was going on beneath the water, an inexplicable struggle, for in his situation Top could not possibly resist; and judging by the bubbling of the surface it must be also a terrible struggle, and could not but terminate in the death of the dog! But suddenly, in the middle of a foaming circle, Top reappeared. Thrown in the air by some unknown power, he rose ten feet above the surface of the lake, fell again into the midst of the agitated waters, and then soon gained the shore, without any severe wounds, miraculously saved.

Cyrus Harding and his companions could not understand it. What was not less inexplicable was that the struggle still appeared to be going on. Doubtless, the dugong, attacked by some powerful animal, after having released the dog, was fighting on its own account. But it did not last long. The water became red with blood, and the body of the dugong, emerging from the sheet of scarlet which spread around, soon stranded on a little beach at the south angle of the lake. The colonists ran towards it. The dugong was dead. It was an enormous animal, fifteen or sixteen feet long, and must have weighed from three to four thousand pounds. At its neck was a wound, which appeared to have been produced by a sharp blade.

What could the amphibious creature have been, who, by this terrible blow had destroyed the formidable dugong? No one could tell, and much interested in this incident, Harding and his companions returned to the Chimneys.

Chapter 17

The next day, the 7th of May, Harding and Gideon Spilett, leaving Neb to prepare breakfast, climbed Prospect Heights, while Herbert and Pencroft ascended by the river, to renew their store of wood.

The engineer and the reporter soon reached the little beach on which the dugong had been stranded. Already flocks of birds had attacked the mass of flesh, and had to be driven away with stones, for Cyrus wished to keep the fat for the use of the colony. As to the animal's flesh it would furnish excellent food, for in the islands of the Malay Archipelago and elsewhere, it is especially reserved for the table of the native princes. But that was Neb's affair.

At this moment Cyrus Harding had other thoughts. He was much interested in the incident of the day before. He wished to penetrate the mystery of that submarine combat, and to ascertain what monster could have given the dugong so strange a wound. He remained at the edge of the lake, looking, observing; but nothing appeared under the tranquil waters, which sparkled in the first rays of the rising sun.

At the beach, on which lay the body of the dugong, the water was tolerably shallow, but from this point the bottom of the lake sloped gradually, and it was probable that the depth was considerable in the centre. The lake might be considered as a large centre basin, which was filled by the water from the Red Creek.

'Well, Cyrus,' said the reporter, 'there seems to be nothing suspicious in this water.'

'No, my dear Spilett,' replied the engineer, 'and I really do not know how to account for the incident of yesterday.'

'I acknowledge,' returned Spilett, 'that the wound given this creature is, at least, very strange, and I cannot explain either how Top was so vigorously cast up out of the water. One could have thought that a powerful arm hurled him up, and that the same arm with a dagger killed the dugong!'

'Yes,' replied the engineer, who had become thoughtful; 'there is something there that I cannot understand. But do you better understand either, my dear Spilett, in what way I was saved myself—how I was drawn from the waves, and carried to the downs? No! Is it not true? Now, I feel sure that there is some mystery there, which, doubtless, we shall discover some day. Let us observe, but do not dwell on these singular incidents before our companions. Let us keep our remarks to ourselves, and continue our work.'

It will be remembered that the engineer had not as yet been able to discover the place where the surplus water escaped, but he knew it must exist somewhere. He was much surprised to see a strong current at this place. By throwing in some bits of wood he found that it set towards the southern angle. He followed the current, and arrived at the south point of the lake.

There was there a sort of depression in the water, as if it was suddenly lost in some fissure in the ground.

Harding listened; placing his ear to the level of the lake, he very distinctly heard the noise of a subterranean fall.

'There,' said he, rising, 'is the discharge of the water; there, doubtless, by a passage in the granite cliff, it joins the sea, through cavities which we can use to our profit. Well, I can find it!'

The engineer cut a long branch, stripped it of its leaves, and plunging it into the angle between the two banks, he found that there was a large hole one foot only beneath the surface of the water. This hole was the opening so long looked for in vain, and the force of the current was such that the branch was torn from the engineer's hands and disappeared.

'There is no doubt about it now,' repeated Harding. 'There is the outlet, and I will lay it open to view!'

'How?' asked Gideon Spilett.

'By lowering the level of the water of the lake three feet.' 'And how will you lower the level?'

'By opening another outlet larger than this.'

'At what place, Cyrus?'

'At the part of the bank nearest the coast.'

'But it is a mass of granite!' observed Spilett.

'Well,' replied Cyrus Harding, 'I will blow up the granite, and the water escaping, will subside, so as to lay bare this opening—'

'And make a waterfall, by falling on to the beach,' added the reporter.

'A fall that we shall make use of!' replied Cyrus. 'Come, come!'

The engineer hurried away his companion, whose confidence in Harding was such that he did not doubt the enterprise would succeed. And yet, how was this granite wall to be opened without powder, and with imperfect instruments? Was not this work upon which the engineer was so bent above their strength?

When Harding and the reporter entered the Chimneys, they found Herbert and Pencroft unloading their raft of wood.

'The woodmen have just finished, captain.' said the sailor, laughing, 'and when you want masons—'

'Masons,—no, but chemists,' replied the engineer.

'Yes,' added the reporter, 'we are going to blow up the island—'

'Blow up the island?' cried Pencroft.

'Part of it, at least,' replied Spilett.

'Listen to me, my friends,' said the engineer. And he made known to them the result of his observations.

According to him, a cavity, more or less considerable, must exist in the mass of granite which supported Prospect Heights, and he intended to penetrate into it. To do this, the opening through which the water rushed must first be cleared, and the level lowered by making a larger outlet. Therefore an explosive substance must be manufactured, which would make a deep trench in some other part of the shore. This was what Harding was going to attempt with the minerals which nature placed at his disposal.

It is useless to say with what enthusiasm all, especially Pencroft, received this project. To employ great means, open the granite, create a cascade, that suited the sailor. And he would just as soon be a chemist as a mason or bootmaker, since the engineer wanted chemicals. He would be all that they liked, 'even a professor of dancing and deportment,' said he to Neb, if that was ever necessary.

Neb and Pencroft were first of all told to extract the grease from the dugong, and to keep the flesh, which was destined for food. Such perfect confidence had they in the engineer, that they set out directly, without even asking a question. A few minutes after them, Cyrus Harding, Herbert, and Gideon Spilett, dragging the hurdle, went towards the vein of coals, where those shistose pyrites abound which are met with in the most recent transition soil, and of which Harding had already found a specimen. All the day being employed in carrying a quantity of these stones to the Chimneys, by evening they had several tons.

The next day, the 8th of May, the engineer began his manipulations. These shistose pyrites being composed principally of coal, flint, alumina, and sulphuret of iron—the latter in excess—it was necessary to separate the sulphuret of iron, and transform it into sulphate as rapidly as possible. The sulphate obtained, the sulphuric acid could then be extracted.

This was the object to be attained. Sulphuric acid is one of the agents the most frequently employed, and the manufacturing importance of a nation can be measured by the consumption which is made of it. This acid would later be of great use to the settlers, in the manufacturing of candles, tanning skins, etc., but this time the engineer reserved it for another use.

Cyrus Harding chose, behind the Chimneys, a site where the ground was perfectly level. On this ground he placed a layer of branches and chopped wood, on which were piled some pieces of shistose pyrites, buttressed one against the other, the whole being covered with a thin layer of pyrites, previously reduced to the size of a nut.

This done, they set fire to the wood, the heat was communicated to the shist, which soon kindled, since it contains coal and sulphur. Then new layers of bruised pyrites were arranged so as to form an immense heap, the exterior of which was covered with earth and grass, several air-holes being left, as if it was a stack of wood which was to be carbonized to make charcoal.

They then left the transformation to complete itself, and it would not take less than ten or twelve days for the sulphuret of iron to be changed to sulphate of iron and the alumina into sulphate of alumina, two equally soluble substances, the others, flint, burnt coal, and cinders, not being so.

While this chemical work was going on, Cyrus Harding proceeded with other operations, which were pursued with more than zeal,—it was eagerness.

Neb and Pencroft had taken away the fat from the dugong, and placed it in large earthen pots. It was then necessary to separate the glycerine from the fat by saponifying it. Now, to obtain this result, it had to be treated either with soda or lime. In fact, one or other of these substances, after having attacked the fat, would form a soap by separating the glycerine, and it was just this glycerine which the engineer wished to obtain. There was no want of lime, only treatment by lime would give calcareous soap, insoluble, and consequently useless, while treatment by soda would furnish, on the contrary, a soluble soap, which could be put to domestic use. Now, a practical man, like Cyrus Harding, would rather try to obtain soda. Was this difficult? No; for marine plants abounded on the shore, glass-wort, ficoides, and all those fucaceae which form wrack. A large quantity of these plants was collected, first dried, then burnt in holes in the open air. The combustion of these plants was kept up for several days, and the result was a compact gray mass, which has been long known under the name of 'natural soda.'

This obtained, the engineer treated the fat with soda, which gave both a soluble soap and that neutral substance, glycerine.

But this was not all. Cyrus Harding still needed, in view of his future preparation, another substance, nitrate of potash, which is better known under the name of salt niter, or of saltpetre.

Cyrus Harding could have manufactured this substance by treating the carbonate of potash, which would be easily extracted from the cinders of the vegetables, by azotic acid. But this acid was wanting, and he would have been in some difficulty, if nature had not happily furnished the saltpetre, without giving them any other trouble than that of picking it up. Herbert found a vein of it at the foot of Mount Franklin, and they had nothing to do but purify this salt.

These different works lasted a week. They were finished before the transformation of the sulphuret into sulphate of iron had been accomplished. During the following days the settlers had time to construct a furnace of bricks of a particular arrangement, to serve for the distillation of the sulphate or iron when it had been obtained. All this was finished about the 18th of May, nearly at the time when the chemical transformation terminated. Gideon Spilett, Herbert, Neb, and Pencroft, skilfully directed by the engineer, had become most clever workmen. Before all masters, necessity is the one most listened to, and who teaches the best.

When the heap of pyrites had been entirely reduced by fire, the result of the operation, consisting of sulphate of iron, sulphate of alumina, flint, remains of coal, and cinders was placed in a basinful of water. They stirred this mixture, let it settle, then decanted it, and obtained a clear liquid containing in solution sulphate of iron and sulphate of alumina, the other matters remaining solid, since they are insoluble. Lastly, this liquid being partly evapourated, crystals of sulphate of iron were deposited, and the not evapourated liquid, which contained the sulphate of alumina, was thrown away.

Cyrus Harding had now at his disposal a large quantity of these sulphate of iron crystals, from which the sulphuric acid had to be extracted. The making of sulphuric acid is a very expensive manufacture. Considerable works are necessary—a special set of tools, an apparatus of platina, leaden chambers, unassailable by the acid, and in which the transformation is performed, etc. The engineer had none of these at his disposal, but he knew that, in Bohemia especially, sulphuric acid is manufactured by very simple means, which have also the advantage of producing it to a superior degree of concentration. It is thus that the acid known under the name of Nordhausen acid is made.

To obtain sulphuric acid, Cyrus Harding had only one operation to make, to calcine the sulphate of iron crystals in a closed vase, so that the sulphuric acid should distil in vapour, which vapour, by condensation, would produce the acid.

The crystals were placed in pots, and the heat from the furnace would distil the sulphuric acid. The operation was successfully completed, and on the 20th of May, twelve days after commencing it, the engineer was the possessor of the agent which later he hoped to use in so many different ways.

Now, why did he wish for this agent? Simply to produce azotic acid; and that was easy, since saltpetre, attacked by sulphuric acid, gives azotic, or nitric, acid by distillation.

But, after all, how was he going to employ this azotic acid? His companions were still ignorant of this, for he had not informed them of the result at which he aimed.

However, the engineer had nearly accomplished his purpose, and by a last operation he would procure the substance which had given so much trouble.

Taking some azotic acid, he mixed it with glycerine, which had been previously concentrated by evapouration, subjected to the water-bath, and he obtained, without even employing a refrigerant mixture, several pints of an oily yellow mixture.

This last operation Cyrus Harding had made alone, in a retired place, at a distance from the Chimneys, for he feared the danger of an explosion, and when he showed a bottle of this liquid to his friends, he contented himself with saying,—

'Here is nitroglycerine!'

It was really this terrible production, of which the explosive power is perhaps tenfold that of ordinary powder, and which has already caused so many accidents. However, since a way has been found to transform it into dynamite, that is to say, to mix with it some solid substance, clay or sugar, porous enough to hold it, the dangerous liquid has been used with some security. But dynamite was not yet known at the time when the settlers worked on Lincoln Island.

'And is it that liquid that is going to blow up our rocks?' said Pencroft incredulously.

'Yes, my friend,' replied the engineer, 'and this nitroglycerine will produce so much the more effect, as the granite is extremely hard, and will oppose a greater resistance to the explosion.'

'And when shall we see this, captain?'

'Tomorrow, as soon as we have dug a hole for the mine, replied the engineer.

The next day, the 21st of May, at daybreak, the miners went to the point which formed the eastern shore of Lake Grant, and was only five hundred feet from the coast. At this place, the plateau inclined downwards from the waters, which were only restrained by their granite case. Therefore, if this case was broken, the water would escape by the opening and form a stream, which, flowing over the inclined surface of the plateau, would rush on to the beach. Consequently, the level of the lake would be greatly lowered, and the opening where the water escaped would be exposed, which was their final aim.

Under the engineer's directions, Pencroft, armed with a pickaxe, which he handled skilfully and vigorously, attacked the granite. The hole was made on the point of the shore, slanting, so that it should meet a much lower level than that of the water of the lake. In this way the explosive force, by scattering the rock, would open a large place for the water to rush out.

The work took some time, for the engineer, wishing to produce a great effect, intended to devote not less than seven quarts of nitroglycerine to the operation. But Pencroft, relieved by Neb, did so well, that towards four o'clock in the evening, the mine was finished.

Now the question of setting fire to the explosive substance was raised. Generally, nitroglycerine is ignited by caps of fulminate, which in bursting cause the explosion. A shock is therefore needed to produce the explosion, for, simply lighted, this substance would burn without exploding.

Cyrus Harding could certainly have fabricated a percussion cap. In default of fulminate, he could easily obtain a substance similar to guncotton, since he had azotic acid at his disposal. This substance, pressed in a cartridge, and introduced among the nitroglycerine, would burst by means of a fuse, and cause the explosion.

But Cyrus Harding knew that nitroglycerine would explode by a shock. He resolved to employ this means, and try another way, if this did not succeed.

In fact, the blow of a hammer on a few drops of nitroglycerine, spread out on a hard surface, was enough to create an explosion. But the operator could not be there to give the blow, without becoming a victim to the operation. Harding, therefore, thought of suspending a mass of iron, weighing several pounds, by means of a fibre, to an upright just above the mine. Another long fibre, previously impregnated with sulphur, was attached to the middle of the first, by one end, while the other lay on the ground several feet distant from the mine. The second fibre being set on fire, it would burn till it reached the first. This catching fire in its turn, would break, and the mass of iron would fall on the nitroglycerine. This apparatus being then arranged, the engineer, after having sent his companions to a distance, filled the hole, so that the nitroglycerine was on a level with the opening; then he threw a few drops of it on the surface of the rock, above which the mass of iron was already suspended.

This done, Harding lit the end of the sulphured fibre, and leaving the place, he returned with his companions to the Chimneys.

The fibre was intended to burn five and twenty minutes, and, in fact, five and twenty minutes afterwards a most tremendous explosion was heard. The island appeared to tremble to its very foundation. Stones were projected in the air as if by the eruption of a volcano. The shock produced by the displacing of the air was such, that the rocks of the Chimneys shook. The settlers, although they were more than two miles from the mine, were thrown on the ground.

They rose, climbed the plateau, and ran towards the place where the bank of the lake must have been shattered by the explosion.

A cheer escaped them! A large rent was seen in the granite! A rapid stream of water rushed foaming across the plateau and dashed down a height of three hundred feet on to the beach!

Chapter 18

Cyrus Harding's project had succeeded, but, according to his usual habit he showed no satisfaction; with closed lips and a fixed look, he remained motionless. Herbert was in ecstasies, Neb bounded with joy, Pencroft nodded his great head, murmuring these words,—

'Come, our engineer gets on capitally!'

The nitroglycerine had indeed acted powerfully. The opening which it had made was so large that the volume of water which escaped through this new outlet was at least treble that which before passed through the old one. The result was, that a short time after the operation the level of the lake would be lowered two feet, or more.

The settlers went to the Chimneys to take some pickaxes, iron-tipped spears, string made of fibres, flint and steel; they then returned to the plateau, Top accompanying them.

On the way the sailor could not help saying to the engineer,—

'Don't you think, captain, that by means of that charming liquid you have made, one could blow up the whole of our island?'

'Without any doubt, the island, continents, and the world itself,' replied the engineer. 'It is only a question of quantity.'

'Then could you not use this nitroglycerine for loading firearms?' asked the sailor.

'No, Pencroft; for it is too explosive a substance. But it would be easy to make some guncotton, or even ordinary powder, as we have azotic acid, saltpetre, sulphur, and coal. Unhappily, it is the guns which we have not got.

'Oh, captain,' replied the sailor, 'with a little determination—'

Pencroft had erased the word 'impossible' from the dictionary of Lincoln Island.

The settlers, having arrived at Prospect Heights, went immediately towards that point of the lake near which was the old opening now uncovered. This outlet had now become practicable, since the water no longer rushed through it, and it would doubtless be easy to explore the interior.

In a few minutes the settlers had reached the lower point of the lake, and a glance showed them that the object had been attained.

In fact, in the side of the lake, and now above the surface of the water, appeared the long-looked-for opening. A narrow ridge, left bare by the retreat of the water, allowed them to approach it. This orifice was nearly twenty feet in width, but scarcely two in height. It was like the mouth of a drain at the edge of the pavement, and therefore did not offer an easy passage to the settlers; but Neb and Pencroft, taking their pickaxes, soon made it of a suitable height.

The engineer then approached, and found that the sides of the opening, in its upper part at least, had not a slope of more than from thirty to thirty-five degrees. It was therefore practicable, and, provided that the declivity did not increase, it would be easy to descend even to the level of the sea. If then, as was probable, some vast cavity existed in the interior of the granite, it might, perhaps, be of great use.

'Well, captain, what are we stopping for?' asked the sailor, impatient to enter the narrow passage. You see Top has got before us!'

'Very well,' replied the engineer. 'But we must see our way. Neb, go and cut some resinous branches.'

Neb and Herbert ran to the edge of the lake, shaded with pines and other green trees, and soon returned with some branches, which they made into torches. The torches were lighted with flint and steel, and Cyrus Harding leading, the settlers ventured into the dark passage, which the overplus of the lake had formerly filled.

Contrary to what might have been supposed, the diameter of the passage increased as the explorers proceeded, so that they very soon were able to stand upright. The granite, worn by the water for an infinite time, was very slippery, and falls were to be dreaded. But the settlers were all attached to each other by a cord, as is frequently done in ascending mountains. Happily some projections of the granite, forming regular steps, made the descent less perilous. Drops, still hanging from the rocks, shone here and there under the light of the torches, and the explorers guessed that the sides were clothed with innumerable stalactites. The engineer examined this black granite. There was not a stratum, not a break in it. The mass was compact, and of an extremely close grain. The passage dated, then, from the very origin of the island. It was not the water which little by little had hollowed it. Pluto and not Neptune had bored it with his own hand, and on the wall traces of an eruptive work could be distinguished, which all the washing of the water had not been able totally to efface.

The settlers descended very slowly. They could not but feel a certain awe, in this venturing into these unknown depths, for the first time visited by human beings. They did not speak, but they thought; and the thought came to more than one, that some polypus or other gigantic cephalopod might inhabit the interior cavities, which were in communication with the sea. However, Top kept at the head of the little band, and they could rely on the sagacity of the dog, who would not fail to give the alarm if there was any need for it.

After having descended about a hundred feet, following a winding road, Harding who was walking on before, stopped, and his companions came up with him. The place where they had halted was wider, so as to form a cavern of moderate dimensions. Drops of water fell from the vault, but that did not prove that they oozed through the rock. They were simply the last traces left by the torrent which had so long thundered through this cavity, and the air there was pure though slightly damp, but producing no mephitic exhalation.

'Well, my dear Cyrus,' said Gideon Spilett, 'here is a very secure retreat, well hid in the depths of the rock, but it is, however, uninhabitable.'

'Why uninhabitable?' asked the sailor.

'Because it is too small and too dark.'

'Couldn't we enlarge it, hollow it out, make openings to let in light and air?' replied Pencroft, who now thought nothing impossible.

'Let us go on with our exploration,' said Cyrus Harding. 'Perhaps lower down, nature will have spared us this labour.'

'We have only gone a third of the way,' observed Herbert.

'Nearly a third,' replied Harding, 'for we have descended a hundred feet from the opening, and it is not impossible that a hundred feet farther down—'

'Where is Top?' asked Neb, interrupting his master.

They searched the cavern, but the dog was not there.

'Most likely he has gone on,' said Pencroft.

'Let us join him,' replied Harding.

The descent was continued. The engineer carefully observed all the deviations of the passage, and notwithstanding so many detours, he could easily have given an account of its general direction, which went towards the sea.

The settlers had gone some fifty feet farther, when their attention was attracted by distant sounds which came up from the depths. They stopped and listened. These sounds, carried through the passage as through an acoustic tube, came clearly to the ear.

'That is Top barking!' cried Herbert.

'Yes,' replied Pencroft, 'and our brave dog is barking furiously!'

'We have our iron-tipped spears,' said Cyrus Harding. 'Keep on your guard, and forward!'

'It is becoming more and more interesting,' murmured Gideon Spilett in the sailor's ear, who nodded. Harding and his companions rushed to the help of their dog. Top's barking became more and more perceptible, and it seemed strangely fierce. Was he engaged in a struggle with some animal whose retreat he had disturbed? Without thinking of the danger to which they might be exposed, the explorers were now impelled by an irresistible curiosity, and in a few minutes, sixteen feet lower they rejoined Top.

There the passage ended in a vast and magnificent cavern.

Top was running backwards and forwards, barking furiously. Pencroft and Neb, waving their torches, threw the light into every crevice; and at the same time, Harding, Gideon Spilett, and Herbert, their spears raised, were ready for any emergency which might arise. The enormous cavern was empty. The settlers explored it in every direction. There was nothing there, not an animal, not a human being; and yet Top continued to bark. Neither caresses nor threats could make him be silent.

'There must be a place somewhere, by which the waters of the lake reached the sea,' said the engineer.

'Of course,' replied Pencroft, 'and we must take care not to tumble into a hole.'

'Go, Top, go!' cried Harding.

The dog, excited by his master's words, ran towards the extremity of the cavern, and there redoubled his barking.

They followed him, and by the light of the torches, perceived the mouth of a regular well in the granite. It was by this that the water escaped; and this time it was not an oblique and practicable passage, but a perpendicular well, into which it was impossible to venture.

The torches were held over the opening: nothing could be seen. Harding took a lighted branch, and threw it into the abyss. The blazing resin, whose illuminating power increased still more by the rapidity of its fall, lighted up the interior of the well, but yet nothing appeared. The flame then went out with a slight hiss, which showed that it had reached the water, that is to say, the level of the sea.

The engineer, calculating the time employed in its fall, was able to calculate the depth of the well, which was found to be about ninety feet.

The floor of the cavern must thus be situated ninety feet above the level of the sea.

'Here is our dwelling,' said Cyrus Harding.

'But it was occupied by some creature,' replied Gideon Spilett, whose curiosity was not yet satisfied.

'Well, the creature, amphibious or otherwise, has made off through this opening,' replied the engineer, 'and has left the place for us.'

'Never mind,' added the sailor, 'I should like very much to be Top just for a quarter of an hour, for he doesn't bark for nothing!'

Cyrus Harding looked at his dog, and those of his companions who were near him might have heard him murmur these words,—

'Yes, I believe that Top knows more than we do about a great many things.'

However, the wishes of the settlers were for the most part satisfied. Chance, aided by the marvellous sagacity of their leader, had done them great service. They had now at their disposal a vast cavern, the size of which could not be properly calculated by the feeble light of their torches, but it would certainly be easy to divide it into rooms, by means of brick partitions, or to use it, if not as a house, at least as a spacious apartment. The water which had left it could not return. The place was free.

Two difficulties remained; firstly, the possibility of lighting this excavation in the midst of solid rock; secondly, the necessity of rendering the means of access more easy. It was useless to think of lighting it from above, because of the enormous thickness of the granite which composed the ceiling; but perhaps the outer wall next the sea might be pierced. Cyrus Harding, during the descent, had roughly calculated its obliqueness, and consequently the length of the passage, and was therefore led to believe that the outer wall could not be very thick. If light was thus obtained, so would a means of access, for it would be as easy to pierce a door as windows, and to establish an exterior ladder.

Harding made known his ideas to his companions.

'Then, captain, let us set to work!' replied Pencroft. 'I have my pickaxe, and I shall soon make my way through this wall. Where shall I strike?'

'Here,' replied the engineer, showing the sturdy sailor a considerable recess in the side, which would much diminish the thickness.

Pencroft attacked the granite, and for half an hour, by the light of the torches, he made the splinters fly around him. Neb relieved him, then Spilett took Neb's place.

This work had lasted two hours, and they began to fear that at this spot the wall would not yield to the pickaxe, when at a last blow given by Gideon Spilett, the instrument, passing through the rock, fell outside.

'Hurrah! hurrah!' cried Pencroft.

The wall only measured there three feet in thickness.

Harding applied his eye to the aperture, which overlooked the ground from a height of eighty feet. Before him was extended the seacoast, the islet, and beyond the open sea.

Floods of light entered by this hole, inundating the splendid cavern and producing a magic effect! On its left side it did not measure more than thirty feet in height and breadth, but on the right it was enormous, and its vaulted roof rose to a height of more than eighty feet.

In some places granite pillars, irregularly disposed, supported the vaulted roof, as those in the nave of a cathedral, here forming lateral piers, there elliptical arches, adorned with pointed mouldings, losing themselves in dark bays, amid the fantastic arches of which glimpses could be caught in the shade, covered with a profusion of projections formed like so many pendants. This cavern was a picturesque mixture of all the styles of Byzantine, Roman, or Gothic architecture ever produced by the hand of man. And yet this was only the work of nature. She alone had hollowed this fairy Alhambra in a mass of granite.

The settlers were overwhelmed with admiration. Where they had only expected to find a narrow cavity, they had found a sort of marvellous palace, and Neb had taken off his hat, as if he had been transported into a temple!

Cries of admiration issued from every mouth. Hurrahs resounded, and the echo was repeated again and again till it died away in the dark naves.

'Ah, my friends!' exclaimed Cyrus Harding, 'when we have lighted the interior of this place, and have arranged our rooms and storehouses in the left part, we shall still have this splendid cavern, which we will make our study and our museum!'

'And we will call it?—' asked Herbert.

'Granite House,' replied Harding; a name which his companions again saluted with a cheer.

The torches were now almost consumed, and as they were obliged to return by the passage to reach the summit of the plateau, it was decided to put off the work necessary for the arrangement of their new dwelling till the next day.

Before departing, Cyrus Harding leaned once more over the dark well, which descended perpendicularly to the level of the sea. He listened attentively. No noise was heard, not even that of the water, which the undulations of the surge must sometimes agitate in its depths. A flaming branch was again thrown in. The sides of the well were lighted up for an instant, but as at the first time, nothing suspicious was seen.

If some marine monster had been surprised unawares by the retreat of the water, he would by this time have regained the sea by the subterranean passage, before the new opening had been offered to him.

Meanwhile, the engineer was standing motionless, his eyes fixed on the gulf, without uttering a word.

The sailor approached him, and touching his arm, 'Captain!' said he.

'What do you want, my friend?' asked the engineer, as if he had returned from the land of dreams.

'The torches will soon go out.'

'Forward!' replied Cyrus Harding.

The little band left the cavern and began to ascend through the dark passage. Top closed the rear, still growling every now and then. The ascent was painful enough. The settlers rested a few minutes in the upper grotto, which made a sort of landing-place halfway up the long granite staircase. Then they began to climb again.

Soon fresher air was felt. The drops of water, dried by evapouration, no longer sparkled on the walls. The flaring torches began to grow dim. The one which Neb carried went out, and if they did not wish to find their way in the dark, they must hasten.

This was done, and a little before four o'clock, at the moment when the sailor's torch went out in its turn, Cyrus Harding and his companions passed out of the passage.

Chapter 19

The next day, the 22nd of May, the arrangement of their new dwelling was commenced. In fact, the settlers longed to exchange the insufficient shelter of the Chimneys for this large and healthy retreat, in the midst of solid rock, and sheltered from the water both of the sea and sky. Their former dwelling was not, however, to be entirely abandoned, for the engineer intended to make a manufactory of it for important works. Cyrus Harding's first care was to find out the position of the front of Granite House from the outside. He went to the beach, and as the pickaxe when it escaped from the hands of the reporter must have fallen perpendicularly to the foot of the cliff, the finding it would be sufficient to show the place where the hole had been pierced in the granite.

The pickaxe was easily found, and the hole could be seen in a perpendicular line above the spot where it was stuck in the sand. Some rock pigeons were already flying in and out of the narrow opening; they evidently thought that Granite House had been discovered on purpose for them. It was the engineer's intention to divide the right portion of the cavern into several rooms, preceded by an entrance passage, and to light it by means of five windows and a door, pierced in the front. Pencroft was much pleased with the five windows, but he could not understand the use of the door, since the passage offered a natural staircase, through which it would always be easy to enter Granite House.

'My friend,' replied Harding, 'if it is easy for us to reach our dwelling by this passage, it will be equally easy for others besides us. I mean, on the contrary, to block up that opening, to seal it hermetically, and, if it is necessary, to completely hide the entrance by making a dam, and thus causing the water of the lake to rise.'

'And how shall we get in?' asked the sailor.

'By an outside ladder,' replied Cyrus Harding, 'a rope ladder, which, once drawn up, will render access to our dwelling impossible.'

'But why so many precautions?' asked Pencroft. 'As yet we have seen no dangerous animals. As to our island being inhabited by natives, I don't believe it!'

'Are you quite sure of that, Pencroft?' asked the engineer, looking at the sailor.

'Of course we shall not be quite sure, till we have explored it in every direction,' replied Pencroft.

'Yes,' said Harding, 'for we know only a small portion of it as yet. But at any rate, if we have no enemies in the interior, they may come from the exterior, for parts of the Pacific are very dangerous. We must be provided against every contingency.'

Cyrus Harding spoke wisely; and without making any further objection, Pencroft prepared to execute his orders.

The front of Granite House was then to be lighted by five windows and a door, besides a large bay window and some smaller oval ones, which would admit plenty of light to enter into the marvellous nave which was to be their chief room. This facade, situated at a height of eighty feet above the ground, was exposed to the east, and the rising sun saluted it with its first rays. It was found to be just at that part of the cliff which was between the projection at the mouth of the Mercy and a perpendicular line traced above the heap of rocks which formed the Chimneys. Thus the winds from the northeast would only strike it obliquely, for it was protected by the projection. Besides, until the window-frames were made, the engineer meant to close the openings with thick shutters, which would prevent either wind or rain from entering, and which could be concealed in need.

The first work was to make the openings. This would have taken too long with the pickaxe alone, and it is known that Harding was an ingenious man. He had still a quantity of nitroglycerine at his disposal, and he employed it usefully. By means of this explosive substance the rock was broken open at the very places chosen by the engineer. Then, with the pickaxe and spade, the windows and doors were properly shaped, the jagged edges were smoothed off, and a few days alter the beginning of the work, Granite House was abundantly lighted by the rising sun, whose rays penetrated into its most secret recesses. Following the plan proposed by Cyrus Harding, the space was to be divided into five compartments looking out on the sea; to the right, an entry with a door, which would meet the ladder; then a kitchen, thirty feet long; a dining-room, measuring forty feet; a sleeping- room, of equal size; and lastly, a 'Visitor's room,' petitioned for by Pencroft, and which was next to the great hall. These rooms, or rather this suite of rooms, would not occupy all the depth of the cave. There would be also a corridor and a storehouse, in which their tools, provisions, and stores would be kept. All the productions of the island, the flora as well as the fauna, were to be there in the best possible state of preservation, and completely sheltered from the damp. There was no want of space, so that each object could be methodically arranged. Besides, the colonists had still at their disposal the little grotto above the great cavern, which was like the garret of the new dwelling.

This plan settled, it had only to be put into execution. The miners became brickmakers again, then the bricks were brought to the foot of Granite House. Till then, Harding and his companions had only entered the cavern by the long passage. This mode of communication obliged them first to climb Prospect Heights, making a detour by the river's bank, and then to descend two hundred feet through the passage, having to climb as far when they wished to return to the plateau. This was a great loss of time, and was also very fatiguing. Cyrus Harding, therefore, resolved to proceed without any further delay to the fabrication of a strong rope ladder, which, once raised, would render Granite House completely inaccessible.

This ladder was manufactured with extreme care, and its uprights, formed of the twisted fibres of a species of cane, had the strength of a thick cable. As to the rounds, they were made of a sort of red cedar, with light, strong branches; and this apparatus was wrought by the masterly hand of Pencroft.

Other ropes were made with vegetable fibres, and a sort of crane with a tackle was fixed at the door. In this way bricks could easily be raised into Granite House. The transport of the materials being thus simplified, the arrangement of the interior could begin immediately. There was no want of lime, and some thousands of bricks were there ready to be used. The framework of the partitions was soon raised, very roughly at first, and in a short time, the cave was divided into rooms and storehouses, according to the plan agreed upon.

These different works progressed rapidly under the direction of the engineer, who himself handled the hammer and the trowel. No labour came amiss to Cyrus Harding, who thus set an example to his intelligent and zealous companions. They worked with confidence, even gaily, Pencroft always having some joke to crack, sometimes carpenter, sometimes rope- maker, sometimes mason, while he communicated his good humour to all the members of their little world. His faith in the engineer was complete; nothing could disturb it. He believed him capable of undertaking anything and succeeding in everything. The question of boots and clothes—assuredly a serious question,—that of light during the winter months, utilizing the fertile parts of the island, transforming the wild flora into cultivated flora, it all appeared easy to him; Cyrus Harding helping, everything would be done in time. He dreamed of canals facilitating the transport of the riches of the ground; workings of quarries and mines; machines for every industrial manufacture; railroads; yes, railroads! of which a network would certainly one day cover Lincoln Island.

The engineer let Pencroft talk. He did not put down the aspirations of this brave heart. He knew how communicable confidence is; he even smiled to hear him speak, and said nothing of the uneasiness for the future which he felt. In fact, in that part of the Pacific, out of the course of vessels, it was to be feared that no help would ever come to them. It was on themselves, on themselves alone, that the settlers must depend, for the distance of Lincoln Island from all other land was such, that to hazard themselves in a boat, of a necessarily inferior construction, would be a serious and perilous thing.

'But,' as the sailor said, 'they quite took the wind out of the sails of the Robinsons, for whom everything was done by a miracle.'

In fact, they were energetic; an energetic man will succeed where an indolent one would vegetate and inevitably perish.

Herbert distinguished himself in these works. He was intelligent and active; understanding quickly, he performed well; and Cyrus Harding became more and more attached to the boy. Herbert had a lively and reverent love for the engineer. Pencroft saw the close sympathy which existed between the two, but he was not in the least jealous. Neb was Neb: he was what he would be always, courage, zeal, devotion, self-denial personified. He had the same faith in his master that Pencroft had, but he showed it less vehemently. When the sailor was enthusiastic, Neb always looked as if he would say, 'Nothing could be more natural.' Pencroft and he were great friends.

As to Gideon Spilett, he took part in the common work, and was not less skilful in it than his companions, which always rather astonished the sailor. A 'journalist,' clever, not only in understanding, but in performing everything.

The ladder was finally fixed on the 28th of May. There were not less than a hundred rounds in this perpendicular height of eighty feet. Harding had been able, fortunately, to divide it in two parts, profiting by an overhanging of the cliff which made a projection forty feet above the ground. This projection, carefully levelled by the pickaxe, made a sort of platform, to which they fixed the first ladder, of which the oscillation was thus diminished one-half, and a rope permitted it to be raised to the level of Granite House. As to the second ladder, it was secured both at its lower part, which rested on the projection, and at its upper end, which was fastened to the door. In short the ascent had been made much easier. Besides, Cyrus Harding hoped later to establish an hydraulic apparatus, which would avoid all fatigue and loss of time, for the inhabitants of Granite House.

The settlers soon became habituated to the use of this ladder. They were light and active, and Pencroft, as a sailor, accustomed to run up the masts and shrouds, was able to give them lessons. But it was also necessary to give them to Top. The poor dog, with his four paws, was not formed for this sort of exercise. But Pencroft was such a zealous master, that Top ended by properly performing his ascents, and soon mounted the ladder as readily as his brethren in the circus. It need not be said that the sailor was proud of his pupil. However, more than once Pencroft hoisted him on his back, which Top never complained of.

It must be mentioned here, that during these works, which were actively conducted, for the bad season was approaching, the alimentary question was not neglected. Every day, the reporter and Herbert, who had been voted purveyors to the colony, devoted some hours to the chase. As yet, they only hunted in Jacamar Wood, on the left of the river, because, for want of a bridge or boat, the Mercy had not yet been crossed. All the immense woods, to which the name of the Forests of the Far West had been given, were not explored. They reserved this important excursion for the first fine days of the next spring. But Jacamar Wood was full of game; kangaroos and boars abounded, and the hunters iron-tipped spears and bows and arrows did wonders. Besides, Herbert discovered towards the southwest point of the lagoon a natural warren, a slightly damp meadow, covered with willows and aromatic herbs which scented the air, such as thyme, basil, savoury, all the sweet-scented species of the labiated plants, which the rabbits appeared to be particularly fond of.

On the reporter observing that since the table was spread for the rabbits, it was strange that the rabbits themselves should be wanting, the two sportsmen carefully explored the warren. At any rate, it produced an abundance of useful plants, and a naturalist would have had a good opportunity of studying many specimens of the vegetable kingdom.

Herbert gathered several shoots of the basil, rosemary, balm, betony, etc., which possess different medicinal properties, some pectoral, astringent, febrifuge, others antispasmodic, or antirheumatic. When, afterwards, Pencroft asked the use of this collection of herbs,—

'For medicine,' replied the lad, 'to treat us when we are ill.'

'Why should we be ill, since there are no doctors in the island?' asked Pencroft quite seriously.

There was no reply to be made to that, but the lad went on with his collection all the same, and it was well received at Granite House. Besides these medicinal herbs, he added a plant known in North America as 'Oswego tea,' which made an excellent beverage.

At last, by searching thoroughly, the hunters arrived at the real site of the warren. There the ground was perforated like a sieve.

'Here are the burrows!' cried Herbert.

'Yes,' replied the reporter, 'so I see.'

'But are they inhabited?'

'That is the question.'

This was soon answered. Almost immediately, hundreds of little animals, similar to rabbits, fled in every direction, with such rapidity that even Top could not overtake them. Hunters and dog ran in vain; these rodents escaped them easily. But the reporter resolved not to leave the place, until he had captured at least half-a-dozen of the quadrupeds. He wished to stock their larder first, and domesticate those which they might take later. It would not have been difficult to do this, with a few snares stretched at the openings of the burrows. But at this moment they had neither snares, nor anything to make them of. They must, therefore, be satisfied with visiting each hole, and rummaging in it with a stick, hoping by dint of patience to do what could not be done in any other way.

At last, after half an hour, four rodents were taken in their holes. They were similar to their European brethren, and are commonly known by the name of American rabbits.

This produce of the chase was brought back to Granite House, and figured at the evening repast. The tenants of the warren were not at all to be despised, for they were delicious. It was a valuable resource of the colony, and it appeared to be inexhaustible.

On the 31st of May the partitions were finished. The rooms had now only to be furnished, and this would be work for the long winter days. A chimney was established in the first room, which served as a kitchen. The pipe destined to conduct the smoke outside gave some trouble to these amateur bricklayers. It appeared simplest to Harding to make it of brick clay; as creating an outlet for it to the upper plateau was not to be thought of, a hole was pierced in the granite above the window of the kitchen, and the pipe met it like that of an iron stove. Perhaps the winds which blew directly against the facade would make the chimney smoke, but these winds were rare, and besides, Master Neb, the cook, was not so very particular about that.

When these interior arrangements were finished, the engineer occupied himself in blocking up the outlet by the lake, so as to prevent any access by that way. Masses of rock were rolled to the entrance and strongly cemented together. Cyrus Harding did not yet realize his plan of drowning this opening under the waters of the lake, by restoring them to their former level by means of a dam. He contented himself with hiding the obstruction with grass and shrubs, which were planted in the interstices of the rocks, and which next spring would sprout thickly. However, he used the waterfall so as to lead a small stream of fresh water to the new dwelling. A little trench, made below their level, produced this result; and this derivation from a pure and inexhaustible source yielded twenty-five or thirty gallons a day. There would never be any want of water at Granite House. At last all was finished, and it was time, for the bad season was near. Thick shutters closed the windows of the facade, until the engineer had time to make glass.

Gideon Spilett had very artistically arranged on the rocky projections around the windows plants of different kinds, as well as long streaming grass, so that the openings were picturesquely framed in green, which had a pleasing effect.

The inhabitants of this solid, healthy, and secure dwelling, could not but be charmed with their work. The view from the windows extended over a boundless horizon, which was closed by the two Mandible Capes on the north, and Claw Cape on the south. All Union Bay was spread before them. Yes, our brave settlers had reason to be satisfied, and Pencroft was lavish in his praise of what he humorously called, 'his apartments on the fifth floor above the ground!'

Chapter 20

The winter season set in with the month of June, which corresponds with the month of December in the Northern Hemisphere. It began with showers and squalls, which succeeded each other without intermission. The tenants of Granite House could appreciate the advantages of a dwelling which sheltered them from the inclement weather. The Chimneys would have been quite insufficient to protect them against the rigor of winter, and it was to be feared that the high tides would make another irruption. Cyrus Harding had taken precautions against this contingency, so as to preserve as much as possible the forge and furnace which were established there.

During the whole of the month of June the time was employed in different occupations, which excluded neither hunting nor fishing, the larder being, therefore, abundantly supplied. Pencroft, so soon as he had leisure, proposed to set some traps, from which he expected great results. He soon made some snares with creepers, by the aid of which the warren henceforth every day furnished its quota of rodents. Neb employed nearly all his time in salting or smoking meat, which insured their always having plenty of provisions. The question of clothes was now seriously discussed, the settlers having no other garments than those they wore when the balloon threw them on the island. These clothes were warm and good; they had taken great care of them as well as of their linen, and they were perfectly whole, but they would soon need to be replaced. Moreover, if the winter was severe, the settlers would suffer greatly from cold.

On this subject the ingenuity of Harding was at fault. They must provide for their most pressing wants, settle their dwelling, and lay in a store of food; thus the cold might come upon them before the question of clothes had been settled. They must therefore make up their minds to pass this first winter without additional clothing. When the fine season came round again, they would regularly hunt those musmons which had been seen on the expedition to Mount Franklin, and the wool once collected, the engineer would know how to make it into strong warm stuff.... How? He would consider.

'Well, we are free to roast ourselves at Granite House!' said Pencroft. 'There are heaps of fuel, and no reason for sparing it.'

'Besides,' added Gideon Spilett, 'Lincoln Island is not situated under a very high latitude, and probably the winters here are not severe. Did you not say, Cyrus, that this thirty-fifth parallel corresponded to that of Spain in the other hemisphere?'

'Doubtless,' replied the engineer, 'but some winters in Spain are very cold! No want of snow and ice; and perhaps Lincoln Island is just as rigourously tried. However, it is an island, and as such, I hope that the temperature will be more moderate.'

'Why, captain?' asked Herbert.

'Because the sea, my boy, may be considered as an immense reservoir, in which is stored the heat of the summer. When winter comes, it restores this heat, which insures for the regions near the ocean a medium temperature, less high in summer, but less low in winter.'

'We shall prove that,' replied Pencroft. 'But I don't want to bother myself about whether it will be cold or not. One thing is certain, that is that the days are already short, and the evenings long. Suppose we talk about the question of light.'

'Nothing is easier,' replied Harding.

'To talk about?' asked the sailor.

'To settle.'

'And when shall we begin?'

'Tomorrow, by having a seal hunt.'

'To make candles?'

'Yes.'

Such was the engineer's project; and it was quite feasible, since he had lime and sulphuric acid, while the amphibians of the islet would furnish the fat necessary for the manufacture.

They were now at the 4th of June. It was Whit Sunday and they agreed to observe this feast. All work was suspended, and prayers were offered to Heaven. But these prayers were now thanksgivings. The settlers in Lincoln Island were no longer the miserable castaways thrown on the islet. They asked for nothing more—they gave thanks. The next day, the 5th of June, in rather uncertain weather, they set out for the islet. They had to profit by the low tide to cross the Channel, and it was agreed that they would construct, for this purpose, as well as they could, a boat which would render communication so much easier, and would also permit them to ascend the Mercy, at the time of their grand exploration of the southwest of the island, which was put off till the first fine days.

The seals were numerous, and the hunters, armed with their iron-tipped spears, easily killed half-a-dozen. Neb and Pencroft skinned them, and only brought back to Granite House their fat and skin, this skin being intended for the manufacture of boots.

The result of the hunt was this: nearly three hundred pounds of fat, all to be employed in the fabrication of candles.

The operation was extremely simple, and if it did not yield absolutely perfect results, they were at least very useful. Cyrus Harding would only have had at his disposal sulphuric acid, but by heating this acid with the neutral fatty bodies he could separate the glycerine; then from this new combination, he easily separated the olein, the margarin, and the stearin, by employing boiling water. But to simplify the operation, he preferred to saponify the fat by means of lime. By this he obtained a calcareous soap, easy to decompose by sulphuric acid, which precipitated the lime into the state of sulphate, and liberated the fatty acids.

From these three acids-oleic, margaric, and stearic-the first, being liquid, was driven out by a sufficient pressure. As to the two others, they formed the very substance of which the candles were to be moulded.

This operation did not last more than four and twenty hours. The wicks, after several trials, were made of vegetable fibres, and dipped in the liquefied substance, they formed regular stearic candles, moulded by the hand, which only wanted whiteness and polish. They would not doubtless have the advantages of the wicks which are impregnated with boracic acid, and which vitrify as they burn and are entirely consumed, but Cyrus Harding having manufactured a beautiful pair of snuffers, these candles would be greatly appreciated during the long evenings in Granite House.

During this month there was no want of work in the interior of their new dwelling. The joiners had plenty to do. They improved their tools, which were very rough, and added others also.

Scissors were made among other things, and the settlers were at last able to cut their hair, and also to shave, or at least trim their beards. Herbert had none, Neb but little, but their companions were bristling in a way which justified the making of the said scissors.

The manufacture of a handsaw cost infinite trouble, but at last an instrument was obtained which, when vigorously handled, could divide the ligneous fibres of the wood. They then made tables, seats, cupboards, to furnish the principal rooms, and bedsteads, of which all the bedding consisted of grass mattresses. The kitchen, with its shelves, on which rested the cooking utensils, its brick stove, looked very well, and Neb worked away there as earnestly as if he was in a chemist's laboratory.

But the joiners had soon to be replaced by carpenters. In fact, the waterfall created by the explosion rendered the construction of two bridges necessary, one on Prospect Heights, the other on the shore. Now the plateau and the shore were transversely divided by a watercourse, which had to be crossed to reach the northern part of the island. To avoid it the colonists had been obliged to make a considerable detour, by climbing up to the source of the Red Creek. The simplest thing was to establish on the plateau, and on the shore, two bridges from twenty to five and twenty feet in length. All the carpenter's work that was needed was to clear some trees of their branches: this was a business of some days. Directly the bridges were established, Neb and Pencroft profited by them to go to the oysterbed which had been discovered near the downs. They dragged with them a sort of rough cart, which replaced the former inconvenient hurdle, and brought back some thousands of oysters, which soon increased among the rocks and formed a bed at the mouth of the Mercy. These molluscs were of excellent quality, and the colonists consumed some daily.

It has been seen that Lincoln Island, although its inhabitants had as yet only explored a small portion of it, already contributed to almost all their wants. It was probable that if they hunted into its most secret recesses, in all the wooded part between the Mercy and Reptile Point, they would find new treasures.

The settlers in Lincoln Island had still one privation. There was no want of meat, nor of vegetable products; those ligneous roots which they had found, when subjected to fermentation, gave them an acid drink, which was preferable to cold water; they also made sugar, without canes or beet- roots, by collecting the liquor which distils from the 'acer saccharinum,' a son of maple-tree, which flourishes in all the temperate zones, and of which the island possessed a great number; they made a very agreeable tea by employing the herbs brought from the warren; lastly, they had an abundance of salt, the only mineral which is used in food,... but bread was wanting.

Perhaps in time the settlers could replace this want by some equivalent, it was possible that they might find the sago or the breadfruit tree among the forests of the south, but they had not as yet met with these precious trees. However, Providence came directly to their aid, in an infinitesimal proportion it is true, but Cyrus Harding, with all his intelligence, all his ingenuity, would never have been able to produce that which, by the greatest chance, Herbert one day found in the lining of his waistcoat, which he was occupied in setting to rights.

On this day, as it was raining in torrents, the settlers were assembled in the great hall in Granite House, when the lad cried out all at once,—

'Look here, captain—A grain of corn!'

And he showed his companions a grain—a single grain—which from a hole in his pocket had got into the lining of his waistcoat.

The presence of this grain was explained by the fact that Herbert, when at Richmond, used to feed some pigeons, of which Pencroft had made him a present.

'A grain of corn?' said the engineer quickly.

'Yes, captain; but one, only one!'

'Well, my boy,' said Pencroft, laughing, 'we're getting on capitally, upon my word! What shall we make with one grain of corn?'

'We will make bread of it,' replied Cyrus Harding.

'Bread, cakes, tarts!' replied the sailor. 'Come, the bread that this grain of corn will make won't choke us very soon!'

Herbert, not attaching much importance to his discovery, was going to throw away the grain in question; but Harding took it, examined it, found that it was in good condition, and looking the sailor full in the face— 'Pencroft,' he asked quietly, 'do you know how many ears one grain of corn can produce?'

'One, I suppose!' replied the sailor, surprised at the question.

'Ten, Pencroft! And do you know how many grains one ear bears?'

'No, upon my word.'

'About eighty!' said Cyrus Harding. 'Then, if we plant this grain, at the first crop we shall reap eight hundred grains which at the second will produce six hundred and forty thousand; at the third, five hundred and twelve millions; at the fourth, more than four hundred thousands of millions! There is the proportion.'

Harding's companions listened without answering. These numbers astonished them. They were exact, however.

'Yes, my friends,' continued the engineer, 'such are the arithmetical progressions of prolific nature; and yet what is this multiplication of the grain of corn, of which the ear only bears eight hundred grains, compared to the poppy-plant, which bears thirty-two thousand seeds; to the tobacco- plant, which produces three hundred and sixty thousand? In a few years, without the numerous causes of destruction, which arrests their fecundity, these plants would overrun the earth.'

But the engineer had not finished his lecture.

'And now, Pencroft,' he continued, 'do you know how many bushels four hundred thousand millions of grains would make?'

'No,' replied the sailor; 'but what I do know is, that I am nothing better than a fool!'

'Well, they would make more than three millions, at a hundred and thirty thousand a bushel, Pencroft.'

'Three millions!' cried Pencroft.

'Three millions.'

'In four years?'

'In four years,' replied Cyrus Harding, 'and even in two years, if, as I hope, in this latitude we can obtain two crops a year.'

At that, according to his usual custom, Pencroft could not reply otherwise than by a tremendous hurrah.

'So, Herbert,' added the engineer, 'you have made a discovery of great importance to us. Everything, my friends, everything can serve us in the condition in which we are. Do not forget that, I beg of you.'

'No, captain, no, we shan't forget it,' replied Pencroft; 'and if ever I find one of those tobacco-seeds, which multiply by three hundred and sixty thousand, I assure you I won't throw it away! And now, what must we do?'

'We must plant this grain,' replied Herbert.

'Yes,' added Gideon Spilett, 'and with every possible care, for it bears in itself our future harvests.'

'Provided it grows!' cried the sailor.

'It will grow,' replied Cyrus Harding.

This was the 20th of June. The time was then propitious for sowing this single precious grain of corn. It was first proposed to plant it in a pot, but upon reflection it was decided to leave it to nature, and confide it to the earth. This was done that very day, and it is needless to add, that every precaution was taken that the experiment might succeed.

The weather having cleared, the settlers climbed the height above Granite House. There, on the plateau, they chose a spot, well sheltered from the wind, and exposed to all the heat of the midday sun. The place was cleared, carefully weeded, and searched for insects and worms; then a bed of good earth, improved with a little lime, was made; it was surrounded by a railing; and the grain was buried in the damp earth.

Did it not seem as if the settlers were laying the first stone of some edifice? It recalled to Pencroft the day on which he lighted his only match, and all the anxiety of the operation. But this time the thing was more serious. In fact, the castaways would have been always able to procure fire, in some mode or other, but no human power could supply another grain of corn, if unfortunately this should be lost!

Chapter 21

From this time Pencroft did not let a single day pass without going to visit what he gravely called his 'cornfield.' And woe to the insects which dared to venture there! No mercy was shown them.

Towards the end of the month of June, after incessant rain, the weather became decidedly colder, and on the 29th a Fahrenheit thermometer would certainly have announced only twenty degrees above zero, that is considerably below the freezing-point. The next day, the 30th of June, the day which corresponds to the 31st of December in the northern year, was a Friday. Neb remarked that the year finished on a bad day, but Pencroft replied that naturally the next would begin on a good one, which was better.

At any rate it commenced by very severe cold. Ice accumulated at the mouth of the Mercy, and it was not long before the whole expanse of the lake was frozen.

The settlers had frequently been obliged to renew their store of wood. Pencroft also had wisely not waited till the river was frozen, but had brought enormous rafts of wood to their destination. The current was an indefatigable moving power, and it was employed in conveying the floating wood to the moment when the frost enchained it. To the fuel which was so abundantly supplied by the forest, they added several cartloads of coal, which had to be brought from the foot of the spurs of Mount Franklin. The powerful heat of the coal was greatly appreciated in the low temperature, which on the 4th of July fell to eight degrees of Fahrenheit, that is, thirteen degrees below zero. A second fireplace had been established in the dining-room, where they all worked together at their different avocations. During this period of cold, Cyrus Harding had great cause to congratulate himself on having brought to Granite House the little stream of water from Lake Grant. Taken below the frozen surface, and conducted through the passage, it preserved its fluidity, and arrived at an interior reservoir which had been hollowed out at the back part of the storeroom, while the overflow ran through the well to the sea.

About this time, the weather being extremely dry, the colonists, clothed as warmly as possible, resolved to devote a day to the exploration of that part of the island between the Mercy and Claw Cape. It was a wide extent of marshy land, and they would probably find good sport, for water-birds ought to swarm there.

They reckoned that it would be about eight or nine miles to go there, and as much to return, so that the whole of the day would be occupied. As an unknown part of the island was about to be explored, the whole colony took part in the expedition. Accordingly, on the 5th of July, at six o'clock in the morning, when day had scarcely broken, Cyrus Harding, Gideon Spilett, Herbert, Neb, and Pencroft, armed with spears, snares, bows and arrows, and provided with provisions, left Granite House, preceded by Top, who bounded before them.

Their shortest way was to cross the Mercy on the ice, which then covered it.

'But,' as the engineer justly observed, 'that could not take the place of a regular bridge!' So, the construction of a regular bridge was noted in the list of future works.

It was the first time that the settlers had set foot on the right bank of the Mercy, and ventured into the midst of those gigantic and superb coniferae now sprinkled over with snow.

But they had not gone half a mile when from a thicket a whole family of quadrupeds, who had made a home there, disturbed by Top, rushed forth into the open country.

'Ah! I should say those are foxes!' cried Herbert, when he saw the troop rapidly decamping.

They were foxes, but of a very large size, who uttered a sort of barking, at which Top seemed to be very much astonished, for he stopped short in the chase, and gave the swift animals time to disappear.

The dog had reason to be surprised, as he did not know Natural History. But, by their barking, these foxes, with reddish-gray hair, black tails terminating in a white tuft, had betrayed their origin. So Herbert was able, without hesitating, to give them their real name of 'Arctic foxes.' They are frequently met with in Chile, in the Falkland Islands, and in all parts of America traversed by the thirtieth and fortieth parallels. Herbert much regretted that Top had not been able to catch one of these carnivore.

'Are they good to eat?' asked Pencroft, who only regarded the representatives of the fauna in the island from one special point of view.

'No,' replied Herbert; 'but zoologists have not yet found out if the eye of these foxes is diurnal or nocturnal, or whether it is correct to class them in the genus dog, properly so called.'

Harding could not help smiling on hearing the lad's reflection, which showed a thoughtful mind. As to the sailor, from the moment when he found that the foxes were not classed in the genus eatable, they were nothing to him. However, when a poultry-yard was established at Granite House, he observed that it would be best to take some precautions against a probable visit from these four-legged plunderers, and no one disputed this.

After having turned the point, the settlers saw a long beach washed by the open sea. It was then eight o'clock in the morning. The sky was very clear, as it often is after prolonged cold; but warmed by their walk, neither Harding nor his companions felt the sharpness of the atmosphere too severely. Besides there was no wind, which made it much more bearable. A brilliant sun, but without any calorific action, was just issuing from the ocean. The sea was as tranquil and blue as that of a Mediterranean gulf, when the sky is clear. Claw Cape, bent in the form of a yataghan, tapered away nearly four miles to the southeast. To the left the edge of the marsh was abruptly ended by a little point. Certainly, in this part of Union Bay, which nothing sheltered from the open sea, not even a sandbank, ships beaten by the east winds would have found no shelter. They perceived by the tranquillity of the sea, in which no shallows troubled the waters, by its uniform colour, which was stained by no yellow shades, by the absence of even a reef, that the coast was steep and that the ocean there covered a deep abyss. Behind in the west, but at a distance of four miles, rose the first trees of the forests of the Far West. They might have believed themselves to be on the desolate coast of some island in the Antarctic regions which the ice had invaded. The colonists halted at this place for breakfast. A fire of brushwood and dried seaweed was lighted, and Neb prepared the breakfast of cold meat, to which he added some cups of Oswego tea.

While eating they looked around them. This part of Lincoln Island was very sterile, and contrasted with all the western part. The reporter was thus led to observe that if chance had thrown them at first on the shore, they would have had but a deplorable idea of their future domain.

'I believe that we should not have been able to reach it,' replied the engineer, 'for the sea is deep, and there is not a rock on which we could have taken refuge. Before Granite House, at least, there were sandbanks, an islet, which multiplied our chances of safety. Here, nothing but the depths!'

'It is singular enough,' remarked Spilett, 'that this comparatively small island should present such varied ground. This diversity of aspect, logically only belongs to continents of a certain extent. One would really say, that the western part of Lincoln Island, so rich and so fertile, is washed by the warm waters of the Gulf of Mexico, and that its shores to the north and the southeast extend over a sort of Arctic sea.'

'You are right, my dear Spilett,' replied Cyrus Harding, 'I have also observed this. I think the form and also the nature of this island strange. It is a summary of all the aspects which a continent presents, and I should not be surprised if it was a continent formerly.'

'What! a continent in the middle of the Pacific?' cried Pencroft.

'Why not?' replied Cyrus Harding. 'Why should not Australia, New Ireland, Australasia, united to the archipelagoes of the Pacific, have once formed a sixth part of the world, as important as Europe or Asia, as Africa or the two Americas? To my mind, it is quite possible that all these islands, emerging from this vast ocean, are but the summits of a continent, now submerged, but which was above the waters at a prehistoric period.'

'As the Atlantis was formerly,' replied Herbert.

'Yes, my boy... if, however, it existed.'

'And would Lincoln Island have been a part of that continent?' asked Pencroft.

'It is probable,' replied Cyrus Harding, 'and that would sufficiently, explain the variety of productions which are seen on its surface.'

'And the great number of animals which still inhabit it,' added Herbert.

'Yes, my boy,' replied the engineer, 'and you furnish me with an argument to support my theory. It is certain, after what we have seen, that animals are numerous in this island, and what is more strange, that the species are extremely varied. There is a reason for that, and to me it is that Lincoln Island may have formerly been a part of some vast continent which had gradually sunk below the Pacific.'

'Then, some fine day,' said Pencroft, who did not appear to be entirely convinced, 'the rest of this ancient continent may disappear in its turn, and there will be nothing between America and Asia.'

'Yes,' replied Harding, 'there will be new continents which millions and millions of animalculae are building at this moment.'

'And what are these masons?' asked Pencroft.

'Coral insects,' replied Cyrus Harding. 'By constant work they made the island of Clermont-Tonnerre, and numerous other coral islands in the Pacific Ocean. Forty-seven millions of these insects are needed to weigh a grain, and yet, with the sea-salt they absorb, the solid elements of water which they assimilate, these animalculae produce limestone, and this limestone forms enormous submarine erections, of which the hardness and solidity equal granite. Formerly, at the first periods of creation, nature employing fire, heaved up the land, but now she entrusts to these microscopic creatures the task of replacing this agent, of which the dynamic power in the interior of the globe has evidently diminished—which is proved by the number of volcanoes on the surface of the earth, now actually extinct. And I believe that centuries succeeding to centuries, and insects to insects, this Pacific may one day be changed into a vast continent, which new generations will inhabit and civilize in their turn.'

'That will take a long time,' said Pencroft.

'Nature has time for it,' replied the engineer.

'But what would be the use of new continents?' asked Herbert. 'It appears to me that the present extent of habitable countries is sufficient for humanity. Yet nature does nothing uselessly.'

'Nothing uselessly, certainly,' replied the engineer, 'but this is how the necessity of new continents for the future, and exactly on the tropical zone occupied by the coral islands, may be explained. At least to me this explanation appears plausible.'

'We are listening, captain,' said Herbert.

'This is my idea: philosophers generally admit that some day our globe will end, or rather that animal and vegetable life will no longer be possible, because of the intense cold to which it will be subjected. What they are not agreed upon, is the cause of this cold. Some think that it will arise from the falling of the temperature, which the sun will experience alter millions of years; others, from the gradual extinction of the fires in the interior of our globe, which have a greater influence on it than is generally supposed. I hold to this last hypothesis, grounding it on the fact that the moon is really a cold star, which is no longer habitable, although the sun continues to throw on its surface the same amount of heat. If, then, the moon has become cold, it is because the interior fires to which, as do all the stars of the stellar world, it owes its origin, are completely extinct. Lastly, whatever may be the cause, our globe will become cold some day, but this cold will only operate gradually. What will happen, then? The temperate zones, at a more or less distant period, will not be more habitable than the polar regions now are. Then the population of men, as well as the animals, will flow towards the latitudes which are more directly under the solar influence. An immense emigration will take place. Europe, Central Asia, North America, will gradually be abandoned, as well as Australasia and the lower parts of South America. The vegetation will follow the human emigration. The flora will retreat towards the Equator at the same time as the fauna. The central parts of South America and Africa will be the continents chiefly inhabited. The Laplanders and the Samoides will find the climate of the polar regions on the shores of the Mediterranean. Who can say, that at this period, the equatorial regions will not be too small, to contain and nourish terrestrial humanity? Now, may not provident nature, so as to give refuge to all the vegetable and animal emigration, be at present laying the foundation of a new continent under the Equator, and may she not have entrusted these insects with the construction of it? I have often thought of all these things, my friends, and I seriously believe that the aspect of our globe will some day be completely changed; that by the raising of new continents the sea will cover the old, and that, in future ages, a Columbus will go to discover the islands of Chimborazo, of the Himalayas, or of Mont Blanc, remains of a submerged America, Asia, and Europe. Then these new continents will become, in their turn, uninhabitable; heat will die away, as does the heat from a body when the soul has left it; and life will disappear from the globe, if not for ever, at least for a period. Perhaps then, our spheroid will rest— will be left to death—to revive some day under superior conditions! But all that, my friends, is the secret of the Author of all things; and beginning by the work of the insects, I have perhaps let myself be carried too far, in investigating the secrets of the future.

'My dear Cyrus,' replied Spilett, 'these theories are prophecies to me, and they will be accomplished some day.'

'That is the secret of God,' said the engineer.

'All that is well and good,' then said Pencroft, who had listened with all his might, 'but will you tell me, captain, if Lincoln Island has been made by your insects?'

'No,' replied Harding; 'it is of a purely volcanic origin.'

'Then it will disappear some day?'

'That is probable.

'I hope we won't be here then.'

'No, don't be uneasy, Pencroft; we shall not be here then, as we have no wish to die here, and hope to get away some time.'

'In the meantime,' replied Gideon Spilett, 'let us establish ourselves here as if forever. There is no use in doing things by halves.'

This ended the conversation. Breakfast was finished, the exploration was continued, and the settlers arrived at the border of the marshy region. It was a marsh of which the extent, to the rounded coast which terminated the island at the southeast, was about twenty square miles. The soil was formed of clayey flint-earth, mingled with vegetable matter, such as the remains of rushes, reeds, grass, etc. Here and there beds of grass, thick as a carpet, covered it. In many places icy pools sparkled in the sun. Neither rain nor any river, increased by a sudden swelling, could supply these ponds. They therefore naturally concluded that the marsh was fed by the infiltrations of the soil and it was really so. It was also to be feared that during the heat miasmas would arise, which might produce fevers.

Above the aquatic plants, on the surface of the stagnant water, fluttered numbers of birds. Wild duck, teal, snipe lived there in flocks, and those fearless birds allowed themselves to be easily approached.

One shot from a gun would certainly have brought down some dozen of the birds, they were so close together. The explorers were, however, obliged to content themselves with bows and arrows. The result was less, but the silent arrow had the advantage of not frightening the birds, while the noise of firearms would have dispersed them to all parts of the marsh. The hunters were satisfied, for this time, with a dozen ducks, which had white bodies with a band of cinnamon, a green head, wings black, white, and red, and flattened beak. Herbert called them tadorns. Top helped in the capture of these birds, whose name was given to this marshy part of the island. The settlers had here an abundant reserve of aquatic game. At some future time they meant to explore it more carefully, and it was probable that some of the birds there might be domesticated, or at least brought to the shores of the lake, so that they would be more within their reach.

About five o'clock in the evening Cyrus Harding and his companions retraced their steps to their dwelling by traversing Tadorn's Fens, and crossed the Mercy on the ice-bridge.

At eight in the evening they all entered Granite House.

Chapter 22

This intense cold lasted till the 15th of August, without, however, passing the degree of Fahrenheit already mentioned. When the atmosphere was calm, the low temperature was easily borne, but when the wind blew, the poor settlers, insufficiently clothed, felt it severely. Pencroft regretted that Lincoln Island was not the home of a few families of bears rather than of so many foxes and seals.

'Bears,' said he, 'are generally very well dressed, and I ask no more than to borrow for the winter the warm cloaks which they have on their backs.'

'But,' replied Neb, laughing, 'perhaps the bears would not consent to give you their cloaks, Pencroft. These beasts are not St. Martins.'

'We would make them do it, Neb, we would make them,' replied Pencroft, in quite an authoritative tone.

But these formidable carnivora did not exist in the island, or at any rate they had not yet shown themselves.

In the meanwhile, Herbert, Pencroft, and the reporter occupied themselves with making traps on Prospect Heights and at the border of the forest.

According to the sailor, any animal, whatever it was, would be a lawful prize, and the rodents or carnivora which might get into the new snares would be well received at Granite House.

The traps were besides extremely simple; being pits dug in the ground, a platform of branches and grass above, which concealed the opening, and at the bottom some bait, the scent of which would attract animals. It must be mentioned also, that they had not been dug at random, but at certain places where numerous footprints showed that quadrupeds frequented the ground. They were visited every day, and at three different times, during the first days, specimens of those Antarctic foxes which they had already seen on the right bank of the Mercy were found in them.

'Why, there are nothing but foxes in this country!' cried Pencroft, when for the third time he drew one of the animals out of the pit. Looking at it in great disgust, he added, 'beasts which are good for nothing!'

'Yes,' said Gideon Spilett, 'they are good for something!'

'And what is that?'

'To make bait to attract other creatures!'

The reporter was right, and the traps were henceforward baited with the foxes carcasses.

The sailor had also made snares from the long tough fibres of a certain plant, and they were even more successful than the traps. Rarely a day passed without some rabbits from the warren being caught. It was always rabbit, but Neb knew how to vary his sauces and the settlers did not think of complaining.

However, once or twice in the second week of August, the traps supplied the hunters with other animals more useful than foxes, namely, several of those small wild boars which had already been seen to the north of the lake. Pencroft had no need to ask if these beasts were eatable. He could see that by their resemblance to the pig of America and Europe.

'But these are not pigs,' said Herbert to him, 'I warn you of that, Pencroft.'

'My boy,' replied the sailor, bending over the trap and drawing out one of these representatives of the family of sus by the little appendage which served it as a tail. 'Let me believe that these are pigs.'

'Why?'

'Because that pleases me!'

'Are you very fond of pig then, Pencroft?'

'I am very fond of pig,' replied the sailor, 'particularly of its feet, and if it had eight instead of four, I should like it twice as much!'

As to the animals in question, they were peccaries belonging to one of the four species which are included in the family, and they were also of the species of Tajacu, recognizable by their deep colour and the absence of those long teeth with which the mouths of their congeners are armed. These peccaries generally live in herds, and it was probable that they abounded in the woody parts of the island.

At any rate, they were eatable from head to foot, and Pencroft did not ask more from them.

Towards the 15th of August, the state of the atmosphere was suddenly moderated by the wind shifting to the northwest. The temperature rose some degrees, and the accumulated vapour in the air was not long in resolving into snow. All the island was covered with a sheet of white, and showed itself to its inhabitants under a new aspect. The snow fell abundantly for several days, and it soon reached a thickness of two feet.

The wind also blew with great violence, and at the height of Granite House the sea could be heard thundering against the reefs. In some places, the wind, eddying round the corners, formed the snow into tall whirling columns, resembling those waterspouts which turn round on their base, and which vessels attack with a shot from a gun. However, the storm, coming from the northwest, blew across the island, and the position of Granite House preserved it from a direct attack.

But in the midst of this snowstorm, as terrible as if it had been produced in some polar country, neither Cyrus Harding nor his companions could, notwithstanding their wish for it, venture forth, and they remained shut up for five days, from the 20th to the 25th of August. They could hear the tempest raging in Jacamar Wood, which would surely suffer from it. Many of the trees would no doubt be torn up by the roots, but Pencroft consoled himself by thinking that he would not have the trouble of cutting them down.

'The wind is turning woodman, let it alone,' he repeated.

Besides, there was no way of stopping it, if they had wished to do so.

How grateful the inhabitants of Granite House then were to Heaven for having prepared for them this solid and immovable retreat! Cyrus Harding had also his legitimate share of thanks, but after all, it was Nature who had hollowed out this vast cavern, and he had only discovered it. There all were in safety, and the tempest could not reach them. If they had constructed a house of bricks and wood on Prospect Heights, it certainly would not have resisted the fury of this storm. As to the Chimneys, it must have been absolutely uninhabitable, for the sea, passing over the islet, would beat furiously against it. But here, in Granite House, in the middle of a solid mass, over which neither the sea nor air had any influence, there was nothing to fear.

During these days of seclusion the settlers did not remain inactive.

There was no want of wood, cut up into planks, in the storeroom, and little by little they completed their furnishing; constructing the most solid of tables and chairs, for material was not spared. Neb and Pencroft were very proud of this rather heavy furniture, which they would not have changed on any account.

Then the carpenters became basket-makers, and they did not succeed badly in this new manufacture. At the point of the lake which projected to the north, they had discovered an osier-bed in which grew a large number of purple osiers. Before the rainy season, Pencroft and Herbert had cut down these useful shrubs, and their branches, well prepared, could now be effectively employed. The first attempts were somewhat crude, but in consequence of the cleverness and intelligence of the workmen, by consulting, and recalling the models which they had seen, and by emulating each other, the possessions of the colony were soon increased by several baskets of different sizes. The storeroom was provided with them, and in special baskets Neb placed his collection of rhizomes, stone-pine almonds, etc.

During the last week of the month of August the weather moderated again. The temperature fell a little, and the tempest abated. The colonists sallied out directly. There was certainly two feet of snow on the shore, but they were able to walk without much difficulty on the hardened surface. Cyrus Harding and his companions climbed Prospect Heights.

What a change! The woods, which they had left green, especially in the part at which the firs predominated, had disappeared under a uniform colour. All was white, from the summit of Mount Franklin to the shore, the forests, the plains, the lake, the river. The waters of the Mercy flowed under a roof of ice, which, at each rising and ebbing of the tide, broke up with loud crashes. Numerous birds fluttered over the frozen surface of the lake. Ducks and snipe, teal and guillemots were assembled in thousands. The rocks among which the cascade flowed were bristling with icicles. One might have said that the water escaped by a monstrous gargoyle, shaped with all the imagination of an artist of the Renaissance. As to the damage caused by the storm in the forest, that could not as yet be ascertained; they would have to wait till the snowy covering was dissipated.

Gideon Spilett, Pencroft, and Herbert did not miss this opportunity of going to visit their traps. They did not find them easily, under the snow with which they were covered. They had also to be careful not to fall into one or other of them, which would have been both dangerous and humiliating; to be taken in their own snares! But happily they avoided this unpleasantness, and found their traps perfectly intact. No animal had fallen into them, and yet the footprints in the neighbourhood were very numerous, among others, certain very clear marks of claws. Herbert did not hesitate to affirm that some animal of the feline species had passed there, which justified the engineer's opinion that dangerous beasts existed in Lincoln Island. These animals doubtless generally lived in the forests of the Far West, but pressed by hunger, they had ventured as far as Prospect Heights. Perhaps they had smelled out the inhabitants of Granite House. 'Now, what are these feline creatures?' asked Pencroft. 'They are tigers,' replied Herbert. 'I thought those beasts were only found in hot countries?'

'On the new continent,' replied the lad, 'they are found from Mexico to the Pampas of Buenos Aires. Now, as Lincoln Island is nearly under the same latitude as the provinces of La Plata, it is not surprising that tigers are to be met with in it.'

'Well, we must look out for them,' replied Pencroft.

However, the snow soon disappeared, quickly dissolving under the influence of the rising temperature. Rain fell, and the sheet of white soon vanished. Notwithstanding the bad weather, the settlers renewed their stores of different things, stone-pine almonds, rhizomes, syrup from the maple-tree, for the vegetable part; rabbits from the warren, agouties, and kangaroos for the animal part. This necessitated several excursions into the forest, and they found that a great number of trees had been blown down by the last hurricane. Pencroft and Neb also pushed with the cart as far as the vein of coal, and brought back several tons of fuel. They saw in passing that the pottery kiln had been severely damaged by the wind, at least six feet of it having been blown off.

At the same time as the coal, the store of wood was renewed at Granite House, and they profited by the current of the Mercy having again become free, to float down several rafts. They could see that the cold period was not ended.

A visit was also paid to the Chimneys, and the settlers could not but congratulate themselves on not having been living there during the hurricane. The sea had left unquestionable traces of its ravages. Sweeping over the islet, it had furiously assailed the passages, half filling them with sand, while thick beds of seaweed covered the rocks. While Neb, Herbert, and Pencroft hunted or collected wood, Cyrus Harding and Gideon Spilett busied themselves in putting the Chimneys to rights, and they found the forge and the bellows almost unhurt, protected as they had been from the first by the heaps of sand.

The store of fuel had not been made uselessly. The settlers had not done with the rigorous cold. It is known that, in the Northern Hemisphere, the month of February is principally distinguished by rapid fallings of the temperature. It is the same in the Southern Hemisphere, and the end of the month of August, which is the February of North America, does not escape this climatic law.

About the 25th, after another change from snow to rain, the wind shifted to the southeast, and the cold became, suddenly, very severe. According to the engineer's calculation, the mercurial column of a Fahrenheit thermometer would not have marked less than eight degrees below zero, and this intense cold, rendered still more painful by a sharp gale, lasted for several days. The colonists were again shut up in Granite House, and as it was necessary to hermetically seal all the openings of the facade, only leaving a narrow passage for renewing the air, the consumption of candles was considerable. To economize them, the cavern was often only lighted by the blazing hearths, on which fuel was not spared. Several times, one or other of the settlers descended to the beach in the midst of ice which the waves heaped up at each tide, but they soon climbed up again to Granite House, and it was not without pain and difficulty that their hands could hold to the rounds of the ladder. In consequence of the intense cold, their fingers felt as if burned when they touched the rounds. To occupy the leisure hours, which the tenants of

Granite House now had at their disposal, Cyrus Harding undertook an operation which could be performed indoors.

We know that the settlers had no other sugar at their disposal than the liquid substance which they drew from the maple, by making deep incisions in the tree. They contented themselves with collecting this liquor in jars and employing it in this state for different culinary purposes, and the more so, as on growing old, this liquid began to become white and to be of a syrupy consistence.

But there was something better to be made of it, and one day Cyrus Harding announced that they were going to turn into refiners.

'Refiners!' replied Pencroft. 'That is rather a warm trade, I think.'

'Very warm,' answered the engineer.

'Then it will be seasonable!' said the sailor.

This word refining need not awake in the mind thoughts of an elaborate manufactory with apparatus and numerous workmen. No! to crystallize this liquor, only an extremely easy operation is required. Placed on the fire in large earthen pots, it was simply subjected to evapouration, and soon a scum arose to its surface. As soon as this began to thicken, Neb carefully removed it with a wooden spatula; this accelerated the evapouration, and at the same time prevented it from contracting an empyreumatic flavour.

After boiling for several hours on a hot fire, which did as much good to the operators as the substance operated upon, the latter was transformed into a thick syrup. This syrup was poured into clay moulds, previously fabricated in the kitchen stove, and to which they had given various shapes. The next day this syrup had become cold, and formed cakes and tablets. This was sugar of rather a reddish colour, but nearly transparent and of a delicious taste.

The cold continued to the middle of September, and the prisoners in Granite House began to find their captivity rather tedious. Nearly every day they attempted sorties which they could not prolong. They constantly worked at the improvement of their dwelling. They talked while working. Harding instructed his companions in many things, principally explaining to them the practical applications of science. The colonists had no library at their disposal; but the engineer was a book which was always at hand, always open at the page which one wanted, a book which answered all their questions, and which they often consulted. The time thus passed away pleasantly, these brave men not appearing to have any fears for the future.

However, all were anxious to see, if not the fine season, at least the cessation of the insupportable cold. If only they had been clothed in a way to meet it, how many excursions they would have attempted, either to the downs or to Tadorn's Fens! Game would have been easily approached, and the chase would certainly have been most productive. But Cyrus Harding considered it of importance that no one should injure his health, for he had need of all his hands, and his advice was followed.

But it must be said, that the one who was most impatient of this imprisonment, after Pencroft perhaps, was Top. The faithful dog found Granite House very narrow. He ran backwards and forwards from one room to another, showing in his way how weary he was of being shut up. Harding often remarked that when he approached the dark well which communicated with the sea, and of which the orifice opened at the back of the storeroom, Top uttered singular growlings. He ran round and round this hole, which had been covered with a wooden lid. Sometimes even he tried to put his paws under the lid, as if he wished to raise it. He then yelped in a peculiar way, which showed at once anger and uneasiness.

The engineer observed this manoeuvre several times.

What could there be in this abyss to make such an impression on the intelligent animal? The well led to the sea, that was certain. Could narrow passages spread from it through the foundations of the island? Did some marine monster come from time to time, to breathe at the bottom of this well? The engineer did not know what to think, and could not refrain from dreaming of many strange improbabilities. Accustomed to go far into the regions of scientific reality, he would not allow himself to be drawn into the regions of the strange and almost of the supernatural; but yet how to explain why Top, one of those sensible dogs who never waste their time in barking at the moon, should persist in trying with scent and hearing to fathom this abyss, if there was nothing there to cause his uneasiness? Top's conduct puzzled Cyrus Harding even more than he cared to acknowledge to himself.

At all events, the engineer only communicated his impressions to Gideon Spilett, for he thought it useless to explain to his companions the suspicions which arose from what perhaps was only Top's fancy.

At last the cold ceased. There had been rain, squalls mingled with snow, hailstorms, gusts of wind, but these inclemencies did not last. The ice melted, the snow disappeared; the shore, the plateau, the banks of the Mercy, the forest, again became practicable. This return of spring delighted the tenants of Granite House, and they soon only passed it in the hours necessary for eating and sleeping.

They hunted much in the second part of September, which led Pencroft to again entreat for the firearms, which he asserted had been promised by Cyrus Harding. The latter, knowing well that without special tools it would be nearly impossible for him to manufacture a gun which would be of any use, still drew back and put off the operation to some future time, observing in his usual dry way, that Herbert and Spilett had become very skilful archers, so that many sorts of excellent animals, agouties, kangaroos, capybaras, pigeons, bustards, wild ducks, snipes, in short, game both with fur and feathers, fell victims to their arrows, and that, consequently, they could wait. But the obstinate sailor would listen to nothing of this, and he would give the engineer no peace till he promised to satisfy his desire. Gideon Spilett, however, supported Pencroft.

'If, which may be doubted,' said he, 'the island is inhabited by wild beasts, we must think how to fight with and exterminate them. A time may come when this will be our first duty.'

But at this period, it was not the question of firearms which occupied Harding, but that of clothes. Those which the settlers wore had passed this winter, but they would not last until next winter. Skins of carnivora or the wool of ruminants must be procured at any price, and since there were plenty of musmons, it was agreed to consult on the means of forming a flock which might be brought up for the use of the colony. An enclosure for the domestic animals, a poultry-yard for the birds, in a word to establish a sort of farm in the island, such were the two important projects for the fine season.

In consequence and in view of these future establishments, it became of much importance that they should penetrate into all the yet unknown parts of Lincoln Island, that is to say, through that thick forest which extended on the right bank of the Mercy, from its mouth to the extremity of the Serpentine Peninsula, as well as on the whole of its western side. But this needed settled weather, and a month must pass before this exploration could be profitably undertaken.

They therefore waited with some impatience, when an incident occurred which increased the desire the settlers had to visit the whole of their domain.

It was the 24th of October. On this day, Pencroft had gone to visit his traps, which he always kept properly baited. In one of them he found three animals which would be very welcome for the larder. They were a female peccary and her two young ones.

Pencroft then returned to Granite House, enchanted with his capture, and, as usual, he made a great show of his game.

'Come, we shall have a grand feast, captain!' he exclaimed. 'And you too, Mr. Spilett, you will eat some!'

'I shall be very happy,' replied the reporter; 'but what is it that I am going to eat?'

'Suckling-pig.'

'Oh, indeed, suckling-pig, Pencroft? To hear you, I thought that you were bringing back a young partridge stuffed with truffles!'

'What?' cried Pencroft. 'Do you mean to say that you turn up your nose at suckling-pig?'

'No,' replied Gideon Spilett, without showing any enthusiasm; 'provided one doesn't eat too much'

'That's right, that's right,' returned the sailor, who was not pleased whenever he heard his chase made light of. 'You like to make objections. Seven months ago, when we landed on the island, you would have been only too glad to have met with such game!'

'Well, well,' replied the reporter, 'man is never perfect, nor contented.'

'Now,' said Pencroft, 'I hope that Neb will distinguish himself. Look here! These two little peccaries are not more than three months old! They will be as tender as quails! Come along, Neb, come! I will look after the cooking myself.'

And the sailor, followed by Neb, entered the kitchen, where they were soon absorbed in their culinary labours.

They were allowed to do it in their own way. Neb, therefore, prepared a magnificent repast—the two little peccaries, kangaroo soup, a smoked ham, stone-pine almonds, Oswego tea; in fact, all the best that they had, but among all the dishes figured in the first rank the savoury peccaries.

At five o'clock dinner was served in the dining-room of Granite House. The kangaroo soup was smoking on the table. They found it excellent.

To the soup succeeded the peccaries, which Pencroft insisted on carving himself, and of which he served out monstrous portions to each of the guests.

These suckling-pigs were really delicious, and Pencroft was devouring his share with great gusto, when all at once a cry and an oath escaped him.

'What's the matter?' asked Cyrus Harding.

'The matter? the matter is that I have just broken a tooth!' replied the sailor.

'What, are there pebbles in your peccaries?' said Gideon Spilett.

'I suppose so,' replied Pencroft, drawing from his lips the object which had cost him a grinder!—

It was not a pebble—it was a leaden bullet.

PART TWO

ABANDONED

Chapter 1

It was now exactly seven months since the balloon voyagers had been thrown on Lincoln Island. During that time, notwithstanding the researches they had made, no human being had been discovered. No smoke even had betrayed the presence of man on the surface of the island. No vestiges of his handiwork showed that either at an early or at a late period had man lived there. Not only did it now appear to be uninhabited by any but themselves, but the colonists were compelled to believe that it never had been inhabited. And now, all this scaffolding of reasonings fell before a simple ball of metal, found in the body of an inoffensive rodent! In fact, this bullet must have issued from a firearm, and who but a human being could have used such a weapon?

When Pencroft had placed the bullet on the table, his companions looked at it with intense astonishment. All the consequences likely to result from this incident, notwithstanding its apparent insignificance, immediately took possession of their minds. The sudden apparition of a supernatural being could not have startled them more completely.

Cyrus Harding did not hesitate to give utterance to the suggestions which this fact, at once surprising and unexpected, could not fail to raise in his mind. He took the bullet, turned it over and over, rolled it between his finger and thumb; then, turning to Pencroft, he asked,—

Are you sure that the peccary wounded by this bullet was not more than three months old?'

'Not more, captain,' replied Pencroft. 'It was still sucking its mother when I found it in the trap.'

'Well,' said the engineer, 'that proves that within three months a gun-shot was fired in Lincoln Island.'

'And that a bullet,' added Gideon Spilett, 'wounded, though not mortally, this little animal.'

'That is unquestionable,' said Cyrus Harding, 'and these are the deductions which must be drawn from this incident: that the island was inhabited before our arrival, or that men have landed here within three months. Did these men arrive here voluntarily or involuntarily, by disembarking on the shore or by being wrecked? This point can only be cleared up later. As to what they were, Europeans or Malays, enemies or friends of our race, we cannot possibly guess; and if they still inhabit the island, or if they have left it, we know not. But these questions are of too much importance to be allowed to remain long unsettled.'

'No! a hundred times no! a thousand times no!' cried the sailor, springing up from the table. 'There are no other men than ourselves on Lincoln Island! By my faith! The island isn't large and if it had been inhabited, we should have seen some of the inhabitants long before this!'

'In fact, the contrary would be very astonishing,' said Herbert.

'But it would be much more astonishing, I should think, observed the reporter, 'if this peccary had been born with a bullet in its inside!'

'At least,' said Neb seriously, 'if Pencroft has not had—'

'Look here, Neb,' burst out Pencroft. 'Do you think I could have a bullet in my jaw for five or six months without finding it out? Where could it be hidden?' he asked, opening his mouth to show the two-and-thirty teeth with which it was furnished. 'Look well, Neb, and if you find one hollow tooth in this set, I will let you pull out half a dozen!'

'Neb's supposition is certainly inadmissible,' replied Harding, who, notwithstanding the gravity of his thoughts, could not restrain a smile. 'It is certain that a gun has been fired in the island, within three months at most. But I am inclined to think that the people who landed on this coast were only here a very short time ago, or that they just touched here; for if, when we surveyed the island from the summit of Mount Franklin, it had been inhabited, we should have seen them or we should have been seen ourselves. It is therefore, probable that within only a few weeks castaways have been thrown by a storm on some part of the coast. However that may be, it is of consequence to us to have this point settled.'

'I think that we should act with caution,' said the reporter.

'Such is my advice,' replied Cyrus Harding, 'for it is to be feared that Malay pirates have landed on the island!'

'Captain,' asked the sailor, 'would it not be a good plan, before setting out, to build a canoe in which we could either ascend the river, or, if we liked, coast round the inland? It will not do to be unprovided.'

'Your idea is good, Pencroft,' replied the engineer, 'but we cannot wait for that. It would take at least a month to build a boat.'

'Yes, a real boat,' replied the sailor; 'but we do not want one for a sea voyage, and in five days at the most, I will undertake to construct a canoe fit to navigate the Mercy.'

'Five days,' cried Neb, 'to build a boat?'

'Yes, Neb; a boat in the Indian fashion.'

'Of wood?' asked the Negro, looking still unconvinced.

'Of wood,' replied Pencroft, 'of rather of bark. I repeat, captain, that in five days the work will be finished!'

'In five days, then, be it,' replied the engineer.

'But till that time we must be very watchful,' said Herbert.

'Very watchful indeed, my friends,' replied Harding; 'and I beg you to confine your hunting excursions to the neighbourhood of Granite House.'

The dinner ended less gaily than Pencroft had hoped.

So, then, the island was, or had been, inhabited by others than the settlers. Proved as it was by the incident of the bullet, it was hereafter an unquestionable fact, and such a discovery could not but cause great uneasiness among the colonists.

Cyrus Harding and Gideon Spilett, before sleeping, conversed long about the matter. They asked themselves if by chance this incident might not have some connection with the inexplicable way in which the engineer had been saved, and the other peculiar circumstances which had struck them at different times. However, Cyrus Harding, after having discussed the pros and cons of the question, ended by saying,—

'In short, would you like to know my opinion, my dear Spilett?'

'Yes, Cyrus.'

'Well, then, it is this: however minutely we explore the island, we shall find nothing.'

The next day Pencroft set to work. He did not mean to build a boat with boards and planking, but simply a flat-bottomed canoe, which would be well suited for navigating the Mercy—above all, for approaching its source, where the water would naturally be shallow. Pieces of bark, fastened one to the other, would form a light boat; and in case of natural obstacles, which would render a portage necessary, it would be easily carried. Pencroft intended to secure the pieces of bark by means of nails, to insure the canoe being watertight.

It was first necessary to select the trees which would afford a strong and supple bark for the work. Now the last storm had brought down a number of large birch-trees, the bark of which would be perfectly suited for their purpose. Some of these trees lay on the ground, and they had only to be barked, which was the most difficult thing of all, owing to the imperfect tools which the settlers possessed. However, they overcame all difficulties.

While the sailor, seconded by the engineer, thus occupied himself without losing an hour, Gideon Spilett and Herbert were not idle.

They were made purveyors to the colony. The reporter could

not but admire the boy, who had acquired great skill in handling the bow and spear. Herbert also showed great courage and much of that presence of mind which may justly be called 'the reasoning of bravery.' These two companions of the chase, remembering Cyrus Harding's recommendations, did not go beyond a radius of two miles round Granite House; but the borders of the forest furnished a sufficient tribute of agoutis, capybaras, kangaroos, peccaries, etc.; and if the result from the traps was less than during the cold, still the warren yielded its accustomed quota, which might have fed all the colony in Lincoln Island.

Often during these excursions, Herbert talked with Gideon Spilett on the incident of the bullet, and the deductions which the engineer drew from it, and one day—it was the 26th of October—he said—'But, Mr. Spilett, do you not think it very extraordinary that, if any castaways have landed on the island, they have not yet shown themselves near Granite House?'

'Very astonishing if they are still here,' replied the reporter, 'but not astonishing at all if they are here no longer!'

'So you think that these people have already quilted the island?' returned Herbert.

'It is more than probable, my boy; for if their stay was prolonged, and above all, if they were still here, some accident would have at last betrayed their presence.'

'But if they were able to go away,' observed the lad, 'they could not have been castaways.'

'No, Herbert; or, at least, they were what might be called provisional castaways. It is very possible that a storm may have driven them to the island without destroying their vessel, and that, the storm over, they went away again.'

'I must acknowledge one thing,' said Herbert, 'it is that Captain Harding appears rather to fear than desire the presence of human beings on our island.'

'In short,' responded the reporter, 'there are only Malays who frequent these seas, and those fellows are ruffians which it is best to avoid.'

'It is not impossible, Mr. Spilett,' said Herbert, 'that some day or other we may find traces of their landing.'

'I do not say no, my boy. A deserted camp, the ashes of a fire, would put us on the track, and this is what we will look for in our next expedition.'

The day on which the hunters spoke thus, they were in a part of the forest near the Mercy, remarkable for its beautiful trees. There, among others, rose, to a height of nearly 200 feet above the ground, some of those superb coniferae, to which, in New Zealand, the natives give the name of Kauris.

'I have an idea, Mr. Spilett,' said Herbert. 'If I were to climb to the top of one of these kauris, I could survey the country for an immense distance round.'

'The idea is good,' replied the reporter; 'but could you climb to the top of those giants?'

'I can at least try,' replied Herbert.

The light and active boy then sprang on the first branches, the arrangement of which made the ascent of the kauri easy, and in a few minutes he arrived at the summit, which emerged from the immense plain of verdure.

From this elevated situation his gaze extended over all the southern portion of the island, from Claw Cape on the southeast, to Reptile End on the southwest. To the northwest rose Mount Franklin, which concealed a great part of the horizon.

But Herbert, from the height of his observatory, could examine all the yet unknown portion of the island, which might have given shelter to the strangers whose presence they suspected.

The lad looked attentively. There was nothing in sight on the sea, not a sail, neither on the horizon nor near the island. However, as the bank of trees hid the shore, it was possible that a vessel, especially if deprived of her masts, might lie close to the land and thus be invisible to Herbert.

Neither in the forests of the Far West was anything to be seen. The wood formed an impenetrable screen, measuring several square miles, without a break or an opening. It was impossible even to follow the course of the Mercy, or to ascertain in what part of the mountain it took its source. Perhaps other creeks also ran towards the west, but they could not be seen.

But at last, if all indication of an encampment escaped Herbert's sight could he not even catch a glimpse of smoke, the faintest trace of which would be easily discernible in the pure atmosphere?

For an instant Herbert thought he could perceive a slight smoke in the west, but a more attentive examination showed that he was mistaken. He strained his eyes in every direction, and his sight was excellent. No, decidedly there was nothing there.

Herbert descended to the foot of the kauri, and the two sportsmen returned to Granite House. There Cyrus Harding listened to the lad's account, shook his head and said nothing. It was very evident that no decided opinion could be pronounced on this question until after a complete exploration of the island.

Two days after—the 28th of October—another incident occurred, for which an explanation was again required.

While strolling along the shore about two miles from Granite House, Herbert and Neb were fortunate enough to capture a magnificent specimen of the order of chelonia. It was a turtle of the species Midas, the edible green turtle, so called from the colour both of its shell and fat.

Herbert caught sight of this turtle as it was crawling among the rocks to reach the sea.

'Help, Neb, help!' he cried.

Neb ran up.

'What a fine animal!' said Neb; 'but how are we to catch it?'

'Nothing is easier, Neb,' replied Herbert. 'We have only to turn the turtle on its back, and it cannot possibly get away. Take your spear and do as I do.'

The reptile, aware of danger, had retired between its carapace and plastron. They no longer saw its head or feet, and it was motionless as a rock.

Herbert and Neb then drove their sticks underneath the animal, and by their united efforts managed without difficulty to turn it on its back. The turtle, which was three feet in length, would have weighed at least four hundred pounds.

'Capital!' cried Neb; 'this is something which will rejoice friend Pencroft's heart.'

In fact, the heart of friend Pencroft could not fail to be rejoiced, for the flesh of the turtle, which feeds on wrack-grass, is extremely savoury. At this moment the creature's head could be seen, which was small, flat, but widened behind by the large temporal fossae hidden under the long roof.

'And now, what shall we do with our prize?' said Neb. 'We can't drag it to Granite House!'

'Leave it here, since it cannot turn over,' replied Herbert, 'and we will come back with the cart to fetch it.'

'That is the best plan.'

However, for greater precaution, Herbert took the trouble, which Neb deemed superfluous, to wedge up the animal with great stones; after which the two hunters returned to Granite House, following the beach, which the tide had left uncovered. Herbert, wishing to surprise Pencroft, said nothing about the 'superb specimen of a chelonian' which they had turned over on the sand; but, two hours later, he and Neb returned with the cart to the place where they had left it. The 'superb specimen of a chelonian' was no longer there!

Neb and Herbert stared at each other first; then they stared about them. It was just at this spot that the turtle had been left. The lad even found the stones which he had used, and therefore he was certain of not being mistaken.

'Well!' said Neb, 'these beasts can turn themselves over, then?"

'It appears so,' replied Herbert, who could not understand it at all, and was gazing at the stones scattered on the sand.

'Well, Pencroft will be disgusted!'

'And Captain Harding will perhaps be very perplexed how to explain this disappearance,' thought Herbert.

'Look here,' said Neb, who wished to hide his ill-luck, 'we won't speak about it.'

'On the contrary, Neb, we must speak about it,' replied Herbert.

And the two, taking the cart, which there was now no use for, returned to Granite House.

Arrived at the dockyard, where the engineer and the sailor were working together, Herbert recounted what had happened.

'Oh! the stupids!' cried the sailor, 'to have let at least fifty meals escape!'

'But, Pencroft,' replied Neb, 'it wasn't our fault that the beast got away; as I tell you, we had turned it over on its back!'

'Then you didn't turn it over enough!' returned the obstinate sailor.

'Not enough!' cried Herbert.

And he told how he had taken care to wedge up the turtle with stones.

'It is a miracle, then!' replied Pencroft.

'I thought, captain,' said Herbert, 'that turtles, once placed on their backs, could not regain their feet, especially when they are of a large size?'

'That is true, my boy,' replied Cyrus Harding.

'Then how did it manage?'

'At what distance from the sea did you leave this turtle?' asked the engineer, who, having suspended his work, was reflecting on this incident.

'Fifteen feet at the most,' replied Herbert.

'And the tide was low at the time?'

'Yes, captain.'

'Well,' replied the engineer, 'what the turtle could not do on the sand it might have been able to do in the water. It turned over when the tide overtook it, and then quietly returned to the deep sea.'

'Oh! what stupids we were!' cried Neb.

'That is precisely what I had the honour of telling you before!' returned the sailor.

Cyrus Harding had given this explanation, which, no doubt, was admissible. But was he himself convinced of the accuracy of this explanation? It cannot be said that he was.

Chapter 2

On the 9th of October the bark canoe was entirely finished. Pencroft had kept his promise, and a light boat, the shell of which was joined together by the flexible twigs of the crejimba, had been constructed in five days. A seat in the stern, a second seat in the middle to preserve the equilibrium, a third seat in the bows, rowlocks for the two oars, a scull to steer with, completed the little craft, which was twelve feet long, and did not weigh more than two hundred pounds. The operation of launching it was extremely simple. The canoe was carried to the beach and laid on the sand before Granite House, and the rising tide floated it. Pencroft, who leaped in directly, manoeuvred it with the scull and declared it to be just the thing for the purpose to which they wished to put it.

'Hurrah!' cried the sailor, who did not disdain to celebrate thus his own triumph. 'With this we could go round—'

'The world?' asked Gideon Spilett.

'No, the island. Some stones for ballast, a mast and a sail, which the captain will make for us some day, and we shall go splendidly! Well, captain—and you, Mr. Spilett; and you, Herbert; and you, Neb—aren't you coming to try our new vessel? Come along! we must see if it will carry all five of us!'

This was certainly a trial which ought to be made. Pencroft soon brought the canoe to the shore by a narrow passage among the rocks, and it was agreed that they should make a trial of the boat that day by following the shore as far as the first point at which the rocks of the south ended.

As they embarked, Neb cried,—

'But your boat leaks rather, Pencroft.'

'That's nothing, Neb,' replied the sailor; 'the wood will get seasoned. In two days there won't be a single leak, and our boat will have no more water in her than there is in the stomach of a drunkard. Jump in!'

They were soon all seated, and Pencroft shoved off. The weather was magnificent, the sea as calm as if its waters were contained within the narrow limits of a lake. Thus the boat could proceed with as much security as if it was ascending the tranquil current of the Mercy.

Neb took one of the oars, Herbert the other, and Pencroft remained in the stern in order to use the scull.

The sailor first crossed the channel, and steered close to the southern point of the islet. A light breeze blew from the south. No roughness was found either in the channel or the green sea. A long swell, which the canoe scarcely felt, as it was heavily laden, rolled regularly over the surface of the water. They pulled out about half a mile distant from the shore, that they might have a good view of Mount Franklin.

Pencroft afterwards returned towards the mouth of the river. The boat then skirted the shore, which, extending to the extreme point, hid all Tadorn's Fens.

This point, of which the distance was increased by the irregularity of the coast, was nearly three miles from the Mercy. The settlers resolved to go to its extremity, and only go beyond it as much as was necessary to take a rapid survey of the coast as far as Claw Cape.

The canoe followed the windings of the shore, avoiding the rocks which fringed it, and which the rising tide began to cover. The cliff gradually sloped away from the mouth of the river to the point. This was formed of granite reeks, capriciously distributed, very different from the cliff at Prospect Heights, and of an extremely wild aspect. It might have been said that an immense cartload of rocks had been emptied out there. There was no vegetation on this sharp promontory, which projected two miles from the forest, and it thus represented a giant's arm stretched out from a leafy sleeve.

The canoe, impelled by the two oars, advanced without difficulty. Gideon Spilett, pencil in one hand and notebook in the other, sketched the coast in bold strokes. Neb, Herbert, and Pencroft chatted, while examining this part of their domain, which was new to them, and, in proportion as the canoe proceeded towards the south, the two Mandible Capes appeared to move, and surround Union Bay more closely.

As to Cyrus Harding, he did not speak; he simply gazed, and by the mistrust which his look expressed, it appeared that he was examining some strange country.

In the meantime, after a voyage of three-quarters of an hour, the canoe reached the extremity of the point, and Pencroft was preparing to return, when Herbert, rising, pointed to a black object, saying,—

'What do I see down there on the beach?'

All eyes turned towards the point indicated.

'Why,' said the reporter, 'there is something. It looks like part of a wreck half buried in the sand.'

'Ah!' cried Pencroft, 'I see what it is!'

'What?' asked Neb.

'Barrels, barrels, which perhaps are full,' replied the sailor.

'Pull to the shore, Pencroft!' said Cyrus.

A few strokes of the oar brought the canoe into a little creek, and its passengers leaped on shore.

Pencroft was not mistaken. Two barrels were there, half buried in the sand, but still firmly attached to a large chest, which, sustained by them, had floated to the moment when it stranded on the beach.

'There has been a wreck, then, in some part of the island,' said Herbert.

'Evidently,' replied Spilett.

'But what's in this chest?' cried Pencroft, with very natural impatience. 'What's in this chest? It is shut up, and nothing to open it with! Well, perhaps a stone—'

And the sailor, raising a heavy block, was about to break in one of the sides of the chest, when the engineer arrested his hand.

'Pencroft,' said he, 'can you restrain your impatience for one hour only?'

But, captain, just think! Perhaps there is everything we want in there!'

'We shall find that out, Pencroft,' replied the engineer; 'but trust to me, and do not break the chest, which may be useful to us. We must convey it to Granite House, where we can open it easily, and without breaking it. It is quite prepared for a voyage; and since it has floated here, it may just as well float to the mouth of the river.'

'You are right, captain, and I was wrong, as usual,' replied the sailor.

The engineer's advice was good. In fact, the canoe probably would not have been able to contain the articles possibly enclosed in the chest, which doubtless was heavy, since two empty barrels were required to buoy it up. It was, therefore, much better to tow it to the beach at Granite House.

And now, whence had this chest come? That was the important question. Cyrus Harding and his companions looked attentively around them, and examined the shore for several hundred steps. No other articles or pieces of wreck could be found. Herbert and Neb climbed a high rock to survey the sea, but there was nothing in sight—neither a dismasted vessel nor a ship under sail.

However, there was no doubt that there had been a wreck. Perhaps this incident was connected with that of the bullet? Perhaps strangers had landed on another part of the island? Perhaps they were still there? But the thought which came naturally to the settlers was, that these strangers could not be Malay pirates, for the chest was evidently of American or European make.

All the party returned to the chest, which was of an unusually large size. It was made of oak wood, very carefully closed and covered with a thick hide, which was secured by copper nails. The two great barrels, hermetically sealed, but which sounded hollow and empty, were fastened to its sides by strong ropes, knotted with a skill which Pencroft directly pronounced sailors alone could exhibit. It appeared to be in a perfect state of preservation, which was explained by the fact that it had stranded on a sandy beach, and not among rocks. They had no doubt whatever, on examining it carefully, that it had not been long in the water, and that its arrival on this coast was recent. The water did not appear to have penetrated to the inside, and the articles which it contained were no doubt uninjured.

It was evident that this chest had been thrown overboard from some dismasted vessel driven towards the island, and that, in the hope that it would reach the land, where they might afterwards find it, the passengers had taken the precaution to buoy it up by means of this floating apparatus.

'We will tow this chest to Granite House,' said the engineer, 'where we can make an inventory of its contents; then, if we discover any of the survivors from the supposed wreck, we can return it to those to whom it belongs. If we find no one—'

'We will keep it for ourselves!' cried Pencroft. 'But what in the world can there be in it?'

The sea was already approaching the chest, and the high tide would evidently float it. One of the ropes which fastened the barrels was partly unleashed and used as a cable to unite the floating apparatus with the canoe. Pencroft and Neb then dug away the sand with their oars, so as to facilitate the moving of the chest, towing which the boat soon began to double the point, to which the name of Flotsam Point was given.

The chest was heavy, and the barrels were scarcely sufficient to keep it above water. The sailor also feared every instant that it would get loose and sink to the bottom of the sea. But happily his fears were not realized, and an hour and a half after they set out—all that time had been taken up in going a distance of three miles—the boat touched the beach below Granite House.

Canoe and chest were then hauled up on the sands; and as the tide was then going out, they were soon left high and dry. Neb, hurrying home, brought back some tools with which to open the chest in such a way that it might be injured as little as possible, and they proceeded to its inventory. Pencroft did not try to hide that he was greatly excited.

The sailor began by detaching the two barrels, which, being in good condition, would of course be of use. Then the locks were forced with a cold chisel and hammer, and the lid thrown back. A second casing of zinc lined the interior of the chest, which had been evidently arranged that the articles which it enclosed might under any circumstances be sheltered from damp.

'Oh!' cried Neb, 'suppose it's jam!

'I hope not,' replied the reporter.

'If only there was—' said the sailor in a low voice.

'What?' asked Neb, who overheard him.

'Nothing!'

The covering of zinc was torn off and thrown back over the sides of the chest, and by degrees numerous articles of very varied character were produced and strewn about on the sand. At each new object Pencroft uttered fresh hurrahs, Herbert clapped his hands, and Neb danced up and down. There were books which made Herbert wild with joy, and cooking utensils which Neb covered with kisses!

In short, the colonists had reason to be extremely satisfied, for this chest contained tools, weapons, instruments, clothes, books; and this is the exact list of them as stated in Gideon Spilett's notebook:

Tools:—3 knives with several blades, 2 woodmen's axes, 2 carpenter's hatchets, 3 planes, 2 adzes, 1 twibil or mattock, 6 chisels, 2 files, 3 hammers, 3 gimlets, 2 augers, 10 bags of nails and screws, 3 saws of different sizes, 2 boxes of needles.

Weapons:—2 flint-lock guns, 2 for percussion caps, 2 breach-loader carbines, 5 boarding cutlasses, 4 sabres, 2 barrels of powder, each containing twenty-five pounds; 12 boxes of percussion caps.

Instruments:—1 sextant, 1 double opera-glass, 1 telescope, 1 box of mathematical instruments, 1 mariner's compass, 1 Fahrenheit thermometer, 1 aneroid barometer, 1 box containing a photographic apparatus, object-glass, plates, chemicals, etc.

Clothes:-2 dozen shirts of a peculiar material resembling wool, but evidently of a vegetable origin; 3 dozen stockings of the same material.

Utensils:-1 iron pot, 6 copper saucepans, 3 iron dishes, 10 metal plates, 2 kettles, 1 portable stove, 6 table-knives,

Books:-1 Bible, 1 atlas, 1 dictionary of the different Polynesian idioms, 1 dictionary of natural science, in six volumes; 3 reams of white paper, 2 books with blank pages.

'It must be allowed,' said the reporter, after the inventory had been made, 'that the owner of this chest was a practical man! Tools, weapons, instruments, clothes, utensils, books—nothing is wanting! It might really be said that he expected to be wrecked, and had prepared for it beforehand.'

'Nothing is wanting, indeed,' murmured Cyrus Harding thoughtfully.

'And for a certainty,' added Herbert, 'the vessel which carried this chest and its owner was not a Malay pirate!'

'Unless,' said Pencroft, 'the owner had been taken prisoner by pirates—'

'That is not admissible,' replied the reporter. 'It is more probable that an American or European vessel has been driven into this quarter, and that her passengers, wishing to save necessaries at least, prepared this chest and threw it overboard.'

'Is that your opinion, captain?' asked Herbert.

'Yes, my boy,' replied the engineer, 'that may have been the case. It is possible that at the moment, or in expectation of a wreck, they collected into this chest different articles of the greatest use in hopes of finding it again on the coast—'

'Even the photographic box!' exclaimed the sailor incredulously.

'As to that apparatus,' replied Harding, 'I do not quite see the use of it; and a more complete supply of clothes or more abundant ammunition would have been more valuable to us as well as to any other castaways!'

'But isn't there any mark or direction on these instruments, tools, or books, which would tell us something about them?' asked Gideon Spilett.

That might be ascertained. Each article was carefully examined, especially the books, instruments and weapons. Neither the weapons nor the instruments, contrary to the usual custom, bore the name of the maker; they were, besides, in a perfect state, and did not appear to have been used. The same peculiarity marked the tools and utensils; all were new, which proved that the articles had not been taken by chance and thrown into the chest, but, on the contrary, that the choice of things had been well considered and arranged with care. This was also indicated by the second case of metal which had preserved them from damp, and which could not have been soldered in a moment of haste.

As to the dictionaries of natural science and Polynesian idioms, both were English; but they neither bore the name of the publisher nor the date of publication.

The same with the Bible printed in English, in quarto, remarkable from a typographic point of view, and which appeared to have been often used.

The atlas was a magnificent work, comprising maps of every country in the world, and several planispheres arranged upon Mercator's projection, and of which the nomenclature was in French—but which also bore neither date nor name of publisher.

There was nothing, therefore, on these different articles by which they could be traced, and nothing consequently of a nature to show the nationality of the vessel which must have recently passed these shores.

But, wherever the chest might have come from, it was a treasure to the settlers on Lincoln Island. Till then, by making use of the productions of nature, they had created everything for themselves, and, thanks to their intelligence, they had managed without difficulty. But did it not appear as if Providence had wished to reward them by sending them these productions of human industry? Their thanks rose unanimously to Heaven.

However, one of them was not quite satisfied: it was Pencroft. It appeared that the chest did not contain something which he evidently held in great esteem, for in proportion as they approached the bottom of the box, his hurrahs diminished in heartiness, and, the inventory finished, he was heard to mutter these words:—'That's all very fine, but you can see that there is nothing for me in that box!'

This led Neb to say,—

'Why, friend Pencroft, what more do you expect?'

'Half a pound of tobacco,' replied Pencroft seriously, 'and nothing would have been wanting to complete my happiness!'

No one could help laughing at this speech of the sailor's.

But the result of this discovery of the chest was, that it was now more than ever necessary to explore the island thoroughly. It was therefore agreed that the next morning at break of day, they should set out, by ascending the Mercy so as to reach the western shore. If any castaways had landed on the coast, it was to be feared they were without resources, and it was therefore the more necessary to carry help to them without delay.

During the day the different articles were carried to Granite House, where they were methodically arranged in the great hall. This day—the 29th of October—happened to be a Sunday, and, before going to bed, Herbert asked the engineer if he would not read them something from the Gospel.

'Willingly,' replied Cyrus Harding.

He took the sacred volume, and was about to open it, when Pencroft stopped him, saying,—'Captain, I am superstitious. Open at random and read the first verse which, your eye falls upon. We will see if it applies to our situation.'

Cyrus Harding smiled at the sailor's idea, and, yielding to his wish, he opened exactly at a place where the leaves were separated by a marker.

Immediately his eyes were attracted by a cross which, made with a pencil, was placed against the eighth verse of the seventh chapter of the Gospel of St. Matthew. He read the verse, which was this:—

'For every one that asketh receiveth; and he that seeketh findeth.'

Chapter 3

The next day, the 30th of October, all was ready for the proposed exploring expedition, which recent events had rendered so necessary. In fact, things had so come about that the settlers in Lincoln Island no longer needed help for themselves, but were even able to carry it to others.

It was therefore agreed that they should ascend the Mercy as far as the river was navigable. A great part of the distance would thus be traversed without fatigue, and the explorers could transport their provisions and arms to an advanced point in the west of the island.

It was necessary to think not only of the things which they should take with them, but also of those which they might have by chance to bring back to Granite House. If there had been a wreck on the coast, as was supposed, there would be many things cast up, which would be lawfully their prizes. In the event of this, the cart would have been of more use than the light canoe, but it was heavy and clumsy to drag, and therefore more difficult to use; this led Pencroft to express his regret that the chest had not contained, besides 'his half pound of tobacco,' a pair of strong New Jersey horses, which would have been very useful to the colony!

The provisions, which Neb had already packed up, consisted of a store of meat and of several gallons of beer, that is to say enough to sustain them for three days, the time which Harding assigned for the expedition. They hoped besides to supply themselves on the road, and Neb took care not to forget the portable stove.

The only tools the settlers took were the two woodmen's axes, which they could use to cut a path through the thick forests, as also the instruments, the telescope and pocket-compass.

For weapons they selected the two flint-lock guns, which were likely to be more useful to them than the percussion fowling-pieces, the first only requiring flints which could be easily replaced, and the latter needing fulminating caps, a frequent use of which would soon exhaust their limited stock. However, they took also one of the carbines and some cartridges.

As to the powder, of which there was about fifty pounds In the barrel, a small supply of it had to be taken, but the engineer hoped to manufacture an explosive substance which would allow them to husband it. To the firearms were added the five cutlasses well sheathed in leather, and, thus supplied, the settlers could venture into the vast forest with some chance of success.

It is useless to add that Pencroft, Herbert, and Neb, thus armed, were at the summit of their happiness, although Cyrus Harding made them promise not to fire a shot unless it was necessary.

At six in the morning the canoe put off from the shore; all had embarked, including Top, and they proceeded to the mouth of the Mercy.

The tide had begun to come up half an hour before. For several hours, therefore, there would be a current, which it was well to profit by, for later the ebb would make it difficult to ascend the river. The tide was already strong, for in three days the moon would be full, and it was enough to keep the boat in the centre of the current, where it floated swiftly along between the high banks without its being necessary to increase its speed by the aid of the oars. In a few minutes the explorers arrived at the angle formed by the Mercy and exactly at the place where, seven months before, Pencroft had made his first raft of wood.

After this sudden angle the river widened and flowed under the shade of great evergreen firs.

The aspect of the banks was magnificent. Cyrus Harding and his companions could not but admire the lovely effects so easily produced by nature with water and trees. As they advanced the forest element diminished. On the right bank of the river grew magnificent specimens of the ulmaceae tribe, the precious elm, so valuable to builders, and which withstands well the action of water. Then there were numerous groups belonging to the same family, among others one in particular, the fruit of which produces a very useful oil. Further on, Herbert remarked the lardizabala, a twining shrub which, when bruised in water, furnishes excellent cordage; and two or three ebony trees of a beautiful black, crossed with capricious veins.

From time to time, in certain places where the landing was easy, the canoe was stopped, when Gideon Spilett, Herbert, and Pencroft, their guns in their hands, and preceded by Top, jumped on shore. Without expecting game, some useful plant might be met with, and the young naturalist was delighted with discovering a sort of wild spinach, belonging to the order of chenopodiaceae, and numerous specimens of cruciferae, belonging to the cabbage tribe, which it would certainly be possible to cultivate by transplanting. There were cresses, horseradish, turnips, and lastly, little branching hairy stalks, scarcely more than three feet high, which produced brownish grains.

Do you know what this plant is?' asked Herbert of the sailor.

'Tobacco!' cried Pencroft, who evidently had never seen his favourite plant except in the bowl of his pipe.

'No, Pencroft,' replied Herbert; 'this is not tobacco, it is mustard.'

'Mustard be hanged!' returned the sailor; 'but if by chance you happen to come across a tobacco-plant, my boy, pray don't scorn that!'

'We shall find it some day!' said Gideon Spilett.

'Well!' exclaimed Pencroft, 'when that day comes, I do not know what more will be wanting in our island!'

These different plants, which had been carefully rooted up, were carried to the canoe, where Cyrus Harding had remained buried in thought.

The reporter, Herbert, and Pencroft in this manner frequently disembarked, sometimes on the right bank, sometimes on the left bank of the Mercy.

The latter was less abrupt, but the former more wooded. The engineer ascertained by consulting his pocket-compass that the direction of the river from the first turn was obviously southwest and northeast, and nearly straight for a length of about three miles. But it was to be supposed that this direction changed beyond that point, and that the Mercy continued to the north-west, towards the spurs of Mount Franklin, among which the river rose.

During one of these excursions, Gideon Spilett managed to get hold of two couples of living gallinaceae. They were birds with long, thin beaks, lengthened necks, short wings, and without any appearance of a tail. Herbert rightly gave them the name of tinamous, and it was resolved that they should be the first tenants of their future poultry-yard.

But till then the guns had not spoken, and the first report which awoke the echoes of the forest of the Far West was provoked by the appearance of a beautiful bird, resembling the kingfisher.

'I recognize him!' cried Pencroft, and it seemed as if his gun went off by itself.

'What do you recognize?' asked the reporter.

'The bird which escaped us on our first excursion, and from which we gave the name to that part of the forest.'

'A jacamar!' cried Herbert.

It was indeed a jacamar, of which the plumage shines with a metallic lustre. A shot brought it to the ground, and Top carried it to the canoe.

At the same time half a dozen lories were brought down. The lory is of the size of a pigeon, the plumage dashed with green, part of the wings crimson, and its crest bordered with white. To the young boy belonged the honour of this shot, and he was proud enough of it. Lories are better food than the jacamar, the flesh of which is rather tough, but it was difficult to persuade Pencroft that he had not killed the king of eatable birds. It was ten o'clock in the morning when the canoe reached a second angle of the Mercy, nearly five miles from its mouth. Here a halt was made for breakfast under the shade of some splendid trees. The river still measured from sixty to seventy feet in breadth, and its bed from five to six feet in depth. The engineer had observed that it was increased by numerous affluents, but they were unnavigable, being simply little streams. As to the forest, including Jacamar Wood, as well as the forests of the Far West, it extended as far as the eye could reach. In no place, either in the depths of the forests or under the trees on the banks of the Mercy, was the presence of man revealed. The explorers could not discover one suspicious trace. It was evident that the woodman's axe had never touched these trees, that the pioneer's knife had never severed the creepers hanging from one trunk to another in the midst of tangled brushwood and long grass. If castaways had landed on the island, they could not have yet quilted the shore, and it was not in the woods that the survivors of the supposed shipwreck should be sought.

The engineer therefore manifested some impatience to reach the western coast of Lincoln Island, which was at least five miles distant according to his estimation.

The voyage was continued, and as the Mercy appeared to flow not towards the shore, but rather towards Mount Franklin, it was decided that they should use the boat as long as there was enough water under its keel to float it. It was both fatigue spared and time gained, for they would have been obliged to cut a path through the thick wood with their axes. But soon the flow completely failed them, either the tide was going down, and it was about the hour, or it could no longer be felt at this distance from the mouth of the Mercy. They had therefore to make use of the oars. Herbert and Neb each took one, and Pencroft took the scull. The forest soon became less dense, the trees grew further apart and often quite isolated. But the further they were from each other the more magnificent they appeared, profiting, as they did, by the free, pure air which circulated around them.

What splendid specimens of the flora of this latitude! Certainly their presence would have been enough for a botanist to name without hesitation the parallel which traversed Lincoln Island.

'Eucalypti!' cried Herbert.

They were, in fact, those splendid trees, the giants of the extratropical zone, the congeners of the Australian and New Zealand eucalyptus, both situated under the same latitude as Lincoln Island. Some rose to a height of two hundred feet. Their trunks at the base measured twenty feet in circumference, and their bark was covered by a network of farrows containing a red, sweet-smelling gum. Nothing is more wonderful or more singular than those enormous specimens of the order of the myrtaceae, with their leaves placed vertically and not horizontally, so that an edge and not a surface looks upwards, the effect being that the sun's rays penetrate more freely among the trees.

The ground at the foot of the eucalypti was carpeted with grass, and from the bushes escaped flights of little birds, which glittered in the sunlight like winged rubies.

'These are something like trees!' cried Neb; 'but are they good for anything?'

'Pooh!' replied Pencroft. 'Of course there are vegetable giants as well as human giants, and they are no good, except to show themselves at fairs!'

'I think that you are mistaken, Pencroft,' replied Gideon Spilett, 'and that the wood of the eucalyptus has begun to be very advantageously employed in cabinet-making.'

'And I may add,' said Herbert, 'that the eucalyptus belongs to a family which comprises many useful members; the guava-tree, from whose fruit guava jelly is made; the clove-tree, which produces the spice; the pomegranate- tree, which bears pomegranates; the Eugeacia Cauliflora, the fruit of which is used in making a tolerable wine; the Ugui myrtle, which contains an excellent alcoholic liquor; the Caryophyllus myrtle, of which the bark forms an esteemed cinnamon; the Eugenia Pimenta, from whence comes Jamaica pepper; the common myrtle, from whose buds and berries spice is sometimes made; the Eucalyptus manifera, which yields a sweet sort of manna; the Guinea Eucalyptus, the sap of which is transformed into beer by fermentation; in short, all those trees known under the name of gum-trees or iron-bark trees in Australia, belong to this family of the myrtaceae, which contains forty-six genera and thirteen hundred species!'

The lad was allowed to run on, and he delivered his little botanical lecture with great animation. Cyrus Harding listened smiling, and Pencroft with an indescribable feeling of pride.

'Very good, Herbert,' replied Pencroft, 'but I could swear that all those useful specimens you have just told us about are none of them giants like these!'

'That is true, Pencroft.'

'That supports what I said,' returned the sailor, 'namely, that these giants are good for nothing!'

'There you are wrong, Pencroft,' said the engineer; 'these gigantic eucalypti, which shelter us, are good for something.'

'And what is that?'

'To render the countries which they inhabit healthy. Do you know what they are called in Australia and New Zealand?'

'No, captain.'

'They are called 'fever trees.''

'Because they give fevers?'

'No, because they prevent them!'

'Good. I must note that,' said the reporter.

'Note it then, my dear Spilett; for it appears proved that the presence of the eucalyptus is enough to neutralize miasmas. This natural antidote has been tried in certain countries in the middle of Europe and the north of Africa where the soil was absolutely unhealthy, and the sanitary condition of the inhabitants has been gradually ameliorated. No more intermittent fevers prevail in the regions now covered with forests of the myrtaceae. This fact is now beyond doubt, and it is a happy circumstance for us settlers in Lincoln Island.'

'Ah! what an island! What a blessed island!' cried Pencroft. 'I tell you, it wants nothing—unless it is—'

'That will come, Pencroft, that will be found,' replied the engineer; 'but now we must continue our voyage and push on as far as the river will carry our boat!'

The exploration was therefore continued for another two miles in the midst of country covered with eucalypti, which predominated in the woods of this portion of the island. The space which they occupied extended as far as the eye could reach on each side of the Mercy, which wound along between high green banks. The bed was often obstructed by long weeds, and even by pointed rocks, which rendered the navigation very difficult. The action of the oars was prevented, and Pencroft was obliged to push with a pole. They found also that the water was becoming shallower and shallower, and that the canoe must soon stop. The sun was already sinking towards the horizon, and the trees threw long shadows on the ground. Cyrus Harding, seeing that he could not hope to reach the western coast of the island in one journey, resolved to camp at the place where any further navigation was prevented by want of water. He calculated that they were still five or six miles from the coast, and this distance was too great for them to attempt during the night in the midst of unknown woods.

The boat was pushed on through the forest, which gradually became thicker again, and appeared also to have more inhabitants; for if the eyes of the sailor did not deceive him, he thought he saw bands of monkeys springing among the trees. Sometimes even two or three of these animals stopped at a little distance from the canoe and gazed at the settlers without manifesting any terror, as if, seeing men for the first time, they had not yet learned to fear them. It would have been easy to bring down one of these quadramani with a gunshot, and Pencroft was greatly tempted to fire, but Harding opposed so useless a massacre. This was prudent, for the monkeys, or apes rather, appearing to be very powerful and extremely active, it was useless to provoke an unnecessary aggression, and the creatures might, ignorant of the power of the explorers' firearms, have attacked them. It is true that the sailor considered the monkeys from a purely alimentary point of view, for those animals which are herbivorous make very excellent game; but since they had an abundant supply of provisions, it was a pity to waste their ammunition.

Towards four o'clock, the navigation of the Mercy became exceedingly difficult, for its course was obstructed by aquatic plants and rocks. The banks rose higher and higher, and already they were approaching the spurs of Mount Franklin. The source could not be far off, since it was fed by the water from the southern slopes of the mountain.

'In a quarter of an hour,' said the sailor, 'we shall be obliged to stop, captain.'

'Very well, we will stop, Pencroft, and we will make our encampment for the night.'

'At what distance are we from Granite House?' asked Herbert.

'About seven miles,' replied the engineer, 'taking into calculation, however, the detours of the river, which has carried us to the northwest.'

'Shall we go on?' asked the reporter.

'Yes, as long as we can,' replied Cyrus Harding. 'Tomorrow, at break of day, we will leave the canoe, and in two hours I hope we shall cross the distance which separates us from the coast, and then we shall have the whole day in which to explore the shore.'

'Go ahead!' replied Pencroft.

But soon the boat grated on the stony bottom of the river, which was now not more than twenty feet in breadth. The trees met like a bower overhead, and caused a half-darkness. They also heard the noise of a waterfall, which showed that a few hundred feet up the river there was a natural barrier.

Presently, after a sudden turn of the river, a cascade appeared through the trees. The canoe again touched the bottom, and in a few minutes it was moored to a trunk near the right bank.

It was nearly five o'clock. The last rays of the sun gleamed through the thick foliage and glanced on the little waterfall, making the spray sparkle with all the colours of the rainbow. Beyond that, the Mercy was lost in the bushwood, where it was fed from some hidden source. The different streams which flowed into it increased it to a regular river further down, but here it was simply a shallow, limpid brook.

It was agreed to camp here, as the place was charming. The colonists disembarked, and a fire was soon lighted under a clump of trees, among the branches of which Cyrus Harding and his companions could, if it was necessary, take refuge for the night.

Supper was quickly devoured, for they were very hungry, and then there was only sleeping to think of. But, as roarings of rather a suspicious nature had been heard during the evening, a good fire was made up for the night, so as to protect the sleepers with its crackling flames. Neb and Pencroft also watched by turns, and did not spare fuel. They thought they saw the dark forms of some wild animals prowling round the camp among the bushes, but the night passed without incident, and the next day, the 31st of October, at five o'clock in the morning, all were on foot, ready for a start.

Chapter 4

It was six o' clock in the morning when the settlers, after a hasty breakfast, set out to reach by the shortest way, the western coast of the island. And how long would it take to do this? Cyrus Harding had said two hours, but of course that depended on the nature of the obstacles they might meet with As it was probable that they would have to cut a path through the grass, shrubs, and creepers, they marched axe in hand, and with guns also ready, wisely taking warning from the cries of the wild beasts heard in the night.

The exact position of the encampment could be determined by the bearing of Mount Franklin, and as the volcano arose in the north at a distance of less than three miles, they had only to go straight towards the southwest to reach the western coast. They set out, having first carefully secured the canoe. Pencroft and Neb carried sufficient provision for the little band for at least two days. It would not thus he necessary to hunt. The engineer advised his companions to refrain from firing, that their presence might not be betrayed to any one near the shore. The first hatchet blows were given among the brushwood in the midst of some mastic-trees, a little above the cascade; and his compass in his hand, Cyrus Harding led the way.

The forest here was composed for the most part of trees which had already been met with near the lake and on Prospect Heights. There were deodars, Douglas firs, casuarinas, gum trees, eucalypti, hibiscus, cedars, and other trees, generally of a moderate size, for their number prevented their growth.

Since their departure, the settlers had descended the slopes which constituted the mountain system of the island, on to a dry soil, but the luxuriant vegetation of which indicated it to be watered either by some subterranean marsh or by some stream. However, Cyrus Harding did not remember having seen, at the time of his excursion to the crater, any other watercourses but the Red Creek and the Mercy.

During the first part of their excursion, they saw numerous troops of monkeys who exhibited great astonishment at the sight of men, whose appearance was so new to them. Gideon Spilett jokingly asked whether these active and merry quadrupeds did not consider him and his companions as degenerate brothers.

And certainly, pedestrians, hindered at each step by bushes, caught by creepers, barred by trunks of trees, did not shine beside those supple animals, who, bounding from branch to branch, were hindered by nothing on their course. The monkeys were numerous, but happily they did not manifest any hostile disposition.

Several pigs, agoutis, kangaroos, and other rodents were seen, also two or three koalas, at which Pencroft longed to have a shot.

'But,' said he, 'you may jump and play just now; we shall have one or two words to say to you on our way back!'

At half-past nine the way was suddenly found to be barred by an unknown stream, from thirty to forty feet broad, whose rapid current dashed foaming over the numerous rocks which interrupted its course. This creek was deep and clear, but it was absolutely unnavigable.

'We are cut off!' cried Neb.

'No,' replied Herbert, 'it is only a stream, and we can easily swim over.'

'What would be the use of that?' returned Harding. 'This creek evidently runs to the sea. Let us remain on this side and follow the bank, and I shall be much astonished if it does not lead us very quickly to the coast. Forward!'

'One minute,' said the reporter. 'The name of this creek, my friends?

Do not let us leave our geography incomplete.'

'All right!' said Pencroft.

'Name it, my boy,' said the engineer, addressing the lad.

'Will it not be better to wait until we have explored it to its mouth?' answered Herbert.

'Very well,' replied Cyrus Harding. 'Let us follow it as fast as we can without stopping.'

'Still another minute!' said Pencroft.

'What's the matter?' asked the reporter.

'Though hunting is forbidden, fishing is allowed, I suppose,' said the sailor.

'We have no time to lose,' replied the engineer.

'Oh! five minutes!' replied Pencroft, 'I only ask for five minutes to use in the interest of our breakfast!'

And Pencroft, lying down on the bank, plunged his arm into the water, and soon pulled up several dozen of fine crayfish from among the stones.

'These will be good!' cried Neb, going to the sailor's aid.

'As I said, there is everything in this island, except tobacco!' muttered Pencroft with a sigh.

The fishing did not take five minutes, for the crayfish were swarming in the creek. A bag was filled with the crustaceae, whose shells were of a cobalt blue. The settlers then pushed on.

They advanced more rapidly and easily along the bank of the river than in the forest. From time to time they came upon the traces of animals of a large size who had come to quench their thirst at the stream, but none were actually seen, and it was evidently not in this part of the forest that the peccary had received the bullet which had cost Pencroft a grinder.

In the meanwhile, considering the rapid current, Harding was led to suppose that he and his companions were much farther from the western coast than they had at first supposed. In fact, at this hour, the rising tide would have turned back the current of the creek, if its mouth had only been a few miles distant. Now, this effect was not produced, and the water pursued its natural course. The engineer was much astonished at this, and frequently consulted his compass, to assure himself that some turn of the river was not leading them again into the Far West.

However, the creek gradually widened and its waters became less tumultuous. The trees on the right bank were as close together as on the left bank, and it was impossible to distinguish anything beyond them; but these masses of wood were evidently uninhabited, for Top did not bark, and the intelligent animal would not have failed to signal the presence of any stranger in the neighbourhood.

At half-past ten, to the great surprise of Cyrus Harding, Herbert, who was a little in front, suddenly stopped and exclaimed,—

'The sea!'

In a few minutes more, the whole western shore of the island lay extended before the eyes of the settlers.

But what a contrast between this and the eastern coast, upon which chance had first thrown them. No granite cliff, no rocks, not even a sandy beach. The forest reached the shore, and the tall trees bending over the water were beaten by the waves. It was not such a shore as is usually formed by nature, either by extending a vast carpet of sand, or by grouping masses of rock, but a beautiful border consisting of the most splendid trees. The bank was raised a little above the level of the sea, and on this luxuriant soil, supported by a granite base, the fine forest trees seemed to be as firmly planted as in the interior of the island.

The colonists were then on the shore of an unimportant little harbour, which would scarcely have contained even two or three fishing-boats. It served as a neck to the new creek, of which the curious thing was that its waters, instead of joining the sea by a gentle slope, fell from a height of more than forty feet, which explained why the rising tide was not felt up the stream. In fact, the tides of the Pacific, even at their maximum elevation, could never reach the level of the river, and, doubtless, millions of years would pass before the water would have worn away the granite and hollowed a practicable mouth.

It was settled that the name of Falls River should be given to this stream. Beyond, towards the north, the forest border was prolonged for a space of nearly two miles; then the trees became scarcer, and beyond that again the picturesque heights described a nearly straight line, which ran north and south. On the contrary, all the part of the shore between Falls River and Reptile End was a mass of wood, magnificent trees, some straight, others bent, so that the long sea-swell bathed their roots. Now, it was this coast, that is, all the Serpentine Peninsula, that was to be explored, for this part of the shore offered a refuge to castaways, which the other wild and barren side must have refused.

The weather was fine and clear, and from a height of a hillock on which Neb and Pencroft had arranged breakfast, a wide view was obtained. There was, however, not a sail in sight; nothing could be seen along the shore as far as the eye could reach. But the engineer would take nothing for granted until he had explored the coast to the very extremity of the Serpentine Peninsula.

Breakfast was soon despatched, and at half-past eleven the captain gave the signal for departure. Instead of proceeding over the summit of a cliff or along a sandy beach, the settlers were obliged to remain under cover of the trees so that they might continue on the shore.

The distance which separated Falls River from Reptile End was about twelve miles. It would have taken the settlers four hours to do this, on a clear ground and without hurrying themselves; but as it was they needed double the time, for what with trees to go round, bushes to cut down, and creepers to chop away, they were impeded at every step, these obstacles greatly lengthening their journey.

There was, however, nothing to show that a shipwreck had taken place recently. It is true that, as Gideon Spilett observed, any remains of it might have drifted out to sea, and they must not take it for granted that because they could find no traces of it, a ship had not been castaway on the coast.

The reporter's argument was just, and besides, the incident of the bullet proved that a shot must have been fired in Lincoln Island within three months.

It was already five o'clock, and there were still two miles between the settlers and the extremity of the Serpentine Peninsula. It was evident that after having reached Reptile End, Harding and his companions would not have time to return before dark to their encampment near the source of the Mercy. It would therefore be necessary to pass the night on the promontory. But they had no lack of provisions, which was lucky, for there were no animals on the shore, though birds, on the contrary, abound—jacamars, couroucous, tragopans, grouse, lories, parrots, cockatoos, pheasants, pigeons, and a hundred others. There was not a tree without a nest, and not a nest which was not full of flapping wings.

Towards seven o'clock the weary explorers arrived at Reptile End. Here the seaside forest ended, and the shore resumed the customary appearance of a coast, with rocks, reefs, and sands. It was possible that something might be found here, but darkness came on, and the further exploration had to be put off to the next day.

Pencroft and Herbert hastened on to find a suitable place for their camp. Among the last trees of the forest of the Far West, the boy found several thick clumps of bamboos.

'Good,' said he; 'this is a valuable discovery.'

'Valuable?' returned Pencroft.

'Certainly,' replied Herbert. 'I may say, Pencroft, that the bark of the bamboo, cut into flexible laths, is used for making baskets; that this bark, mashed into a paste, is used for the manufacture of Chinese paper; that the stalks furnish, according to their size, canes and pipes and are used for conducting water; that large bamboos make excellent material for building, being light and strong, and being never attacked by insects. I will add that by sawing the bamboo in two at the joint, keeping for the bottom the part of the transverse film which forms the joint, useful cups are obtained, which are much in use among the Chinese. No! you don't care for that. But—'

'But what?'

'But I can tell you, if you are ignorant of it, that in India these bamboos are eaten like asparagus.'

'Asparagus thirty feet high!' exclaimed the sailor. 'And are they good?'

'Excellent,' replied Herbert. 'Only it is not the stems of thirty feet high which are eaten, but the young shoots.'

'Perfect, my boy, perfect!' replied Pencroft.

'I will also add that the pith of the young stalks, preserved in vinegar, makes a good pickle.'

'Better and better, Herbert!'

'And lastly, that the bamboos exude a sweet liquor which can be made into a very agreeable drink.'

'Is that all?' asked the sailor.

'That is all!'

'And they don't happen to do for smoking?'

'No, my poor Pencroft.'

Herbert and the sailor had not to look long for a place in which to pass the night. The rocks, which must have been violently beaten by the sea under the influence of the winds of the southwest, presented many cavities in which shelter could be found against the night air. But just as they were about to enter one of these caves a loud roaring arrested them.

'Back!' cried Pencroft. 'Our guns are only loaded with small shot, and beasts which can roar as loud as that would care no more for it than for grains of salt!' And the sailor, seizing Herbert by the arm, dragged him behind a rock, just as a magnificent animal showed itself at the entrance of the cavern.

It was a jaguar of a size at least equal to its Asiatic congeners, that is to say, it measured five feet from the extremity of its head to the beginning of its tail. The yellow colour of its hair was relieved by streaks and regular oblong spots of black, which contrasted with the white of its chest. Herbert recognized it as the ferocious rival of the tiger, as formidable as the puma, which is the rival of the largest wolf!

The jaguar advanced and gazed around him with blazing eyes, his hair bristling as if this was not the first time he had scented men.

At this moment the reporter appeared round a rock, and Herbert, thinking that he had not seen the jaguar, was about to rush towards him, when Gideon Spilett signed to him to remain where he was. This was not his first tiger, and advancing to within ten feet of the animal he remained motionless, his gun to his shoulder, without moving a muscle. The jaguar collected itself for a spring, but at that moment a shot struck it in the eyes, and it fell dead.

Herbert and Pencroft rushed towards the jaguar. Neb and Harding also ran up, and they remained for some instants contemplating the animal as it lay stretched on the ground, thinking that its magnificent skin would be a great ornament to the hall at Granite House.

'Oh, Mr. Spilett, how I admire and envy you!' cried Herbert, in a fit of very natural enthusiasm.

'Well, my boy,' replied the reporter, 'you could have done the same.'

'I! with such coolness!—'

'Imagine to yourself, Herbert, that the jaguar is only a hare, and you would fire as quietly as possible.'

'That is,' rejoined Pencroft, 'that it is not more dangerous than a hare!'

'And now,' said Gideon Spilett, 'since the jaguar has left its abode, I do not see, my friends, why we should not take possession of it for the night.'

'But others may come,' said Pencroft.

'It will be enough to light a fire at the entrance of the cavern,' said the reporter, 'and no wild beasts will dare to cross the threshold.'

'Into the jaguar's house, then!' replied the sailor, dragging after him the body of the animal.

While Neb skinned the jaguar, his companions collected an abundant supply of dry wood from the forest, which they heaped up at the cave.

Cyrus Harding, seeing the clump of bamboos, cut a quantity, which he mingled with the other fuel.

This done, they entered the grotto, of which the floor was strewn with bones, the guns were carefully loaded, in case of a sudden attack, they had supper, and then just before they lay down to rest, the heap of wood piled at the entrance was set fire to. Immediately, a regular explosion, or rather a series of reports, broke the silence! The noise was caused by the bamboos, which, as the flames reached them, exploded like fireworks. The noise was enough to terrify even the boldest of wild beasts.

It was not the engineer who had invented this way of causing loud explosions, for, according to Marco Polo, the Tartars have employed it for many centuries to drive away from their encampments the formidable wild beasts of Central Asia.

Chapter 5

Cyrus Harding and his companions slept like innocent marmots in the cave which the jaguar had so politely left at their disposal.

At sunrise all were on the shore at the extremity of the promontory, and their gaze was directed towards the horizon, of which two-thirds of the circumference were visible. For the last time the engineer could ascertain that not a sail nor the wreck of a ship was on the sea, and even with the telescope nothing suspicious could be discovered.

There was nothing either on the shore, at least, in the straight line of three miles which formed the south side of the promontory, for beyond that, rising ground had the rest of the coast, and even from the extremity of the Serpentine Peninsula Claw Cape could not be seen.

The southern coast of the island still remained to be explored. Now should they undertake it immediately, and devote this day to it?

This was not included in their first plan. In fact, when the boat was abandoned at the sources of the Mercy, it had been agreed that after having surveyed the west coast, they should go back to it, and return to Granite House by the Mercy. Harding then thought that the western coast would have offered refuge, either to a ship in distress, or to a vessel in her regular course; but now, as he saw that this coast presented no good anchorage, he wished to seek on the south what they had not been able to find on the west.

Gideon Spilett proposed to continue the exploration, that the question of the supposed wreck might be completely settled, and he asked at what distance Claw Cape might be from the extremity of the peninsula.

'About thirty miles,' replied the engineer, 'if we take into consideration the carvings of the coast.'

'Thirty miles!' returned Spilett. 'That would be a long day's march. Nevertheless, I think that we should return to Granite House by the south coast.'

'But,' observed Herbert, 'from Claw Cape to Granite House there must be at least another ten miles.

'Make it forty miles in all,' replied the engineer, 'and do not hesitate to do it. At least we should survey the unknown shore, and then we shall not have to begin the exploration again.'

'Very good,' said Pencroft. 'But the boat?'

'The boat has remained by itself for one day at the sources of the Mercy,' replied Gideon Spilett; 'it may just as well stay there two days!

As yet, we have had no reason to think that the island is infested by thieves!'

'Yet,' said the sailor, 'when I remember the history of the turtle, I am far from confident of that.'

'The turtle! the turtle!' replied the reporter. 'Don't you know that the sea turned it over?'

'Who knows?' murmured the engineer.

'But,—' said Neb.

Neb had evidently something to say, for he opened his mouth to speak and yet said nothing.

'What do you want to say, Neb?' asked the engineer.

'If we return by the shore to Claw Cape,' replied Neb, 'after having doubled the Cape, we shall be stopped—'

'By the Mercy! of course,' replied Herbert, 'and we shall have neither bridge nor boat by which to cross.'

'But, captain,' added Pencroft, 'with a few floating trunks we shall have no difficulty in crossing the river.'

'Never mind,' said Spilett, 'it will be useful to construct a bridge if we wish to have an easy access to the Far West!'

'A bridge!' cried Pencroft. 'Well, is not the captain the best engineer in his profession? He will make us a bridge when we want one. As to transporting you this evening to the other side of the Mercy, and that without wetting one thread of your clothes, I will take care of that. We have provisions for another day, and besides we can get plenty of game. Forward!'

The reporter's proposal, so strongly seconded by the sailor, received general approbation, for each wished to have their doubts set at rest, and by returning by Claw Cape the exploration would he ended. But there was not an hour to lose, for forty miles was a long march, and they could not hope to reach Granite House before night.

At six o'clock in the morning the little band set out. As a precaution the guns were loaded with ball, and Top, who led the van, received orders to beat about the edge of the forest.

From the extremity of the promontory which formed the tail of the peninsula the coast was rounded for a distance of five miles, which was rapidly passed over, without even the most minute investigations bringing to light the least trace of any old or recent landings; no debris, no mark of an encampment, no cinders of a fire, nor even a footprint!

From the point of the peninsula on which the settlers now were their gaze could extend along the southwest. Twenty-five miles off the coast terminated in the Claw Cape, which loomed dimly through the morning mists, and which, by the phenomenon of the mirage, appeared as if suspended between land and water.

Between the place occupied by the colonists and the other side of the immense bay, the shore was composed, first, of a tract of low land, bordered in the background by trees; then the shore became more irregular, projecting sharp points into the sea, and finally ended in the black rocks which, accumulated in picturesque disorder, formed Claw Cape.

Such was the development of this part of the island, which the settlers took in at a glance, while stopping for an instant.

'If a vessel ran in here,' said Pencroft, 'she would certainly be lost. Sandbanks and reefs everywhere! Bad quarters!'

'But at least something would be left of the ship,' observed the reporter.

'There might be pieces of wood on the rocks, but nothing on the sands,' replied the sailor.

'Why?'

'Because the sands are still more dangerous than the rocks, for they swallow up everything that is thrown on them. In a few days the hull of a ship of several hundred tons would disappear entirely in there!'

'So, Pencroft,' asked the engineer, 'if a ship has been wrecked on these banks, is it not astonishing that there is now no trace of her remaining?'

'No, captain, with the aid of time and tempest. However, it would be surprising, even in this case, that some of the masts or spars should not have been thrown on the beach, out of reach of the waves.'

'Let us go on with our search, then,' returned Cyrus Harding.

At one o'clock the colonists arrived at the other side of Washington Bay, they having now gone a distance of twenty miles.

They then halted for breakfast.

Here began the irregular coast, covered with lines of rocks and sandbanks. The long sea-swell could be seen breaking over the rocks in the bay, forming a foamy fringe. From this point to Claw Cape the beach was very narrow between the edge of the forest and the reefs.

Walking was now more difficult, on account of the numerous rocks which encumbered the beach. The granite cliff also gradually increased in height, and only the green tops of the trees which crowned it could be seen.

After half an hour's rest, the settlers resumed their journey, and not a spot among the rocks was left unexamined. Pencroft and Neb even rushed into the surf whenever any object attracted their attention. But they found nothing, some curious formations of the rocks having deceived them. They ascertained, however, that eatable shellfish abounded there, but these could not be of any great advantage to them until some easy means of communication had been established between the two banks of the Mercy, and until the means of transport had been perfected.

Nothing therefore which threw any light on the supposed wreck could be found on this shore, yet an object of any importance, such as the hull of a ship, would have been seen directly, or any of her masts and spans would have been washed on shore, just as the chest had been, which was found twenty miles from here. But there was nothing.

Towards three o'clock Harding and his companions arrived at a snug little creek. It formed quite a natural harbour, invisible from the sea, and was entered by a narrow channel.

At the back of this creek some violent convulsion had torn up the rocky border, and a cutting, by a gentle slope, gave access to an upper plateau, which might be situated at least ten miles from Claw Cape, and consequently four miles in a straight line from Prospect Heights. Gideon Spilett proposed to his companions that they should make a halt here. They agreed readily, for their walk had sharpened their appetites; and although it was not their usual dinner-hour, no one refused to strengthen himself with a piece of venison. This luncheon would sustain them until their supper, which they intended to take at Granite House. In a few minutes the settlers, seated under a clump of fine sea-pines, were devouring the provisions which Neb produced from his bag.

This spot was raised from fifty to sixty feet above the level of the sea. The view was very extensive, but beyond the cape it ended in Union Bay. Neither the islet nor Prospect Heights was visible, and could not be from thence, for the rising ground and the curtain of trees closed the northern horizon.

It is useless to add that notwithstanding the wide extent of sea which the explorers could survey, and though the engineer swept the horizon with his glass, no vessel could be found.

The shore was of course examined with the same care from the edge of the water to the cliff, and nothing could be discovered even with the aid of the instrument.

'Well,' said Gideon Spilett, 'it seems we must make up our minds to console ourselves with thinking that no one will come to dispute with us the possession of Lincoln Island!'

'But the bullet,' cried Herbert. 'That was not imaginary, I suppose!'

'Hang it, no!' exclaimed Pencroft, thinking of his absent tooth.

'Then what conclusion may be drawn?' asked the reporter.

'This,' replied the engineer, 'that three months or more ago, a vessel, either voluntarily or not, came here.'

'What! then you admit, Cyrus, that she was swallowed up without leaving any trace?' cried the reporter.

'No, my dear Spilett; but you see that if it is certain that a human being set foot on the island, it appears no less certain that he has now left it.'

'Then, if I understand you right, captain,' said Herbert, 'the vessel has left again?'

'Evidently.'

'And we have lost an opportunity to get back to our country?' said Neb.

'I fear so.'

'Very well, since the opportunity is lost, let us go on; it can't be helped,' said Pencroft, who felt homesickness for Granite House.

But just as they were rising, Top was heard loudly barking; and the dog issued from the wood, holding in his mouth a rag soiled with mud.

Neb seized it. It was a piece of strong cloth!

Top still barked, and by his going and coming, seemed to invite his master to follow him into the forest.

'Now there's something to explain the bullet!' exclaimed Pencroft.

'A castaway!' replied Herbert.

'Wounded, perhaps!' said Neb.

'Or dead!' added the reporter.

All ran after the dog, among the tall pines on the border of the forest. Harding and his companions made ready their firearms, in case of an emergency.

They advanced some way into the wood, but to their great disappointment, they as yet saw no signs of any human being having passed that way. Shrubs and creepers were uninjured, and they had even to cut them away with the axe, as they had done in the deepest recesses of the forest. It was difficult to fancy that any human creature had ever passed there, but yet Top went backward and forward, not like a dog who searches at random, but like a dog being endowed with a mind, who is following up an idea.

In about seven or eight minutes Top stopped in a glade surrounded with tall trees. The settlers gazed around them, but saw nothing, neither under the bushes nor among the trees.

'What is the matter, Top?' said Cyrus Harding.

Top barked louder, bounding about at the foot of a gigantic pine. All at once Pencroft shouted,—'Ho, splendid! capital!'

'What is it?' asked Spilett.

'We have been looking for a wreck at sea or on land!'

'Well?'

'Well; and here we've found one in the air!'

And the sailor pointed to a great white rag, caught in the top of the pine, a fallen scrap of which the dog had brought to them.

'But that is not a wreck!' cried Gideon Spilett.

'I beg your pardon!' returned Pencroft.

'Why? is it—?'

'It is all that remains of our airy boat, of our balloon, which has been caught up aloft there, at the top of that tree!'

Pencroft was not mistaken, and he gave vent to his feelings in a tremendous hurrah, adding,—

'There is good cloth! There is what will furnish us with linen for years. There is what will make us handkerchiefs and shirts! Ha, ha, Mr. Spilett, what do you say to an island where shirts grow on the trees?'

It was certainly a lucky circumstance for the settlers in Lincoln Island that the balloon, after having made its last bound into the air, had fallen on the island and thus given them the opportunity of finding it again, whether they kept the case under its present form, or whether they wished to attempt another escape by it, or whether they usefully employed the several hundred yards of cotton, which was of fine quality. Pencroft's joy was therefore shared by all.

But it was necessary to bring down the remains of the balloon from the tree, to place it in security, and this was no slight task. Neb, Herbert, and the sailor, climbing to the summit of the tree, used all their skill to disengage the now reduced balloon.

The operation lasted two hours, and then not only the case, with its valve, its springs, its brasswork, lay on the ground, but the net, that is to say a considerable quantity of ropes and cordage, and the circle and the anchor. The case, except for the fracture, was in good condition, only the lower portion being torn.

It was a fortune which had fallen from the sky.

'All the same, captain,' said the sailor, 'if we ever decide to leave the island, it won't be in a balloon, will it? These airboats won't go where we want them to go, and we have had some experience in that way! Look here, we will build a craft of some twenty tons, and then we can make a mainsail, a foresail, and a jib out of that cloth. As to the rest of it, that will help to dress us.'

'We shall see, Pencroft,' replied Cyrus Harding; 'we shall see.'

'In the meantime, we must put it in a safe place,' said Neb.

They certainly could not think of carrying this load of cloth, ropes, and cordage, to Granite House, for the weight of it was very considerable, and while waiting for a suitable vehicle in which to convey it, it was of importance that this treasure should not be left longer exposed to the mercies of the first storm. The settlers, uniting their efforts, managed to drag it as far as the shore, where they discovered a large rocky cavity, which owing to its position could not be visited either by the wind or rain.

'We needed a locker, and now we have one,' said Pencroft; 'but as we cannot lock it up, it will be prudent to hide the opening. I don't mean from two-legged thieves, but from those with four paws!'

At six o'clock, all was stowed away, and after having given the creek the very suitable name of 'Port Balloon,' the settlers pursued their way along Claw Cape. Pencroft and the engineer talked of the different projects which it was agreed to put into execution with the briefest possible delay. It was necessary first of all to throw a bridge over the Mercy, so as to establish an easy communication with the south of the island; then the cart must be taken to bring back the balloon, for the canoe alone could not carry it, then they would build a decked boat, and Pencroft would rig it as a cutter, and they would be able to undertake voyages of circumnavigation round the island, etc.

In the meanwhile night came on, and it was already dark when the settlers reached Flotsam Point, where they had found the precious chest.

The distance between Flotsam Point and Granite House was another four miles, and it was midnight when, after having followed the shore to the mouth of the Mercy, the settlers arrived at the first angle formed by the Mercy.

There the river was eighty feet in breadth, which was awkward to cross, but as Pencroft had taken upon himself to conquer this difficulty, he was compelled to do it. The settlers certainly had reason to be pretty tired. The journey had been long, and the task of getting down the balloon had not rested either their arms or legs. They were anxious to reach Granite House to eat and sleep, and if the bridge had been constructed, in a quarter of an hour they would have been at home.

The night was very dark. Pencroft prepared to keep his promise by constructing a sort of raft, on which to make the passage of the Mercy. He and Neb, armed with axes, chose two trees near the water, and began to attack them at the base.

Cyrus Harding and Spilett, seated on the bank, waited till their companions were ready for their help, while Herbert roamed about, though without going to any distance. All at once, the lad, who had strolled by the river, came running back, and, pointing up the Mercy, exclaimed,—

'What is floating there?'

Pencroft stopped working, and seeing an indistinct object moving through the gloom,—

'A canoe!' cried he.

All approached, and saw to their extreme surprise, a boat floating down the current.

'Boat ahoy!' shouted the sailor, without thinking that perhaps it would be best to keep silence.

No reply. The boat still drifted onward, and it was not more than twelve feet off, when the sailor exclaimed,—

'But it is our own boat! she has broken her moorings, and floated down the current. I must say she has arrived very opportunely.'

'Our boat?' murmured the engineer.

Pencroft was right. It was indeed the canoe, of which the rope had undoubtedly broken, and which had come alone from the sources of the Mercy. It was very important to seize it before the rapid current should have swept it away out of the mouth of the river, but Neb and Pencroft cleverly managed this by means of a long pole.

The canoe touched the shore. The engineer leaped in first, and found, on examining the rope, that it had been really worn through by rubbing against the rocks.

'Well,' said the reporter to him, in a low voice, 'this is a strange thing.'

'Strange indeed!' returned Cyrus Harding.

Strange or not, it was very fortunate. Herbert, the reporter, Neb, and Pencroft, embarked in turn. There was no doubt about the rope having been worn through, but the astonishing part of the affair was, that the boat should arrive just at the moment when the settlers were there to seize it on its way, for a quarter of an hour earlier or later it would have been lost in the sea.

If they had been living in the time of genii, this incident would have given them the right to think that the island was haunted by some supernatural being, who used his power in the service of the castaways!

A few strokes of the oar brought the settlers to the mouth of the Mercy. The canoe was hauled up on the beach near the Chimneys, and all proceeded towards the ladder of Granite House.

But at that moment, Top barked angrily, and Neb, who was looking for the first steps, uttered a cry.

There was no longer a ladder!

Chapter 6

Cyrus Harding stood still, without saying a word. His companions searched in the darkness on the wall, in case the wind should have moved the ladder, and on the ground, thinking that it might have fallen down.... But the ladder had quite disappeared. As to ascertaining if a squall had blown it on the landing-place, half way up, that was impossible in the dark.

'If it is a joke,' cried Pencroft, 'it is a very stupid one! To come home and find no staircase to go up to your room by—that's nothing for weary men to laugh at.'

Neb could do nothing but cry out 'Oh! oh! oh!'

'I begin to think that very curious things happen in Lincoln Island!' said Pencroft.

'Curious?' replied Gideon Spilett, 'not at all, Pencroft, nothing can be more natural. Some one has come during our absence, taken possession of our dwelling and drawn up the ladder.'

'Some one,' cried the sailor. 'But who?'

'Who but the hunter who fired the bullet?' replied the reporter.

'Well, if there is any one up there,' replied Pencroft, who began to lose patience, 'I will give them a hail, and they must answer.'

And in a stentorian voice the sailor gave a prolonged 'Halloo!' which was echoed again and again from the cliff and rocks.

The settlers listened and they thought they heard a sort of chuckling laugh, of which they could not guess the origin. But no voice replied to Pencroft, who in vain repeated his vigorous shouts.

There was something indeed in this to astonish the most apathetic of men, and the settlers were not men of that description. In their situation every incident had its importance, and, certainly, during the seven months which they had spent on the island, they had not before met with anything of so surprising a character.

Be that as it may, forgetting their fatigue in the singularity of the event, they remained below Granite House, not knowing what to think, not knowing what to do, questioning each other without any hope of a satisfactory reply, every one starting some supposition each more unlikely than the last. Neb bewailed himself, much disappointed at not being able to get into his kitchen, for the provisions which they had had on their expedition were exhausted, and they had no means of renewing them.

'My friends,' at last said Cyrus Harding, 'there is only one thing to be done at present; wait for day, and then act according to circumstances. But let us go to the Chimneys. There we shall be under shelter, and if we cannot eat, we can at least sleep.'

'But who is it that has played us this cool trick?' again asked Pencroft, unable to make up his mind to retire from the spot.

Whoever it was, the only thing practicable was to do as the engineer proposed, to go to the Chimneys and there wait for day. In the meanwhile Top was ordered to mount guard below the windows of Granite House, and when Top received an order he obeyed it without any questioning. The brave dog therefore remained at the foot of the cliff while his master with his companions sought a refuge among the rocks.

To say that the settlers, notwithstanding their fatigue, slept well on the sandy floor of the Chimneys would not be true. It was not only that they were extremely anxious to find out the cause of what had happened, whether it was the result of an accident which would be discovered at the return of day, or whether on the contrary it was the work of a human being; but they also had very uncomfortable beds. That could not be helped, however, for in some way or other at that moment their dwelling was occupied, and they could not possibly enter it.

Now Granite House was more than their dwelling, it was their warehouse. There were all the stores belonging to the colony, weapons, instruments, tools, ammunition, provisions, etc. To think that all that might be pillaged and that the settlers would have all their work to do over again, fresh weapons and tools to make, was a serious matter. Their uneasiness led one or other of them also to go out every few minutes to see if Top was keeping good watch. Cyrus Harding alone waited with his habitual patience, although his strong mind was exasperated at being confronted with such an inexplicable fact, and he was provoked at himself for allowing a feeling to which he could not give a name, to gain an influence over him. Gideon Spilett shared his feelings in this respect, and the two conversed together in whispers of the inexplicable circumstance which baffled even their intelligence and experience.

'It is a joke,' said Pencroft; 'it is a trick some one has played us. Well, I don't like such jokes, and the joker had better look out for himself, if he falls into my hands, I can tell him.'

As soon as the first gleam of light appeared in the east, the colonists, suitably armed, repaired to the beach under Granite House. The rising sun now shone on the cliff and they could see the windows, the shutters of which were closed, through the curtains of foliage.

All here was in order; but a cry escaped the colonists when they saw that the door, which they had closed on their departure, was now wide open.

Some one had entered Granite House—there could be no more doubt about that.

The upper ladder, which generally hung from the door to the landing, was in its place, but the lower ladder was drawn up and raised to the threshold. It was evident that the intruders had wished to guard themselves against a surprise.

Pencroft hailed again.

No reply.

'The beggars,' exclaimed the sailor. 'There they are sleeping quietly as if they were in their own house. Hallo there, you pirates, brigands, robbers, sons of John Bull!'

When Pencroft, being a Yankee, treated any one to the epithet of 'son of John Bull,' he considered he had reached the last limits of insult.

The sun had now completely risen, and the whole facade of Granite House became illuminated by its rays; but in the interior as well as on the exterior all was quiet and calm.

The settlers asked if Granite House was inhabited or not, and yet the position of the ladder was sufficient to show that it was; it was also certain that the inhabitants, whoever they might be, had not been able to escape. But how were they to be got at?

Herbert then thought of fastening a cord to an arrow, and shooting the arrow so that it should pass between the first rounds of the ladder which hung from the threshold. By means of the cord they would then be able to draw down the ladder to the ground, and so re-establish the communication between the beach and Granite House. There was evidently nothing else to be done, and, with a little skill, this method might succeed. Very fortunately bows and arrows had been left at the Chimneys, where they also found a quantity of light hibiscus cord. Pencroft fastened this to a well-feathered arrow. Then Herbert fixing it to his bow, took a careful aim for the lower part of the ladder.

Cyrus Harding, Gideon Spilett, Pencroft, and Neb drew back, so as to see if anything appeared at the windows. The reporter lifted his gun to his shoulder and covered the door.

The bow was bent, the arrow flew, taking the cord with it, and passed between the two last rounds.

The operation had succeeded.

Herbert immediately seized the end of the cord, but, at that moment when he gave it a pull to bring down the ladder, an arm, thrust suddenly out between the wall and the door, grasped it and dragged it inside Granite House.

'The rascals!' shouted the sailor. 'If a ball can do anything for you, you shall not have long to wait for it.

'But who was it?' asked Neb.

'Who was it? Didn't you see?'

'No.'

'It was a monkey, a sapajou, an orangoutang, a baboon, a gorilla, a sagoin. Our dwelling has been invaded by monkeys, who climbed up the ladder during our absence.'

And, at this moment, as if to bear witness to the truth of the sailor's words, two or three quadrumana showed themselves at the windows, from which they had pushed back the shutters, and saluted the real proprietors of the place with a thousand hideous grimaces.

'I knew that it was only a joke,' cried Pencroft; 'but one of the jokers shall pay the penalty for the rest.'

So saying, the sailor, raising his piece, took a rapid aim at one of the monkeys and fired. All disappeared, except one who fell mortally wounded on the beach. This monkey, which was of a large size, evidently belonged to the first order of the quadrumana. Whether this was a chimpanzee, an orangoutang, or a gorilla, he took rank among the anthropoid apes, who are so called from their resemblance to the human race. However, Herbert declared it to be an orangoutang.

'What a magnificent beast!' cried Neb.

'Magnificent, if you like,' replied Pencroft; 'but still I do not see how we are to get into our house.'

'Herbert is a good marksman,' said the reporter, 'and his bow is here. He can try again.'

'Why, these apes are so cunning,' returned Pencroft; 'they won't show themselves again at the windows and so we can't kill them; and when I think of the mischief they may do in the rooms and storehouse—'

'Have patience,' replied Harding; 'these creatures cannot keep us long at bay.'

'I shall not be sure of that till I see them down here,' replied the sailor. 'And now, captain, do you know how many dozens of these fellows are up there?'

It was difficult to reply to Pencroft, and as for the young boy making another attempt, that was not easy; for the lower part of the ladder had been drawn again into the door, and when another pull was given, the line broke and the ladder remained firm. The case was really perplexing. Pencroft stormed. There was a comic side to the situation, but he did not think it funny at all. It was certain that the settlers would end by reinstating themselves in their domicile and driving out the intruders, but when and how? this is what they were not able to say.

Two hours passed, during which the apes took care not to show themselves, but they were still there, and three or four times a nose or a paw was poked out at the door or windows, and was immediately saluted by a gun- shot.

'Let us hide ourselves,' at last said the engineer. 'Perhaps the apes will think we have gone quite away and will show themselves again. Let Spilett and Herbert conceal themselves behind those rocks and fire on all that may appear.'

The engineer's orders were obeyed, and while the reporter and the lad, the best marksmen in the colony, posted themselves in a good position, but out of the monkeys' sight, Neb, Pencroft, and Cyrus climbed the plateau and entered the forest in order to kill some game, for it was now time for breakfast and they had no provisions remaining.

In half an hour the hunters returned with a few rock pigeons, which they roasted as well as they could. Not an ape had appeared. Gideon Spilett and Herbert went to take their share of the breakfast, leaving Top to watch under the windows. They then, having eaten, returned to their post.

Two hours later, their situation was in no degree improved. The quadrumana gave no sign of existence, and it might have been supposed that they had disappeared; but what seemed more probable was that, terrified by the death of one of their companions, and frightened by the noise of the firearms, they had retreated to the back part of the house or probably even into the storeroom. And when they thought of the valuables which this storeroom contained, the patience so much recommended by the engineer, fast changed into great irritation, and there certainly was room for it.

'Decidedly it is too bad,' said the reporter; 'and the worst of it is, there is no way of putting an end to it.'

'But we must drive these vagabonds out somehow,' cried the sailor. 'We could soon get the better of them, even if there are twenty of the rascals; but for that, we must meet them hand to hand. Come now, is there no way of getting at them?'

'Let us try to enter Granite House by the old opening at the lake,' replied the engineer.

'Oh!' shouted the sailor, 'and I never thought of that.'

This was in reality the only way by which to penetrate into Granite House so as to fight with and drive out the intruders. The opening was, it is true, closed up with a wall of cemented stones, which it would be necessary to sacrifice, but that could easily be rebuilt. Fortunately, Cyrus

Harding had not as yet effected his project of hiding this opening by raising the waters of the lake, for the operation would then have taken some time.

It was already past twelve o'clock, when the colonists, well armed and provided with picks and spades, left the Chimneys, passed beneath the windows of Granite House, after telling Top to remain at his post, and began to ascend the left bank of the Mercy, so as to reach Prospect Heights.

But they had not made fifty steps in this direction, when they heard the dog barking furiously.

And all rushed down the bank again.

Arrived at the turning, they saw that the situation had changed.

In fact, the apes, seized with a sudden panic, from some unknown cause, were trying to escape. Two or three ran and clambered from one window to another with the agility of acrobats. They were not even trying to replace the ladder, by which it would have been easy to descend; perhaps in their terror they had forgotten this way of escape. The colonists, now being able to take aim without difficulty, fired. Some, wounded or killed, fell back into the rooms, uttering piercing cries. The rest, throwing themselves out, were dashed to pieces in their fall, and in a few minutes, so far as they knew, there was not a living quadrumana in Granite House.

At this moment the ladder was seen to slip over the threshold, then unroll and fall to the ground.

'Hullo!' cried the sailor, 'this is queer!'

'Very strange!' murmured the engineer, leaping first up the ladder.

'Take care, captain!' cried Pencroft, 'perhaps there are still some of these rascals.

'We shall soon see,' replied the engineer, without stopping however.

All his companions followed him, and in a minute they had arrived at the threshold. They searched everywhere. There was no one in the rooms nor in the storehouse, which had been respected by the band of quadrumana.

'Well now, and the ladder,' cried the sailor; 'who can the gentleman have been who sent us that down?'

But at that moment a cry was heard, and a great orang, who had hidden himself in the passage, rushed into the room, pursued by Neb.

'Ah, the robber!' cried Pencroft.

And hatchet in hand, he was about to cleave the head of the animal, when Cyrus Harding seized his arm, saying,—

'Spare him, Pencroft.'

'Pardon this rascal?'

'Yes! it was he who threw us the ladder!'

And the engineer said this in such a peculiar voice that it was difficult to know whether he spoke seriously or not.

Nevertheless, they threw themselves on the orang, who defended himself gallantly, but was soon overpowered and bound.

'There!' said Pencroft. 'And what shall we make of him, now we've got him?'

'A servant!' replied Herbert.

The lad was not joking in saying this, for he knew how this intelligent race could be turned to account.

The settlers then approached the ape and gazed at it attentively. He belonged to the family of anthropoid apes, of which the facial angle is not much inferior to that of the Australians and Hottentots. It was an orangoutang, and as such, had neither the ferocity of the gorilla, nor the stupidity of the baboon. It is to this family of the anthropoid apes that so many characteristics belong which prove them to be possessed of an almost human intelligence. Employed in houses, they can wait at table, sweep rooms, brush clothes, clean boots, handle a knife, fork, and spoon properly, and even drink wine,... doing everything as well as the best servant that ever walked upon two legs. Buffon possessed one of these apes, who served him for a long time as a faithful and zealous servant.

The one which had been seized in the hall of Granite House was a great fellow, six feet high, with an admirably poportioned frame, a broad chest, head of a moderate size, the facial angle reaching sixty-five degrees, round skull, projecting nose, skin covered with soft glossy hair, in short, a fine specimen of the anthropoids. His eyes, rather smaller than human eyes, sparkled with intelligence; his white teeth glittered under his moustache, and he wore a little curly brown beard.

'A handsome fellow!' said Pencroft; 'if we only knew his language, we could talk to him.'

'But, master,' said Neb, 'are you serious? Are we going to take him as a servant?'

'Yes, Neb,' replied the engineer, smiling. 'But you must not be jealous.'

'And I hope he will make an excellent servant,' added Herbert. 'He appears young, and will be easy to educate, and we shall not be obliged to use force to subdue him, nor draw his teeth, as is sometimes done. He will soon grow fond of his masters if they are kind to him.'

'And they will be,' replied Pencroft, who had forgotten all his rancour against 'the jokers.'

Then, approaching the orang,—

'Well, old boy!' he asked, 'how are you?'

The orang replied by a little grunt which did not show any anger.

'You wish to join the colony?' again asked the sailor. 'You are going to enter the service of Captain Cyrus Harding?'

Another respondent grunt was uttered by the ape.

'And you will be satisfied with no other wages than your food?'

Third affirmative grunt.

'This conversation is slightly monotonous,' observed Gideon Spilett.

'So much the better,' replied Pencroft; 'the best servants are those who talk the least. And then, no wages, do you hear, my boy? We will give you no wages at first, but we will double them afterwards if we are pleased with you.'

Thus the colony was increased by a new member. As to his name the sailor begged that in memory of another ape which he had known, he might be called Jupiter, and Jup for short.

And so, without more ceremony, Master Jup was installed in Granite House.

Chapter 7

The settlers in Lincoln Island had now regained their dwelling, without having been obliged to reach it by the old opening, and were therefore spared the trouble of mason's work. It was certainly lucky, that at the moment they were about to set out to do so, the apes had been seized with that terror, no less sudden than inexplicable, which had driven them out of Granite House. Had the animals discovered that they were about to be attacked from another direction? This was the only explanation of their sudden retreat.

During the day the bodies of the apes were carried into the wood, where they were buried; then the settlers busied themselves in repairing the disorder caused by the intruders, disorder but not damage, for although they had turned everything in the rooms topsy-turvy, yet they had broken nothing. Neb relighted his stove, and the stores in the larder furnished a substantial repast, to which all did ample justice.

Jup was not forgotten, and he ate with relish some stonepine almonds and rhizome roots, with which he was abundantly supplied. Pencroft had unfastened his arms, but judged it best to have his legs tied until they were more sure of his submission.

Then, before retiring to rest, Harding and his companions seated round their table, discussed those plans, the execution of which was most pressing. The most important and most urgent was the establishment of a bridge over the Mercy, so as to form a communication with the southern part of the island and Granite House; then the making of an enclosure for the musmons or other woolly animals which they wished to capture.

These two projects would help to solve the difficulty as to their clothing, which was now serious. The bridge would render easy the transport of the balloon case, which would furnish them with linen, and the inhabitants of the enclosure would yield wool which would supply them with winter clothes.

As to the enclosure, it was Cyrus Harding's intention to establish it at the sources of the Red Creek, where the ruminants would find fresh and abundant pasture. The road between Prospect Heights and the sources of the stream was already partly beaten, and with a better cart than the first, the material could be easily conveyed to the spot, especially if they could manage to capture some animals to draw it.

But though there might be no inconvenience in the enclosure being so far from Granite House, it would not be the same with the poultry-yard, to which Neb called the attention of the colonists. It was indeed necessary that the birds should be close within reach of the cook, and no place appeared more favourable for the establishment of the said poultry-yard than that portion of the banks of the lake which was close to the old opening.

Water-birds would prosper there as well as others, and the couple of tinamous taken in their last excursion would be the first to be domesticated.

The next day, the 3rd of November, the new works were begun by the construction of the bridge, and all hands were required for this important task. Saws, hatchets, and hammers were shouldered by the settlers, who, now transformed into carpenters, descended to the shore.

There Pencroft observed,—

'Suppose, that during our absence, Master Jup takes it into his head to draw up the ladder which he so politely returned to us yesterday?'

'Let us tie its lower end down firmly,' replied Cyrus Harding.

This was done by means of two stakes securely fixed in the sand. Then the settlers, ascending the left bank of the Mercy, soon arrived at the angle formed by the river.

There they halted, in order to ascertain if the bridge could be thrown across. The place appeared suitable.

In fact, from this spot, to Port Balloon, discovered the day before on the southern coast, there was only a distance of three miles and a half, and from the bridge to the Port, it would be easy to make a good cart-road which would render the communication between Granite House and the south of the island extremely easy.

Cyrus Harding now imparted to his companions a scheme for completely isolating Prospect Heights so as to shelter it from the attacks both of quadrupeds and quadrumana. In this way, Granite House, the Chimneys, the poultry-yard, and all the upper part of the plateau which was to be used for cultivation, would be protected against the depredations of animals. Nothing could be easier than to execute this project, and this is how the engineer intended to set to work.

The plateau was already defended on three sides by watercourses, either artificial or natural. On the northwest, by the shores of Lake Grant, from the entrance of the passage to the breach made in the banks of the lake for the escape of the water.

On the north, from this breach to the sea, by the new watercourse which had hollowed out a bed for itself across the plateau and shore, above and below the fall, and it would be enough to dig the bed of this creek a little deeper to make it impracticable for animals, on all the eastern border by the sea itself, from the mouth of the aforesaid creek to the mouth of the Mercy.

Lastly, on the south, from the mouth to the turn of the Mercy where the bridge was to be established.

The western border of the plateau now remained between the turn of the river and the southern angle of the lake, a distance of about a mile, which was open to all comers. But nothing could be easier than to dig a broad deep ditch, which could be filled from the lake, and the overflow of which would throw itself by a rapid fall into the bed of the Mercy. The level of the lake would, no doubt, be somewhat lowered by this fresh discharge of its waters, but Cyrus Harding had ascertained that the volume of water in the Red Creek was considerable enough to allow of the execution of this project.

'So then,' added the engineer, 'Prospect Heights will become a regular island, being surrounded with water on all sides, and only communicating with the rest of our domain by the bridge which we are about to throw across the Mercy, the two little bridges already established above and below the fall; and, lastly, two other little bridges which must be constructed, one over the canal which I propose to dig, the other across to the left bank of the Mercy. Now, if these bridges can be raised at will, Prospect Heights will be guarded from any surprise.'

The bridge was the most urgent work. Trees were selected, cut down, stripped of their branches, and cut into beams, joists, and planks. The end of the bridge which rested on the right bank of the Mercy was to be firm, but the other end on the left bank was to be movable, so that it might be raised by means of a counterpoise, as some canal bridges are managed.

This was certainly a considerable work, and though it was skilfully conducted, it took some time, for the Mercy at this place was eighty feet wide. It was therefore necessary to fix piles in the bed of the river so as to sustain the floor of the bridge and establish a pile-driver to act on the tops of these piles, which would thus form two arches and allow the bridge to support heavy loads.

Happily there was no want of tools with which to shape the wood, nor of iron-work to make it firm, nor of the ingenuity of a man who had a marvellous knowledge of the work, nor lastly, the zeal of his companions, who in seven months had necessarily acquired great skill in the use of their tools; and it must be said that not the least skilful was Gideon Spilett, who in dexterity almost equalled the sailor himself. 'Who would ever have expected so much from a newspaper man!' thought Pencroft.

The construction of the Mercy bridge lasted three weeks of regular hard work. They even breakfasted on the scene of their labours, and the weather being magnificent, they only returned to Granite House to sleep.

During this period it may be stated that Master Jup grew more accustomed to his new masters, whose movements he always watched with very inquisitive eyes. However, as a precautionary measure, Pencroft did not as yet allow him complete liberty, rightly wishing to wait until the limits of the plateau should be settled by the projected works. Top and Jup were good friends and played willingly together, but Jup did everything solemnly.

On the 20th of November the bridge was finished. The movable part, balanced by the counterpoise, swung easily, and only a slight effort was needed to rise it; between its hinge and the last crossbar on which it rested when closed, there existed a space of twenty feet, which was sufficiently wide to prevent any animals from crossing.

The settlers now began to talk of fetching the balloon-case, which they were anxious to place in perfect security; but to bring it, it would be necessary to take a cart to Port Balloon, and consequently, necessary to beat a road through the dense forests of the Far West. This would take some time. Also, Neb and Pencroft having gone to examine into the state of things at Port Balloon, and reported that the stock of cloth would suffer no damage in the grotto where it was stored, it was decided that the work at Prospect Heights should not be discontinued.

'That,' observed Pencroft, 'will enable us to establish our poultry-yard under better conditions, since we need have no fear of visits from foxes nor the attacks of other beasts.'

'Then,' added Neb, 'we can clear the plateau, and transplant wild plants to it.'

'And prepare our second cornfield!' cried the sailor with a triumphant air.

In fact, the first cornfield sown with a single grain had prospered admirably, thanks to Pencroft's care. It had produced the ten ears foretold by the engineer, and each ear containing eighty grains, the colony found itself in possession of eight hundred grains, in six months, which promised a double harvest each year.

These eight hundred grains, except fifty, which were prudently reserved, were to be sown in a new field, but with no less care than was bestowed on the single grain.

The field was prepared, then surrounded with a strong palisade, high and pointed, which quadrupeds would have found difficulty in leaping. As to birds, some scarecrows, due to Pencroft's ingenious brain, were enough to frighten them. The seven hundred and fifty grains deposited in very regular furrows were then left for nature to do the rest.

On the 21st of November, Cyrus Harding began to plan the canal which was to close the plateau on the west, from the south angle of Lake Grant to the angle of the Mercy. There was there two or three feet of vegetable earth, and below that granite. It was therefore necessary to manufacture some more nitroglycerine, and the nitroglycerine did its accustomed work. In less than a fortnight a ditch, twelve feet wide and six deep, was dug out in the hard ground of the plateau. A new trench was made by the same means in the rocky border of the lake, forming a small stream, to which they gave the name of Creek Glycerine, and which was thus an affluent of the Mercy. As the engineer had predicted, the level of the lake was lowered, though very slightly. To complete the enclosure the bed of the stream on the beach was considerably enlarged, and the sand supported by means of stakes.

By the end of the first fortnight of December these works were finished, and Prospect Heights—that is to say, a sort of irregular pentagon, having a perimeter of nearly four miles, surrounded by a liquid belt—was completely protected from depredators of every description.

During the month of December, the heat was very great. In spite of it, however, the settlers continued their work, and as they were anxious to possess a poultry-yard they forthwith commenced it.

It is useless to say that since the enclosing of the plateau had been completed, Master Jup had been set at liberty. He did not leave his masters, and evinced no wish to escape. He was a gentle animal, though very powerful and wonderfully active. He was already taught to make himself useful by drawing loads of wood and carting away the stones which were extracted from the bed of Creek Glycerine.

The poultry-yard occupied an area of two hundred square yards, on the southeastern bank of the lake. It was surrounded by a palisade, and in it were constructed various shelters for the birds which were to populate it. These were simply built of branches and divided into compartments, made ready for the expected guests.

The first were the two tinamous, which were not long in having a number of young ones; they had for companions half a dozen ducks, accustomed to the borders of the lake. Some belonged to the Chinese species, of which the wings open like a fan, and which by the brilliancy of their plumage rival the golden pheasants. A few days afterwards, Herbert snared a couple of gallinaceae, with spreading tails composed of long feathers, magnificent alectors, which soon became tame. As to pelicans, kingfishers, water-hens, they came of themselves to the shores of the poultry-yard, and this little community, after some disputes, cooing, screaming, clucking, ended by settling down peacefully, and increased in encouraging proportion for the future use of the colony.

Cyrus Harding, wishing to complete his performance, established a pigeon- house in a corner of the poultry-yard. There he lodged a dozen of those pigeons which frequented the rocks of the plateau. These birds soon became accustomed to returning every evening to their new dwelling, and showed more disposition to domesticate themselves than their congeners, the wood- pigeons.

Lastly, the time had come for turning the balloon-case to use, by cutting it up to make shirts and other articles; for as to keeping it in its present form, and risking themselves in a balloon filled with gas, above a sea of the limits of which they had no idea, it was not to be thought of.

It was necessary to bring the case to Granite House, and the colonists employed themselves in rendering their heavy cart lighter and more manageable. But though they had a vehicle, the moving power was yet to be found.

But did there not exist in the island some animal which might supply the place of the horse, ass, or ox? That was the question.

'Certainly,' said Pencroft, 'a beast of burden would be very useful to us until the captain has made a steam cart, or even an engine, for some day we shall have a railroad from Granite House to Port Balloon, with a branch line to Mount Franklin!'

One day, the 23rd of December, Neb and Top were heard shouting and barking, each apparently trying to see who could make the most noise. The settlers, who were busy at the Chimneys, ran, fearing some vexatious incident.

What did they see? Two fine animals of a large size that had imprudently ventured on the plateau, when the bridges were open. One would have said they were horses, or at least donkeys, male and female, of a fine shape, dove-coloured, the legs and tail white, striped with black on the head and neck. They advanced quietly without showing any uneasiness, and gazed at the men, in whom they could not as yet recognize their future masters.

'These are onagers!' cried Herbert, 'animals something between the zebra and the quagga!'

'Why not donkeys?' asked Neb.

'Because they have not long ears, and their shape is more graceful!'

'Donkeys or horses,' interrupted Pencroft, 'they are 'moving powers,' as the captain would say, and as such must be captured!'

The sailor, without frightening the animals, crept through the grass to the bridge over Creek Glycerine, lowered it, and the onagers were prisoners.

Now, should they seize them with violence and master them by force? No. It was decided that for a few days they should be allowed to roam freely about the plateau, where there was an abundance of grass, and the engineer immediately began to prepare a stable near the poultry-yard, in which the onagers might find food, with a good litter, and shelter during the night.

This done, the movements of the two magnificent creatures were left entirely free, and the settlers avoided even approaching them so as to terrify them. Several times, however, the onagers appeared to wish to leave the plateau, too confined for animals accustomed to the plains and forests. They were then seen following the water-barrier which everywhere presented itself before them, uttering short neighs, then galloping through the grass, and becoming calmer, they would remain entire hours gazing at the woods, from which they were cut off for ever!

In the meantime harness of vegetable fibre had been manufactured, and some days after the capture of the onagers, not only the cart was ready, but a straight road, or rather a cutting, had been made through the forests of the Far West, from the angle of the Mercy to Port Balloon. The cart might then be driven there, and towards the end of December they tried the onagers for the first time.

Pencroft had already coaxed the animals to come and eat out of his hand, and they allowed him to approach without making any difficulty, but once harnessed they reared and could with difficulty be held in. However, it was not long before they submitted to this new service, for the onager, being less refractory than the zebra, is frequently put in harness in the mountainous regions of Southern Africa, and it has even been acclimatized in Europe, under zones of a relative coolness.

On this day all the colony, except Pencroft who walked at the animals' heads, mounted the cart, and set out on the road to Port Balloon.

Of course they were jolted over the somewhat rough road, but the vehicle arrived without any accident, and was soon loaded with the case and rigging of the balloon.

At eight o'clock that evening the cart, after passing over the Mercy bridge, descended the left bank of the river, and stopped on the beach. The onagers being unharnessed, were thence led to their stable, and Pencroft before going to sleep gave vent to his feelings in a deep sigh of satisfaction that awoke all the echoes of Granite House.

Chapter 8

The first week of January was devoted to the manufacture of the linen garments required by the colony. The needles found in the box were used by sturdy if not delicate fingers, and we may be sure that what was sewn was sewn firmly.

There was no lack of thread, thanks to Cyrus Harding's idea of re- employing that which had been already used in the covering of the balloon. This with admirable patience was all unpicked by Gideon Spilett and Herbert, for Pencroft had been obliged to give this work up, as it irritated him beyond measure; but he had no equal in the sewing part of the business. Indeed, everybody knows that sailors have a remarkable aptitude for tailoring.

The cloth of which the balloon-case was made was then cleaned by means of soda and potash, obtained by the incineration of plants, in such a way that the cotton, having got rid of the varnish, resumed its natural softness and elasticity; then, exposed to the action of the atmosphere, it soon became perfectly white. Some dozen shirts and sock—the latter not knitted, of course, but made of cotton—were thus manufactured. What a comfort it was to the settlers to clothe themselves again in clean linen, which was doubtless rather rough, but they were not troubled about that! and then to go to sleep between sheets, which made the couches at Granite House into quite comfortable beds!

It was about this time also that they made boots of seal-leather, which were greatly needed to replace the shoes and boots brought from America. We may be sure that these new shoes were large enough and never pinched the feet of the wearers.

With the beginning of the year 1866 the heat was very great, but the hunting in the forests did not stand still. Agouties, peccaries, capybaras, kangaroos, game of all sorts, actually swarmed there, and Spilett and Herbert were too good marksmen ever to throw away their shot uselessly.

Cyrus Harding still recommended them to husband the ammunition, and he took measures to replace the powder and shot which had been found in the box, and which he wished to reserve for the future. How did he know where chance might one day cast his companions and himself in the event of their leaving their domain? They should, then, prepare for the unknown future by husbanding their ammunition and by substituting for it some easily renewable substance.

To replace lead, of which Harding had found no traces in the island, he employed granulated iron, which was easy to manufacture. These bullets, not having the weight of leaden bullets, were made larger, and each charge contained less, but the skill of the sportsmen made up this deficiency. As to powder, Cyrus Harding would have been able to make that also, for he had at his disposal saltpetre, sulphur, and coal; but this preparation requires extreme care, and without special tools it is difficult to produce it of a good quality. Harding preferred, therefore, to manufacture pyroxyle, that is to say guncotton, a substance in which cotton is not indispensable, as the elementary tissue of vegetables may be used, and this is found in an almost pure state, not only in cotton, but in the textile fibre of hemp and flax, in paper, the pith of the elder, etc. Now, the elder abounded in the island towards the mouth of Red Creek, and the colonists had already made coffee of the berries of these shrubs, which belong to the family of the caprifoliaceae.

The only thing to be collected, therefore, was elder-pith, for as to the other substance necessary for the manufacture of pyroxyle, it was only fuming azotic acid. Now, Harding having sulphuric acid at his disposal, had already been easily able to produce azotic acid by attacking the saltpetre with which nature supplied him. He accordingly resolved to manufacture and employ pyroxyle, although it has some inconveniences, that is to say, a great inequality of effect, an excessive inflammability, since it takes fire at one hundred and seventy degrees instead of two hundred and forty, and lastly, an instantaneous deflagration which might damage the firearms. On the other hand, the advantages of pyroxyle consist in this, that it is not injured by damp, that it does not make the gun-barrels dirty, and that its force is four times that of ordinary powder.

To make pyroxyle, the cotton must be immersed in the fuming azotic acid for a quarter of an hour, then washed in cold water and dried. Nothing could be more simple.

Cyrus Harding had only at his disposal the ordinary azotic acid and not the fuming or monohydrate azotic acid, that is to say, acid which emits white vapours when it comes in contact with damp air; but by substituting for the latter ordinary azotic acid, mixed, in the proportion of from three to five volumes of concentrated sulphuric acid, the engineer obtained the same result. The sportsmen of the island therefore soon had a perfectly prepared substance, which, employed discreetly, produced admirable results.

About this time the settlers cleared three acres of the plateau, and the rest was preserved in a wild state, for the benefit of the onagers. Several excursions were made into the Jacamar Wood and the forests of the Far West, and they brought back from thence a large collection of wild vegetables, spinach, cress, radishes, and turnips, which careful culture would soon improve, and which would temper the regimen on which the settlers had till then subsisted. Supplies of wood and coal were also carted. Each excursion was at the same time a means of improving the roads, which gradually became smoother under the wheels of the cart.

The rabbit-warren still continued to supply the larder of Granite House. As fortunately it was situated on the other side of Creek Glycerine, its inhabitants could not reach the plateau nor ravage the newly-made plantation. The oyster-bed among the rocks was frequently renewed and furnished excellent molluscs. Besides that, the fishing, either in the lake or the Mercy, was very profitable, for Pencroft had made some lines, armed with iron hooks, with which they frequently caught fine trout, and a species of fish whose silvery sides were speckled with yellow, and which were also extremely savoury. Master Neb, who was skilled in the culinary art, knew how to vary agreeably the bill of fare. Bread alone was wanting at the table of the settlers, and as has been said, they felt this privation greatly.

The settlers hunted too the turtles which frequented the shores of Cape Mandible. At this place the beach was covered with little mounds, concealing perfectly spherical turtles' eggs, with white hard shells, the albumen of which does not coagulate as that of birds' eggs. They were hatched by the sun, and their number was naturally considerable, as each turtle can lay annually two hundred and fifty.

'A regular egg-field,' observed Gideon Spilett, 'and we have nothing to do but to pick them up.'

But not being contented with simply the produce, they made chase after the producers, the result of which was that they were able to bring back to Granite House a dozen of these chelonians, which were really valuable from an alimentary point of view. The turtle soup, flavoured with aromatic herbs, often gained well-merited praises for its preparer, Neb.

We must here mention another fortunate circumstance by which new stores for the winter were laid in. Shoals of salmon entered the Mercy, and ascended the country for several miles. It was the time at which the females, going to find suitable places in which to spawn, precede the males and make a great noise through the fresh water. A thousand of these fish, which measured about two feet and a half in length, came up the river, and a large quantity were retained by fixing dams across the stream. More than a hundred were thus taken, which were salted and stored for the time when winter, freezing up the streams, would render fishing impracticable. By this time the intelligent Jup was raised to the duty of valet. He had been dressed in a jacket, white linen breeches, and an apron, the pockets of which were his delight. The clever orang had been marvellously trained by Neb, and any one would have said that the Negro and the ape understood each other when they talked together. Jup had besides a real affection for Neb, and Neb returned it. When his services were not required, either for carrying wood or for climbing to the top of some tree, Jup passed the greatest part of his time in the kitchen, where he endeavoured to imitate Neb in all that he saw him do. The black showed the greatest patience and even extreme zeal in instructing his pupil, and the pupil exhibited remarkable intelligence in profiting by the lessons he received from his master.

Judge then of the pleasure Master Jup gave to the inhabitants of Granite House when, without their having had any idea of it, he appeared one day, napkin on his arm, ready to wait at table. Quick, attentive, he acquitted himself perfectly, changing the plates, bringing dishes, pouring out water, all with a gravity which gave intense amusement to the settlers, and which enraptured Pencroft.

'Jup, some soup!'

'Jup, a little agouti!'

'Jup, a plate!'

'Jup! Good Jup! Honest Jup!'

Nothing was heard but that, and Jup without ever being disconcerted, replied to every one, watched for everything, and he shook his head in a knowing way when Pencroft, referring to his joke of the first day, said to him,—

'Decidedly, Jup, your wages must be doubled.'

It is useless to say that the orang was now thoroughly domesticated at Granite House, and that he often accompanied his masters to the forest without showing any wish to leave them. It was most amusing to see him walking with a stick which Pencroft had given him, and which he carried on his shoulder like a gun. If they wished to gather some fruit from the summit of a tree, how quickly he climbed for it. If the wheel of the cart stuck in the mud, with what energy did Jup with a single heave of his shoulder put it right again.

'What a jolly fellow he is!' cried Pencroft often. 'If he was as mischievous as he is good, there would be no doing anything with him!'

It was towards the end of January the colonists began their labours in the centre of the island. It had been decided that a pen should be established near the sources of the Red Creek, at the foot of Mount Franklin, destined to contain the ruminants, whose presence would have been troublesome at Granite House, and especially for the musmons, who were to supply the wool for the settlers' winter garments.

Each morning, the colony, sometimes entire, but more often represented only by Harding, Herbert, and Pencroft, proceeded to the sources of the Creek, a distance of not more than five miles, by the newly beaten road to which the name of Corral Road had been given.

There a site was chosen, at the back of the southern ridge of the mountain. It was a meadow land, dotted here and there with clumps of trees, and watered by a little stream, which sprung from the slopes which closed it in on one side. The grass was fresh, and it was not too much shaded by the trees which grew about it. This meadow was to be surrounded by a palisade, high enough to prevent even the most agile animals from leaping over. This enclosure would be large enough to contain a hundred musmons and wild goats, with all the young ones they might produce.

The perimeter of the corral was then traced by the engineer, and they would then have proceeded to fell the trees necessary for the construction of the palisade, but as the opening up of the road had already necessitated the sacrifice of a considerable number, those were brought and supplied a hundred stakes, which were firmly fixed in the ground.

The construction of this corral did not take less than three weeks, for besides the palisade, Cyrus Harding built large sheds, in which the animals could take shelter. These buildings had also to be made very strong, for musmons are powerful animals, and their first fury was to be feared. The stakes, sharpened at their upper end and hardened by fire, had been fixed by means of crossbars, and at regular distances props assured the solidity of the whole.

The corral finished, a raid had to be made on the pastures frequented by the ruminants. This was done on the 7th of February, on a beautiful summer's day, and every one took part in it. The onagers, already well trained, were ridden by Spilett and Herbert, and were of great use.

The manoeuvre consisted simply in surrounding the musmons and goats, and gradually narrowing the circle around them. Cyrus Harding, Pencroft, Neb, and Jup, posted themselves in different parts of the wood, while the two cavaliers and Top galloped in a radius of half a mile round the corral.

The musmons were very numerous in this part of the island. These fine animals were as large as deer; their horns were stronger than those of the ram, and their gray-coloured fleece was mixed with long hair.

This hunting day was very fatiguing. Such going and coming, and running and riding and shouting! Of a hundred musmons which had been surrounded, more than two-thirds escaped, but at last, thirty of these animals and ten wild goats were gradually driven back towards the corral, the open door of which appearing to offer a means of escape, they rushed in and were prisoners.

In short, the result was satisfactory, and the settlers had no reason to complain. There was no doubt that the flock would prosper, and that at no distant time not only wool but hides would be abundant.

That evening the hunters returned to Granite House quite exhausted. However, notwithstanding their fatigue, they returned the next day to visit the corral. The prisoners had been trying to overthrow the palisade, but of course had not succeeded, and were not long in becoming more tranquil.

During the month of February, no event of any importance occurred. The daily labours were pursued methodically, and, as well as improving the roads to the corral and to Port Balloon, a third was commenced, which, starting from the enclosure, proceeded towards the western coast. The yet unknown portion of Lincoln Island was that of the wood-covered Serpentine Peninsula, which sheltered the wild beasts, from which Gideon Spilett was so anxious to clear their domain.

Before the cold season should appear the most assiduous care was given to the cultivation of the wild plants which had been transplanted from the forest to Prospect Heights. Herbert never returned from an excursion without bringing home some useful vegetable. One day, it was some specimens of the chicory tribe, the seeds of which by pressure yield an excellent oil; another, it was some common sorrel, whose antiscorbutic qualities were not to be despised; then, some of those precious tubers, which have at all times been cultivated in South America, potatoes, of which more than two hundred species are now known. The kitchen garden, now well stocked and carefully defended from the birds, was divided into small beds, where grew lettuces, kidney potatoes, sorrel, turnips, radishes, and other coneiferae. The soil on the plateau was particularly fertile, and it was hoped that the harvests would be abundant.

They had also a variety of different beverages, and so long as they did not demand wine, the most hard to please would have had no reason to complain. To the Oswego tea, and the fermented liquor extracted from the roots of the dragonnier, Harding had added a regular beer, made from the young shoots of the spruce-fir, which, after having been boiled and fermented, made that agreeable drink called by the Anglo-Americans spring- beer.

Towards the end of the summer, the poultry-yard was possessed of a couple of fine bustards, which belonged to the houbara species, characterized by a sort of feathery mantle; a dozen shovelers, whose upper mandible was prolonged on each side by a membraneous appendage; and also some magnificent cocks, similar to the Mozambique cocks, the comb, caruncle, and epidermis being black. So far, everything had succeeded, thanks to the activity of these courageous and intelligent men. Nature did much for them, doubtless; but faithful to the great precept, they made a right use of what a bountiful Providence gave them.

After the heat of these warm summer days, in the evening when their work was finished and the sea-breeze began to blow, they liked to sit on the edge of Prospect Heights, in a sort of veranda, covered with creepers, which Neb had made with his own hands. There they talked, they instructed each other, they made plans, and the rough good-humour of the sailor always amused this little world, in which the most perfect harmony had never ceased to reign.

They often spoke of their country, of their dear and great America. What was the result of the War of Secession? It could not have been greatly prolonged. Richmond had doubtless soon fallen into the hands of General Grant. The taking of the capital of the Confederates must have been the last action of this terrible struggle. Now the North had triumphed in the good cause, how welcome would have been a newspaper to the exiles in Lincoln Island! For eleven months all communication between them and the rest of their fellow-creatures had been interrupted, and in a short time the 24th of March would arrive, the anniversary of the day on which the balloon had thrown them on this unknown coast. They were then mere castaways, not even knowing how they should preserve their miserable lives from the fury of the elements! And now, thanks to the knowledge of their captain, and their own intelligence, they were regular colonists, furnished with arms, tools, and instruments; they had been able to turn to their profit the animals, plants, and minerals of the island, that is to say, the three kingdoms of Nature.

Yes; they often talked of all these things and formed still more plans.

As to Cyrus Harding he was for the most part silent, and listened to his companions more often than he spoke to them. Sometimes he smiled at Herbert's ideas or Pencroft's nonsense, but always and everywhere he pondered over those inexplicable facts, that strange enigma, of which the secret still escaped him!

Chapter 9

The weather changed during the first week of March. There had been a full moon at the commencement of the month, and the heat was excessive. The atmosphere was felt to be full of electricity, and a period of some length of tempestuous weather was to be feared.

Indeed, on the 2nd, peals of thunder were heard, the wind blew from the east, and hail rattled against the facade of Granite House like volleys of grapeshot. The door and windows were immediately closed, or everything in the rooms would have been drenched. On seeing these hailstones, some of which were the size of a pigeon's egg, Pencroft's first thought was that his cornfield was in serious danger.

He directly rushed to his field, where little green heads were already appearing, and by means of a great cloth he managed to protect his crop.

This bad weather lasted a week, during which time the thunder rolled without cessation in the depths of the sky.

The colonists, not having any pressing work out of doors, profited by the bad weather to work at the interior of Granite House, the arrangement of which was becoming more complete from day to day. The engineer made a turning-lathe, with which he turned several articles both for the toilet and the kitchen, particularly buttons, the want of which was greatly felt. A gunrack had been made for the firearms, which were kept with extreme care, and neither tables nor cupboards were left incomplete. They sawed, they planed, they filed, they turned; and during the whole of this bad season, nothing was heard but the grinding of tools or the humming of the turning-lathe which responded to the growling of the thunder.

Master Jup had not been forgotten, and he occupied a room at the back, near the storeroom, a sort of cabin with a cot always full of good litter, which perfectly suited his taste.

'With good old Jup there is never any quarrelling,' often repeated Pencroft, 'never any improper reply. What a servant, Neb, what a servant!'

Of course Jup was now well used to service. He brushed their clothes, he turned the spit, he waited at table, he swept the rooms, he gathered wood, and he performed another admirable piece of service which delighted Pencroft—he never went to sleep without first coming to tuck up the worthy sailor in his bed.

As to the health of the members of the colony, bipeds or bimana, quadrumana or quadrupeds, it left nothing to be desired. With their life in the open air, on this salubrious soil, under that temperate zone, working both with head and hands, they could not suppose that illness would ever attack them.

All were indeed wonderfully well. Herbert had already grown two inches in the year. His figure was forming and becoming more manly, and he promised to be an accomplished man, physically as well as morally. Besides he improved himself during the leisure hours which manual occupations left to him; he read the books found in the case; and after the practical lessons which were taught by the very necessity of their position, he found in the engineer for science, and the reporter for languages, masters who were delighted to complete his education.

The tempest ended about the 9th of March, but the sky remained covered with clouds during the whole of this last summer month. The atmosphere, violently agitated by the electric commotiones, could not recover its former purity, and there was almost invariably rain and fog, except for three or four fine days on which several excursions were made. About this time the female onager gave birth to a young one which belonged to the same sex as its mother, and which throve capitally. In the corral, the flock of musmons had also increased, and several lambs already bleated in the sheds, to the great delight of Neb and Herbert, who had each their favourite among these newcomers. An attempt was also made for the domestication of the peccaries, which succeeded well. A sty was constructed under the poultry-yard, and soon contained several young ones in the way to become civilized, that is to say, to become fat under Neb's care. Master Jup, entrusted with carrying them their daily nourishment, leavings from the kitchen, etc., acquitted himself conscientiously of his task. He sometimes amused himself at the expense of his little pensioners by tweaking their tails; but this was mischief, and not wickedness, for these little twisted tails amused him like a plaything, and his instinct was that of a child. One day in this month of March,

Pencroft, talking to the engineer, reminded Cyrus Harding of a promise which the latter had not as yet had time to fulfil.

'You once spoke of an apparatus which would take the place of the long ladders at Granite House, captain,' said he; 'won't you make it some day?'

'Nothing will be easier; but is this a really useful thing?'

'Certainly, captain. After we have given ourselves necessaries, let us think a little of luxury. For us it may be luxury, if you like, but for things it is necessary. It isn't very convenient to climb up a long ladder when one is heavily loaded.'

'Well, Pencroft, we will try to please you,' replied Cyrus Harding.

'But you have no machine at your disposal.'

'We will make one.'

'A steam machine?'

'No, a water machine.

And, indeed, to work his apparatus there was already a natural force at the disposal of the engineer which could be used without great difficulty. For this, it was enough to augment the flow of the little stream which supplied the interior of Granite House with water. The opening among the stones and grass was then increased, thus producing a strong fall at the bottom of the passage, the overflow from which escaped by the inner well. Below this fall the engineer fixed a cylinder with paddles, which was joined on the exterior with a strong cable rolled on a wheel, supporting a basket. In this way, by means of a long rope reaching to the ground, which enabled them to regulate the motive power, they could rise in the basket to the door of Granite House.

It was on the 17th of March that the lift acted for the first time, and gave universal satisfaction. Henceforward all the loads, wood, coal, provisions, and even the settlers themselves, were hoisted by this simple system, which replaced the primitive ladder, and, as may be supposed, no one thought of regretting the change. Top particularly was enchanted with this improvement, for he had not, and never could have possessed Master Jup's skill in climbing ladders, and often it was on Neb's back, or even on that of the orang that he had been obliged to make the ascent to Granite House. About this time, too, Cyrus Harding attempted to manufacture glass, and he at first put the old pottery-kiln to this new use. There were some difficulties to be encountered; but, after several fruitless attempts, he succeeded in setting up a glass manufactory, which Gideon Spilett and Herbert, his usual assistants, did not leave for several days. As to the substances used in the composition of glass, they are simply sand, chalk, and soda, either carbonate or sulphate. Now the beach supplied sand, lime supplied chalk, sea-weeds supplied soda, pyrites supplied sulphuric acid, and the ground supplied coal to heat the kiln to the wished-for temperature. Cyrus Harding thus soon had everything ready for setting to work.

The tool, the manufacture of which presented the most difficulty, was the pipe of the glass-maker, an iron tube, five or six feet long, which collects on one end the material in a state of fusion. But by means of a long, thin piece of iron rolled up like the barrel of a gun, Pencroft succeeded in making a tube soon ready for use.

On the 28th of March the tube was heated. A hundred parts of sand, thirty-five of chalk, forty of sulphate of soda, mixed with two or three parts of powdered coal, composed the substance, which was placed in crucibles. When the high temperature of the oven had reduced it to a liquid, or rather a pasty state, Cyrus Harding collected with the tube a quantity of the paste: he turned it about on a metal plate, previously arranged, so as to give it a form suitable for blowing, then he passed the tube to Herbert, telling him to blow at the other extremity.

And Herbert, swelling out his cheeks, blew so much and so well into the tube-taking care to twirl it round at the same time—that his breath dilated the glassy mass. Other quantities of the substance in a state of fusion were added to the first, and in a short time the result was a bubble which measured a foot in diameter. Harding then took the tube out of Herbert's hands, and, giving it a pendulous motion, he ended by lengthening the malleable bubble so as to give it a cylindroconic shape.

The blowing operation had given a cylinder of glass terminated by two hemispheric caps, which were easily detached by means of a sharp iron dipped in cold water; then, by the same proceeding, this cylinder was cut lengthways, and after having been rendered malleable by a second heating, it was extended on a plate and spread out with a wooden roller.

The first pane was thus manufactured, and they had only to perform this operation fifty times to have fifty panes. The windows at Granite House were soon furnished with panes; not very white, perhaps, but still sufficiently transparent.

As to bottles and tumblers, that was only play. They were satisfied with them, besides, just as they came from the end of the tube. Pencroft had asked to be allowed to 'blow' in his turn, and it was great fun for him; but he blew so hard that his productions took the most ridiculous shapes, which he admired immensely.

Cyrus Harding and Herbert, while hunting one day, had entered the forest of the Far West, on the left bank of the Mercy, and, as usual, the lad was asking a thousand questions of the engineer, who answered them heartily. Now, as Harding was not a sportsman, and as, on the other side, Herbert was talking chemistry and natural philosophy, numbers of kangaroos, capybaras, and agouties came within range, which, however, escaped the lad's gun; the consequence was that the day was already advanced, and the two hunters were in danger of having made a useless excursion, when Herbert, stopping, and uttering a cry of joy, exclaimed,—

'Oh, Captain Harding, do you see that tree?' and he pointed to a shrub, rather than a tree, for it was composed of a single stem, covered with a scaly bark, which bore leaves streaked with little parallel veins.

'And what is this tree which resembles a little palm?' asked Harding.

'It is a 'cycas revoluta,' of which I have a picture in our dictionary of Natural History!' said Herbert.

'But I can't see any fruit on this shrub!' observed his companion.

'No, captain,' replied Herbert; 'but its stem contains a flour with which nature has provided us all ready ground.'

'It is, then, the bread-tree?'

'Yes, the bread-tree.'

'Well, my boy,' replied the engineer, 'this is a valuable discovery, since our wheat harvest is not yet ripe; I hope that you are not mistaken!'

Herbert was not mistaken: he broke the stem of a cycas, which was composed of a glandulous tissue, containing a quantity of floury pith, traversed with woody fibre, separated by rings of the same substance, arranged concentrically. With this fecula was mingled a mucilaginous juice of disagreeable flavour, but which it would be easy to get rid of by pressure. This cellular substance was regular flour of a superior quality, extremely nourishing; its exportation was formerly forbidden by the Japanese laws.

Cyrus Harding and Herbert, after having examined that part of the Far West where the cycas grew, took their bearings, and returned to Granite House, where they made known their discovery.

The next day the settlers went to collect some, and returned to Granite House with an ample supply of cycas stems. The engineer constructed a press, with which to extract the mucilaginous juice mingled with the fecula, and he obtained a large quantity of flour, which Neb soon transformed into cakes and puddings. This was not quite real wheaten bread, but it was very like it.

Now, too, the onager, the goats, and the sheep in the corral furnished daily the milk necessary to the colony. The cart, or rather a sort of light carriole which had replaced it, made frequent journeys to the corral, and when it was Pencroft's turn to go he took Jup, and let him drive, and Jup, cracking his whip, acquitted himself with his customary intelligence.

Everything prospered, as well in the corral as in Granite House, and certainly the settlers, if it had not been that they were so far from their native land, had no reason to complain. They were so well suited to this life, and were, besides, so accustomed to the island, that they could not have left its hospitable soil without regret!

And yet so deeply is the love of his country implanted in the heart of man, that if a ship had unexpectedly come in sight of the island, the colonists would have made signals, would have attracted her attention, and would have departed!

It was the 1st of April, a Sunday, Easter Day, which Harding and his companions sanctified by rest and prayer. The day was fine, such as an October day in the Northern Hemisphere might be.

All, towards the evening after dinner, were seated under the veranda on the edge of Prospect Heights, and they were watching the darkness creeping up from the horizon. Some cups of the infusion of elderberries, which took the place of coffee, had been served by Neb. They were speaking of the island and of its isolated situation in the Pacific, which led Gideon Spilett to say,—

'My dear Cyrus, have you ever, since you possessed the sextant found in the case, again taken the position of our island?'

'No,' replied the engineer.

'But it would perhaps be a good thing to do it with this instrument, which is more perfect than that which you before used.'

'What is the good?' said Pencroft. 'The island is quite comfortable where it is!'

'Well, who knows,' returned the reporter, 'who knows but that we may be much nearer inhabited land than we think?'

'We shall know tomorrow,' replied Cyrus Harding, 'and if it had not been for the occupations which left me no leisure, we should have known it already.'

'Good!' said Pencroft. 'The captain is too good an observer to be mistaken, and, if it has not moved from its place, the island is just where he put it.'

'We shall see.'

On the next day, therefore, by means of the sextant, the engineer made the necessary observations to verify the position which he had already obtained, and this was the result of his operation. His first observation had given him the situation of Lincoln Island,—

In west longitude: from 1500 to 1550;

In south latitude: from 300 to 350

The second gave exactly:

In longitude: 1500° 30'

In south latitude: 340° 57'

So then, notwithstanding the imperfection of his apparatus, Cyrus Harding had operated with so much skill that his error did not exceed five degrees.

'Now,' said Gideon Spilett, 'since we possess an atlas as well as a sextant, let us see, my dear Cyrus, the exact position which Lincoln Island occupies in the Pacific.'

Herbert fetched the atlas, and the map of the Pacific was opened, and the engineer, compass in hand, prepared to determine their position.

Suddenly the compasses stopped, and he exclaimed,

'But an island exists in this part of the Pacific already!'

'An island?' cried Pencroft.

'Tabor Island.'

'An important island?'

'No, an islet lost in the Pacific, and which perhaps has never been visited.'

'Well, we will visit it,' said Pencroft.

'We?'

'Yes, captain. We will build a decked boat, and I will undertake to steer her. At what distance are we from this Tabor Island?'

'About a hundred and fifty miles to the northeast,' replied Harding.

'A hundred and fifty miles! And what's that?' returned Pencroft. 'In forty-eight hours, with a good wind, we should sight it!'

And, on this reply, it was decided that a vessel should be constructed in time to be launched towards the month of next October, on the return of the fine season.

Chapter 10

When Pencroft had once got a plan in his head, he had no peace till it was executed. Now he wished to visit Tabor Island, and as a boat of a certain size was necessary for this voyage, he determined to build one.

What wood should he employ? Elm or fir, both of which abounded in the island? They decided for the fir, as being easy to work, but which stands water as well as the elm.

These details settled, it was agreed that since the fine season would not return before six months, Cyrus Harding and Pencroft should work alone at the boat. Gideon Spilett and Herbert were to continue to hunt, and neither Neb nor Master Jup, his assistant, were to leave the domestic duties which had devolved upon them.

Directly the trees were chosen, they were felled, stripped of their branches, and sawn into planks as well as sawyers would have been able to do it. A week after, in the recess between the Chimneys and the cliff, a dockyard was prepared, and a keel five-and-thirty feet long, furnished with a stern-post at the stern and a stem at the bows, lay along the sand.

Cyrus Harding was not working in the dark at this new trade. He knew as much about shipbuilding as about nearly everything else, and he had at first drawn the model of his ship on paper. Besides, he was ably seconded by Pencroft, who, having worked for several years in a dockyard in Brooklyn, knew the practical part of the trade. It was not until after careful calculation and deep thought that the timbers were laid on the keel.

Pencroft, as may be believed, was all eagerness to carry out his new enterprise, and would not leave his work for an instant.

A single thing had the honour of drawing him, but for one day only, from his dockyard. This was the second wheat-harvest, which was gathered in on the 15th of April. It was as much a success as the first, and yielded the number of grains which had been predicted.

'Five bushels, captain,' said Pencroft, alter having scrupulously measured his treasure.

'Five bushels,' replied the engineer; 'and a hundred and thirty thousand grains a bushel will make six hundred and fifty thousand grains.'

'Well, we will sow them all this time,' said the sailor, 'except a little in reserve.'

'Yes, Pencroft, and if the next crop gives a proportionate yield, we shall have four thousand bushels.'

'And shall we eat bread?'

'We shall eat bread.'

'But we must have a mill.

'We will make one.'

The third cornfield was very much larger than the two first, and the soil, prepared with extreme care, received the precious seed. That done, Pencroft returned to his work.

During this time Spilett and Herbert hunted in the neighbourhood, and they ventured deep into the still unknown parts of the Far West, their guns loaded with ball, ready for any dangerous emergency. It was a vast thicket of magnificent trees, crowded together as if pressed for room. The exploration of these dense masses of wood was difficult in the extreme, and the reporter never ventured there without the pocket-compass, for the sun scarcely pierced through the thick foliage and it would have been very difficult for them to retrace their way. It naturally happened that game was more rare in those situations where there was hardly sufficient room to move; two or three large herbivorous animals were however killed during the last fortnight of April. These were koalas, specimens of which the settlers had already seen to the north of the lake, and which stupidly allowed themselves to be killed among the thick branches of the trees in which they took refuge. Their skins were brought back to Granite House, and there, by the help of sulphuric acid, they were subjected to a sort of tanning process which rendered them capable of being used.

On the 30th of April, the two sportsmen were in the depth of the Far West, when the reporter, preceding Herbert a few paces, arrived in a sort of clearing, into which the trees more sparsely scattered had permitted a few rays to penetrate. Gideon Spilett was at first surprised at the odour which exhaled from certain plants with straight stalks, round and branchy, bearing grapelike clusters of flowers and very small berries. The reporter broke off one or two of these stalks and returned to the lad, to whom he said,—

'What can this be, Herbert?'

'Well, Mr. Spilett,' said Herbert, 'this is a treasure which will secure you Pencroft's gratitude forever.'

'Is it tobacco?'

'Yes, and though it may not be of the first quality, it is none the less tobacco!'

'Oh, good old Pencroft! Won't he be pleased! But we must not let him smoke it all, he must give us our share.'

'Ah! an idea occurs to me, Mr, Spilett,' replied Herbert. 'Don't let us say anything to Pencroft yet; we will prepare these leaves, and one fine day we will present him with a pipe already filled!'

'All right, Herbert, and on that day our worthy companion will have nothing left to wish for in this world.'

The reporter and the lad secured a good store of the precious plant, and then returned to Granite House, where they smuggled it in with as much precaution as if Pencroft had been the most vigilant and severe of custom- house officers.

Cyrus Harding and Neb were taken into confidence, and the sailor suspected nothing during the whole time, necessarily somewhat long, which was required in order to dry the small leaves, chop them up, and subject them to a certain torrefaction on hot stones. This took two months; but all these manipulations were successfully carried on unknown to Pencroft, for, occupied with the construction of his boat, he only returned to Granite House at the hour of rest.

For some days they had observed an enormous animal two or three miles out in the open sea swimming around Lincoln Island. This was a whale of the largest size, which apparently belonged to the southern species, called the 'Cape Whale.'

'What a lucky chance it would be if we could capture it!' cried the sailor. 'Ah! if we only had a proper boat and a good harpoon, I would say 'After the beast,' for he would be well worth the trouble of catching!'

'Well, Pencroft,' observed Harding, 'I should much like to watch you handling a harpoon. It would be very interesting.'

'I am astonished,' said the reporter, 'to see a whale in this comparatively high latitude.'

'Why so, Mr. Spilett?' replied Herbert. 'We are exactly in that part of the Pacific which English and American whalemen call the whale field, and it is here, between New Zealand and South America, that the whales of the Southern Hemisphere are met with in the greatest numbers.'

And Pencroft returned to his work, not without uttering a sigh of regret, for every sailor is a born fisherman, and if the pleasure of fishing is in exact proportion to the size of the animal, one can judge how a whaler feels in sight of a whale. And if this had only been for pleasure! But they could not help feeling how valuable such a prize would have been to the colony, for the oil, fat, and bones would have been put to many uses.

Now it happened that this whale appeared to have no wish to leave the waters of the island. Therefore, whether from the windows of Granite House, or from Prospect Heights, Herbert and Gideon Spilett, when they were not hunting, or Neb, unless presiding over his fires, never left the telescope, but watched all the animal's movements. The cetacean, having entered far into Union Bay, made rapid furrows across it from Mandible Cape to Claw Cape, propelled by its enormously powerful flukes, on which it supported itself, and making its way through the water at the rate little short of twelve knots an hour. Sometimes also it approached so near to the island that it could be clearly distinguished. It was the southern whale, which is completely black, the head being more depressed than that of the northern whale.

They could also see it throwing up from its air-holes to a great height a cloud of vapour, or of water, for, strange as it may appear, naturalists and whalers are not agreed on this subject. Is it air or is it water which is thus driven out? It is generally admitted to be vapour, which, condensing suddenly by contact with the cold air, falls again as rain.

However, the presence of this mammifer preoccupied the colonists. It irritated Pencroft especially, as he could think of nothing else while at work. He ended by longing for it, like a child for a thing which it has been denied. At night he talked about it in his sleep, and certainly if he had had the means of attacking it, if the sloop had been in a fit state to put to sea, he would not have hesitated to set out in pursuit.

But what the colonists could not do for themselves chance did for them, and on the 3rd of May shouts from Neb, who had stationed himself at the kitchen window, announced that the whale was stranded on the beach of the island.

Herbert and Gideon Spilett, who were just about to set out hunting, left their guns, Pencroft threw down his axe, and Harding and Neb joining their companions, all rushed towards the scene of action.

The stranding had taken place on the beach of Flotsam Point, three miles from Granite House, and at high tide. It was therefore probable that the cetacean would not be able to extricate itself easily; at any rate it was best to hasten, so as to cut off its retreat if necessary. They ran with pickaxes and iron-tipped poles in their hands, passed over the Mercy bridge, descended the right bank of the river, along the beach, and in less than twenty minutes the settlers were close to the enormous animal, above which flocks of birds already hovered.

'What a monster!' cried Neb.

And the exclamation was natural, for it was a southern whale, eighty feet long, a giant of the species, probably not weighing less than a hundred and fifty thousand pounds!

In the meanwhile, the monster thus stranded did not move, nor attempt by struggling to regain the water while the tide was still high.

It was dead, and a harpoon was sticking out of its left side.

'There are whalers in these quarters, then?' said Gideon Spilett directly.

'Oh, Mr. Spilett, that doesn't prove anything!' replied Pencroft. 'Whales have been known to go thousands of miles with a harpoon in the side, and this one might even have been struck in the north of the Atlantic and come to die in the south of the Pacific, and it would be nothing astonishing.'

Pencroft, having torn the harpoon from the animal's side, read this inscription on it:

MARIA STELLA, VINEYARD

'A vessel from the Vineyard! A ship from my country!' he cried. 'The 'Maria Stella!' A fine whaler, 'pon my word; I know her well! Oh, my friends, a vessel from the Vineyard!—a whaler from the Vineyard!'

And the sailor brandishing the harpoon, repeated, not without emotion, the name which he loved so well—the name of his birthplace.

But as it could not be expected that the 'Maria Stella' would come to reclaim the animal harpooned by her, they resolved to begin cutting it up before decomposition should commence. The birds, who had watched this rich prey for several days, had determined to take possession of it without further delay, and it was necessary to drive them off by firing at them repeatedly.

The whale was a female, and a large quantity of milk was taken from it, which, according to the opinion of the naturalist Duffenbach, might pass for cow's milk, and, indeed, it differs from it neither in taste, colour, nor density.

Pencroft had formerly served on board a whaling-ship, and he could methodically direct the operation of cutting up, a sufficiently disagreeable operation lasting three days, but from which the settlers did not flinch, not even Gideon Spilett, who, as the sailor said, would end by making a 'real good castaway.'

The blubber, cut in parallel slices of two feet and a half in thickness, then divided into pieces which might weigh about a thousand pounds each, was melted down in large earthen pots brought to the spot, for they did not wish to taint the environs of Granite House, and in this fusion it lost nearly a third of its weight.

But there was an immense quantity of it; the tongue alone yielded six thousand pounds of oil, and the lower lip four thousand. Then, besides the fat, which would insure for a long time a store of stearine and glycerine, there were still the bones, for which a use could doubtless be found, although there were neither umbrellas nor stays used at Granite House. The upper part of the mouth of the cetacean was, indeed, provided on both sides with eight hundred horny blades, very elastic, of a fibrous texture, and fringed at the edge like great combs, at which the teeth, six feet long, served to retain the thousands of animalculae, little fish, and molluscs, on which the whale fed.

The operation finished, to the great satisfaction of the operators, the remains of the animal were left to the birds, who would soon make every vestige of it disappear, and their usual daily occupations were resumed by the inmates of Granite House.

However, before returning to the dockyard, Cyrus Harding conceived the idea of fabricating certain machines, which greatly excited the curiosity of his companions. He took a dozen of the whale's bones, cut them into six equal parts, and sharpened their ends.

'This machine is not my own invention, and it is frequently employed by the Aleutian hunters in Russian America. You see these bones, my friends; well, when it freezes, I will bend them, and then wet them with water till they are entirely covered with ice, which will keep them bent, and I will strew them on the snow, having previously covered them with fat. Now, what will happen if a hungry animal swallows one of these baits? Why, the heat of his stomach will melt the ice, and the bone, springing straight, will pierce him with its sharp points.'

'Well! I do call that ingenious!' said Pencroft.

'And it will spare the powder and shot,' rejoined Cyrus Harding.

'That will be better than traps!' added Neb.

In the meanwhile the boat-building progressed, and towards the end of the month half the planking was completed. It could already be seen that her shape was excellent, and that she would sail well.

Pencroft worked with unparalleled ardour, and only a sturdy frame could have borne such fatigue; but his companions were preparing in secret a reward for his labours, and on the 31st of May he was to meet with one of the greatest joys of his life.

On that day, after dinner, just as he was about to leave the table, Pencroft felt a hand on his shoulder.

It was the hand of Gideon Spilett, who said,—

'One moment, Master Pencroft, you mustn't sneak off like that! You've forgotten your dessert.'

'Thank you, Mr. Spilett,' replied the sailor, 'I am going back to my work.'

'Well, a cup of coffee, my friend?'

'Nothing more.'

'A pipe, then?'

Pencroft jumped up, and his great good-natured face grew pale when he saw the reporter presenting him with a ready-filled pipe, and Herbert with a glowing coal.

The sailor endeavoured to speak, but could not get out a word; so, seizing the pipe, he carried it to his lips, then applying the coal, he drew five or six great whiffs. A fragrant blue cloud soon arose, and from its depths a voice was heard repeating excitedly,—

'Tobacco! real tobacco!'

'Yes, Pencroft,' returned Cyrus Harding, 'and very good tobacco too!'

'O, divine Providence; sacred Author of all things!' cried the sailor. 'Nothing more is now wanting to our island.'

And Pencroft smoked, and smoked, and smoked.

'And who made this discovery?' he asked at length. 'You, Herbert, no doubt?'

'No, Pencroft, it was Mr. Spilett.'

'Mr. Spilett!' exclaimed the sailor, seizing the reporter, and clasping him to his breast with such a squeeze that he had never felt anything like it before.

'Oh Pencroft,' said Spilett, recovering his breath at last, 'a truce for one moment. You must share your gratitude with Herbert, who recognized the plant, with Cyrus, who prepared it, and with Neb, who took a great deal of trouble to keep our secret.'

'Well, my friends, I will repay you some day,' replied the sailor. 'Now we are friends for life.'

Chapter 11

Winter arrived with the month of June, which is the December of the northern zones, and the great business was the making of warm and solid clothing.

The musmons in the corral had been stripped of their wool, and this precious textile material was now to be transformed into stuff.

Of course Cyrus Harding, having at his disposal neither carders, combers, polishers, stretchers, twisters, mule-jenny, nor self-acting machine to spin the wool, nor loom to weave it, was obliged to proceed in a simpler way, so as to do without spinning and weaving. And indeed he proposed to make use of the property which the filaments of wool possess when subjected to a powerful pressure of mixing together, and of manufacturing by this simple process the material called felt. This felt could then be obtained by a simple operation which, if it diminished the flexibility of the stuff, increased its power of retaining heat in proportion. Now the wool furnished by the musmons was composed of very short hairs, and was in a good condition to be felted.

The engineer, aided by his companions, including Pencroft, who was once more obliged to leave his boat, commenced the preliminary operations, the subject of which was to rid the wool of that fat and oily substance with which it is impregnated, and which is called grease. This cleaning was done in vats filled with water, which was maintained at the temperature of seventy degrees, and in which the wool was soaked for four-and-twenty hours; it was then thoroughly washed in baths of soda, and, when sufficiently dried by pressure, it was in a state to be compressed, that is to say, to produce a solid material, rough, no doubt, and such as would have no value in a manufacturing centre of Europe or America, but which would be highly esteemed in the Lincoln Island markets.

This sort of material must have been known from the most ancient times, and, in fact, the first woollen stuffs were manufactured by the process which Harding was now about to employ. Where Harding's engineering qualifications now came into play was in the construction of the machine for pressing the wool; for he knew how to turn ingeniously to profit the mechanical force, hitherto unused, which the waterfall on the beach possessed to move a fulling-mill.

Nothing could be more rudimentary. The wool was placed in troughs, and upon it fell in turns heavy wooden mallets; such was the machine in question, and such it had been for centuries until the time when the mallets were replaced by cylinders of compression, and the material was no longer subjected to beating, but to regular rolling.

The operation, ably directed by Cyrus Harding, was a complete success. The wool, previously impregnated with a solution of soap, intended on the one hand to facilitate the interlacing, the compression, and the softening of the wool, and on the other to prevent its diminution by the beating, issued from the mill in the shape of thick felt cloth. The roughnesses with which the staple of wool is naturally filled were so thoroughly entangled and interlaced together that a material was formed equally suitable either for garments or bedclothes. It was certainly neither merino, muslin, cashmere, rep, satin, alpaca, cloth, nor flannel. It was 'Lincolnian felt,' and Lincoln Island possessed yet another manufacture. The colonists had now warm garments and thick bedclothes, and they could without fear await the approach of the winter of 1866-67.

The severe cold began to be felt about the 20th of June, and, to his great regret, Pencroft was obliged to suspend his boat-building, which he hoped to finish in time for next spring.

The sailor's great idea was to make a voyage of discovery to Tabor Island, although Harding could not approve of a voyage simply for curiosity's sake, for there was evidently nothing to be found on this desert and almost arid rock. A voyage of a hundred and fifty miles in a comparatively small vessel, over unknown seas, could not but cause him some anxiety. Suppose that their vessel, once out at sea, should be unable to reach Tabor Island, and could not return to Lincoln Island, what would become of her in the midst of the Pacific, so fruitful of disasters?

Harding often talked over this project with Pencroft, and he found him strangely bent upon undertaking this voyage, for which determination he himself could give no sufficient reason.

'Now,' said the engineer one day to him, 'I must observe, my friend, that after having said so much, in praise of Lincoln Island, after having spoken so often of the sorrow you would feel if you were obliged to forsake it, you are the first to wish to leave it.'

'Only to leave it for a few days,' replied Pencroft, 'only for a few days, captain. Time to go and come back, and see what that islet is like!'

'But it is not nearly as good as Lincoln Island.'

'I know that beforehand.'

'Then why venture there?'

'To know what is going on in Tabor Island.'

'But nothing is going on there; nothing could happen there.'

'Who knows?'

'And if you are caught in a hurricane?'

'There is no fear of that in the fine season,' replied Pencroft. 'But, captain, as we must provide against everything, I shall ask your permission to take Herbert only with me on this voyage.'

'Pencroft,' replied the engineer, placing his hand on the sailor's shoulder, 'if any misfortune happens to you, or to this lad, whom chance has made our child, do you think we could ever cease to blame ourselves?'

'Captain Harding,' replied Pencroft, with unshaken confidence, 'we shall not cause you that sorrow. Besides, we will speak further of this voyage, when the time comes to make it. And I fancy, when you have seen our tight- rigged little craft, when you have observed how she behaves at sea, when we sail round our island, for we will do so together—I fancy, I say, that you will no longer hesitate to let me go. I don't conceal from you that your boat will be a masterpiece.'

'Say 'our' boat, at least, Pencroft,' replied the engineer, disarmed for the moment. The conversation ended thus, to be resumed later on, without convincing either the sailor or the engineer.

The first snow fell towards the end of the month of June. The corral had previously been largely supplied with stores, so that daily visits to it were not requisite; but it was decided that more than a week should never be allowed to pass without someone going to it.

Traps were again set, and the machines manufactured by Harding were tried. The bent whalebones, imprisoned in a case of ice, and covered with a thick outer layer of fat, were placed on the border of the forest at a spot where animals usually passed on their way to the lake.

To the engineer's great satisfaction, this invention, copied from the Aleutian fishermen, succeeded perfectly. A dozen foxes, a few wild boars, and even a jaguar, were taken in this way, the animals being found dead, their stomachs pierced by the unbent bones.

An incident must here be related, not only as interesting in itself, but because it was the first attempt made by the colonists to communicate with the rest of mankind.

Gideon Spilett had already several times pondered whether to throw into the sea a letter enclosed in a bottle, which currents might perhaps carry to an inhabited coast, or to confide it to pigeons.

But how could it be seriously hoped that either pigeons or bottles could cross the distance of twelve hundred miles which separated the island from any inhabited land? It would have been pure folly.

But on the 30th of June the capture was effected, not without difficulty, of an albatross, which a shot from Herbert's gun had slightly wounded in the foot. It was a magnificent bird, measuring ten feet from wing to wing, and which could traverse seas as wide as the Pacific.

Herbert would have liked to keep this superb bird, as its wound would soon heal, and he thought he could tame it; but Spilett explained to him that they should not neglect this opportunity of attempting to communicate by this messenger with the lands of the Pacific; for if the albatross had come from some inhabited region, there was no doubt but that it would return there so soon as it was set free.

Perhaps in his heart Gideon Spilett, in whom the journalist sometimes came to the surface, was not sorry to have the opportunity of sending forth to take its chance an exciting article relating the adventures of the settlers in Lincoln Island. What a success for the authorized reporter of the New York Herald, and for the number which should contain the article, if it should ever reach the address of its editor, the Honourable James Bennett!

Gideon Spilett then wrote out a concise account, which was placed in a strong waterproof bag, with an earnest request to whoever might find it to forward it to the office of the New York Herald. This little bag was fastened to the neck of the albatross, and not to its foot, for these birds are in the habit of resting on the surface of the sea; then liberty was given to this swift courier of the air, and it was not without some emotion that the colonists watched it disappear in the misty west.

'Where is he going to?' asked Pencroft.

'Towards New Zealand,' replied Herbert.

'A good voyage to you,' shouted the sailor, who himself did not expect any great result from this mode of correspondence.

With the winter, work had been resumed in the interior of Granite House, mending clothes and different occupations, among others making the sails for their vessel, which were cut from the inexhaustible balloon-case.

During the month of July the cold was intense, but there was no lack of either wood or coal. Cyrus Harding had established a second fireplace in the dining room, and there the long winter evenings were spent. Talking while they worked, reading when the hands remained idle, the time passed with profit to all.

It was real enjoyment to the settlers when in their room, well lighted with candles, well warmed with coal, after a good dinner, elderberry coffee smoking in the cups, the pipes giving forth an odoriferous smoke, they could hear the storm howling without. Their comfort would have been complete, if complete comfort could ever exist for those who are far from their fellow-creatures, and without any means of communication with them. They often talked of their country, of the friends whom they had left, of the grandeur of the American Republic, whose influence could not but increase; and Cyrus Harding, who had been much mixed up with the affairs of the Union, greatly interested his auditors by his recitals, his views, and his prognostics.

It chanced one day that Spilett was led to say—

'But now, my dear Cyrus, all this industrial and commercial movement to which you predict a continual advance, does it not run the danger of being sooner or later completely stopped?'

'Stopped! And by what?'

'By the want of coal, which may justly be called the most precious of minerals.'

'Yes, the most precious indeed,' replied the engineer; 'and it would seem that nature wished to prove that it was so by making the diamond, which is simply pure carbon crystallized.'

'You don't mean to say, captain,' interrupted Pencroft, 'that we burn diamonds in our stoves in the shape of coal?'

'No, my friend,' replied Harding.

'However,' resumed Gideon Spilett, 'you do not deny that some day the coal will be entirely consumed?'

'Oh! the veins of coal are still considerable, and the hundred thousand miners who annually extract from them a hundred millions of hundredweights have not nearly exhausted them.'

'With the increasing consumption of coal,' replied Gideon Spilett, 'it can be foreseen that the hundred thousand workmen will soon become two hundred thousand, and that the rate of extraction will be doubled.'

'Doubtless; but after the European mines, which will be soon worked more thoroughly with new machines, the American and Australian mines will for a long time yet provide for the consumption in trade.'

'For how long a time?' asked the reporter.

'For at least two hundred and fifty or three hundred years.'

'That is reassuring for us, but a bad lookout for our great-grandchildren!' observed Pencroft.

'They will discover something else,' said Herbert.

'It is to be hoped so,' answered Spilett, 'for without coal there would be no machinery, and without machinery there would be no railways, no steamers, no manufactories, nothing of that which is indispensable to modern civilization!'

'But what will they find?' asked Pencroft. 'Can you guess, captain?'

'Nearly, my friend.'

'And what will they burn instead of coal?'

'Water,' replied Harding.

'Water!' cried Pencroft, 'water as fuel for steamers and engines! water to heat water!'

'Yes, but water decomposed into its primitive elements,' replied Cyrus Harding, 'and decomposed doubtless, by electricity, which will then have become a powerful and manageable force, for all great discoveries, by some inexplicable laws, appear to agree and become complete at the same time. Yes, my friends, I believe that water will one day be employed as fuel, that hydrogen and oxygen which constitute it, used singly or together, will furnish an inexhaustible source of heat and light, of an intensity of which coal is not capable. Some day the coalrooms of steamers and the tenders of locomotives will, instead of coal, be stored with these two condensed gases, which will burn in the furnaces with enormous calorific power. There is, therefore, nothing to fear. As long as the earth is inhabited it will supply the wants of its inhabitants, and there will be no want of either light or heat as long as the productions of the vegetable, mineral or animal kingdoms do not fail us. I believe, then, that when the deposits of coal are exhausted we shall heat and warm ourselves with water. Water will be the coal of the future.'

'I should like to see that,' observed the sailor.

'You were born too soon, Pencroft,' returned Neb, who only took part in the discussion by these words.

However, it was not Neb's speech which interrupted the conversation, but Top's barking, which broke out again with that strange intonation which had before perplexed the engineer. At the same time Top began to run round the mouth of the well, which opened at the extremity of the interior passage.

'What can Top be barking in that way for?' asked Pencroft.

'And Jup be growling like that?' added Herbert.

In fact the orang, joining the dog, gave unequivocal signs of agitation, and, singular to say, the two animals appeared more uneasy than angry.

'It is evident,' said Gideon Spilett, 'that this well is in direct communication with the sea, and that some marine animal comes from time to time to breathe at the bottom.'

'That's evident,' replied the sailor, 'and there can be no other explanation to give. Quiet there, Top!' added Pencroft, turning to the dog, 'and you, Jup, be off to your room!'

The ape and the dog were silent. Jup went off to bed, but Top remained in the room, and continued to utter low growls at intervals during the rest of the evening. There was no further talk on the subject, but the incident, however, clouded the brow of the engineer.

During the remainder of the month of July there was alternate rain and frost. The temperature was not so low as during the preceding winter, and its maximum did not exceed eight degrees Fahrenheit. But although this winter was less cold, it was more troubled by storms and squalls; the sea besides often endangered the safety of the Chimneys. At times it almost seemed as if an undercurrent raised these monstrous billows which thundered against the wall of Granite House.

When the settlers, leaning from their windows, gazed on the huge watery masses breaking beneath their eyes, they could not but admire the magnificent spectacle of the ocean in its impotent fury. The waves rebounded in dazzling foam, the beach entirely disappearing under the raging flood, and the cliff appearing to emerge from the sea itself, the spray rising to a height of more than a hundred feet.

During these storms it was difficult and even dangerous to venture out, owing to the frequently falling trees; however, the colonists never allowed a week to pass without having paid a visit to the corral. Happily, this enclosure, sheltered by the southeastern spur of Mount Franklin, did not greatly suffer from the violence of the hurricanes, which spared its trees, sheds, and palisades; but the poultry-yard on Prospect Heights, being directly exposed to the gusts of wind from the east, suffered considerable damage. The pigeon-house was twice unroofed and the paling blown down. All this required to be remade more solidly than before, for, as may be clearly seen, Lincoln Island was situated in one of the most dangerous parts of the Pacific. It really appeared as if it formed the central point of vast cyclones, which beat it perpetually as the whip does the top, only here it was the top which was motionless and the whip which moved. During the first week of the month of August the weather became more moderate, and the atmosphere recovered the calm which it appeared to have lost forever. With the calm the cold again became intense, and the thermometer fell to eight degrees Fahrenheit, below zero.

On the 3rd of August an excursion which had been talked of for several days was made into the southeastern part of the island, towards Tadorn Marsh. The hunters were tempted by the aquatic game which took up their winter quarters there. Wild duck, snipe, teal and grebe abounded there, and it was agreed that a day should be devoted to an expedition against these birds.

Not only Gideon Spilett and Herbert, but Pencroft and Neb also took part in this excursion. Cyrus Harding alone, alleging some work as an excuse, did not join them, but remained at Granite House.

The hunters proceeded in the direction of Port Balloon, in order to reach the marsh, after having promised to be back by the evening. Top and Jup accompanied them. As soon as they had passed over the Mercy Bridge, the engineer raised it and returned, intending to put into execution a project for the performance of which he wished to be alone.

Now this project was to minutely explore the interior well, the mouth of which was on a level with the passage of Granite House, and which communicated with the sea, since it formerly supplied a way to the waters of the lake.

Why did Top so often run round this opening? Why did he utter such strange barks when a sort of uneasiness seemed to draw him towards this well? Why did Jup join Top in a sort of common anxiety? Had this well branches besides the communication with the sea? Did it spread towards other parts of the island? This is what Cyrus Harding wished to know. He had resolved, therefore, to attempt the exploration of the well during the absence of his companions, and an opportunity for doing so had now presented itself.

It was easy to descend to the bottom of the well by employing the rope ladder which had not been used since the establishment of the lift. The engineer drew the ladder to the hole, the diameter of which measured nearly six feet, and allowed it to unroll itself after having securely fastened its upper extremity. Then, having lighted a lantern, taken a revolver, and placed a cutlass in his belt, he began the descent.

The sides were everywhere entire; but points of rock jutted out here and there, and by means of these points it would have been quite possible for an active creature to climb to the mouth of the well.

The engineer remarked this; but although he carefully examined these points by the light of his lantern, he could find no impression, no fracture which could give any reason to suppose that they had either recently or at any former time been used as a staircase. Cyrus Harding descended deeper, throwing the light of his lantern on all sides.

He saw nothing suspicious.

When the engineer had reached the last rounds he came upon the water, which was then perfectly calm. Neither at its level nor in any other part of the well, did any passage open, which could lead to the interior of the cliff. The wall which Harding struck with the hilt of his cutlass sounded solid. It was compact granite, through which no living being could force a way. To arrive at the bottom of the well and then climb up to its mouth it was necessary to pass through the channel under the rocky subsoil of the beach, which placed it in communication with the sea, and this was only possible for marine animals. As to the question of knowing where this channel ended, at what point of the shore, and at what depth beneath the water, it could not be answered.

Then Cyrus Harding, having ended his survey, re-ascended, drew up the ladder, covered the mouth of the well, and returned thoughtfully to the diningroom, saying to himself,—

'I have seen nothing, and yet there is something there!'

Chapter 12

In the evening the hunters returned, having enjoyed good sport, and being literally loaded with game; indeed, they had as much as four men could possibly carry. Top wore a necklace of teal and Jup wreaths of snipe round his body.

'Here, master,' cried Neb; 'here's something to employ our time! Preserved and made into pies we shall have a welcome store! But I must have some one to help me. I count on you, Pencroft.'

'No, Neb,' replied the sailor; 'I have the rigging of the vessel to finish and to look after, and you will have to do without me.'

'And you, Mr. Herbert?'

'I must go to the corral tomorrow, Neb,' replied the lad.

'It will be you then, Mr. Spilett, who will help me?'

'To oblige you, Neb, I will,' replied the reporter; 'but I warn you that if you disclose your receipts to me, I shall publish them.'

'Whenever you like, Mr. Spilett,' replied Neb; 'whenever you like.'

And so the next day Gideon Spilett became Neb's assistant and was installed in his culinary laboratory. The engineer had previously made known to him the result of the exploration which he had made the day before, and on this point the reporter shared Harding's opinion, that although he had found nothing, a secret still remained to be discovered!

The frost continued for another week, and the settlers did not leave Granite House unless to look after the poultry-yard. The dwelling was filled with appetizing odours, which were emitted from the learned manipulation of Neb and the reporter. But all the results of the chase were not made into preserved provisions; and as the game kept perfectly in the intense cold, wild duck and other fowl were eaten fresh, and declared superior to all other aquatic birds in the known world.

During this week, Pencroft, aided by Herbert, who handled the sailmaker's needle with much skill, worked with such energy that the sails of the vessel were finished. There was no want of cordage. Thanks to the rigging which had been discovered with the case of the balloon, the ropes and cables from the net were all of good quality, and the sailor turned them all to account. To the sails were attached strong bolt ropes, and there still remained enough from which to make the halyards, shrouds, and sheets, etc. The blocks were manufactured by Cyrus Harding under Pencroft's directions by means of the turning lathe. It therefore happened that the rigging was entirely prepared before the vessel was finished. Pencroft also manufactured a flag, that flag so dear to every true American, containing the stars and stripes of their glorious Union. The colours for it were supplied from certain plants used in dyeing, and which were very abundant in the island; only to the thirty-seven stars, representing the thirty- seven States of the Union, which shine on the American flag, the sailor added a thirty-eighth, the star of 'the State of Lincoln,' for he considered his island as already united to the great republic. 'And,' said he, 'it is so already in heart, if not in deed!'

In the meantime, the flag was hoisted at the central window of Granite House, and the settlers saluted it with three cheers.

The cold season was now almost at an end, and it appeared as if this second winter was to pass without any unusual occurrence, when on the night of the 11th of August, the plateau of Prospect Heights was menaced with complete destruction.

After a busy day the colonists were sleeping soundly, when towards four o'clock in the morning they were suddenly awakened by Top's barking.

The dog was not this time barking near the mouth of the well, but at the threshold of the door, at which he was scratching as if he wished to burst it open. Jup was also uttering piercing cries.

'Hello, Top!' cried Neb, who was the first awake. But the dog continued to bark more furiously than ever.

'What's the matter now?' asked Harding.

And all dressing in haste rushed to the windows, which they opened.

Beneath their eyes was spread a sheet of snow which looked gray in the dim light. The settlers could see nothing, but they heard a singular yelping noise away in the darkness. It was evident that the beach had been invaded by a number of animals which could not be seen.

'What are they?' cried Pencroft.

'Wolves, jaguars, or apes?' replied Neb.

'They have nearly reached the plateau,' said the reporter.

'And our poultry-yard,' exclaimed Herbert, 'and our garden!'

'Where can they have crossed?' asked Pencroft.

'They must have crossed the bridge on the shore,' replied the engineer, 'which one of us must have forgotten to close.'

'True,' said Spilett, 'I remember having left it open.'

'A fine job you have made of it, Mr. Spilett,' cried the sailor.

'What is done cannot be undone,' replied Cyrus Harding. 'We must consult what it will now be best to do.'

Such were the questions and answers which were rapidly exchanged between Harding and his companions. It was certain that the bridge had been crossed, that the shore had been invaded by animals, and that whatever they might be they could by ascending the left bank of the Mercy reach Prospect Heights. They must therefore be advanced against quickly and fought with if necessary.

'But what are these beasts?' was asked a second time, as the yelpings were again heard more loudly than before. These yelps made Herbert start, and he remembered having heard them before during his first visit to the sources of the Red Creek.

'They are colpeo foxes!' he exclaimed.

'Forward!' shouted the sailor.

And all arming themselves with hatchets, carbines, and revolvers, threw themselves into the lift and soon set foot on the shore.

Colpeos are dangerous animals when in great numbers and irritated by hunger, nevertheless the colonists did not hesitate to throw themselves into the midst of the troop, and their first shots vividly lighting up the darkness made their assailants draw back.

The chief thing was to hinder these plunderers from reaching the plateau, for the garden and the poultry-yard would then have been at their mercy, and immense, perhaps irreparable mischief, would inevitably be the result, especially with regard to the cornified. But as the invasion of the plateau could only be made by the left bank of the Mercy, it was sufficient to oppose the colpeos on the narrow bank between the river and the cliff of granite.

This was plain to all, and, by Cyrus Harding's orders, they reached the spot indicated by him, while the colpeos rushed fiercely through the gloom. Harding, Gideon Spilett, Herbert, Pencroft and Neb posted themselves in impregnable line. Top, his formidable jaws open, preceded the colonists, and he was followed by Jup, armed with knotty cudgel, which he brandished like a club.

The night was extremely dark, it was only by the flashes from the revolvers as each person fired that they could see their assailants, who were at least a hundred in number, and whose eyes were glowing like hot coals.

'They must not pass!' shouted Pencroft.

'They shall not pass!' returned the engineer.

But if they did not pass it was not for want of having attempted it. Those in the rear pushed on the foremost assailants, and it was an incessant struggle with revolvers and hatchets. Several colpeos already lay dead on the ground, but their number did not appear to diminish, and it might have been supposed that reinforcements were continually arriving over the bridge.

The colonists were soon obliged to fight at close quarters, not without receiving some wounds, though happily very slight ones. Herbert had, with a shot from his revolver, rescued Neb, on whose back a colpeo had sprung like a tiger cat. Top fought with actual fury, flying at the throats of the foxes and strangling them instantaneously. Jup wielded his weapon valiantly, and it was in vain that they endeavoured to keep him in the rear. Endowed doubtless with sight which enabled him to pierce the obscurity, he was always in the thick of the fight uttering from time to time—a sharp hissing sound, which was with him the sign of great rejoicing.

At one moment he advanced so far, that by the light from a revolver he was seen surrounded by five or six large colpeos, with whom he was coping with great coolness.

However, the struggle was ended at last, and victory was on the side of the settlers, but not until they had fought for two long hours! The first signs of the approach of day doubtless determined the retreat of their assailants, who scampered away towards the North, passing over the bridge, which Neb ran immediately to raise. When day had sufficiently lighted up the field of battle, the settlers counted as many as fifty dead bodies scattered about on the shore.

'And Jup!' cried Pencroft; 'where is Jup?' Jup had disappeared. His friend Neb called him, and for the first time Jup did not reply to his friend's call.

Everyone set out in search of Jup, trembling lest he should be found among the slain; they cleared the place of the bodies which stained the snow with their blood. Jup was found in the midst of a heap of colpeos whose broken jaws and crushed bodies showed that they had to do with the terrible club of the intrepid animal.

Poor Jup still held in his hand the stump of his broken cudgel, but deprived of his weapon he had been overpowered by numbers, and his chest was covered with severe wounds.

'He is living,' cried Neb, who was bending over him.

'And we will save him,' replied the sailor. 'We will nurse him as if he was one of ourselves.'

It appeared as if Jup understood, for he leaned his head on Pencroft's shoulder as if to thank him. The sailor was wounded himself, but his wound was insignificant, as were those of his companions; for thanks to their firearms they had been almost always able to keep their assailants at a distance. It was therefore only the orang whose condition was serious.

Jup, carried by Neb and Pencroft, was placed in the lift, and only a slight moan now and then escaped his lips. He was gently drawn up to Granite House. There he was laid on a mattress taken from one of the beds, and his wounds were bathed with the greatest care. It did not appear that any vital part had been reached, but Jup was very weak from loss of blood, and a high fever soon set in after his wounds had been dressed. He was laid down, strict diet was imposed, 'just like a real person,' as Neb said, and they made him swallow several cups of a cooling drink, for which the ingredients were supplied from the vegetable medicine chest of Granite House. Jup was at first restless, but his breathing gradually became more regular, and he was left sleeping quietly. From time to time Top, walking on tiptoe, as one might say, came to visit his friend, and seemed to approve of all the care that had been taken of him. One of Jup's hands hung over the side of his bed, and Top licked it with a sympathizing air.

They employed the day in interring the dead, who were dragged to the forest of the Far West, and there buried deep.

This attack, which might have had such serious consequences, was a lesson to the settlers, who from this time never went to bed until one of their number had made sure that all the bridges were raised, and that no invasion was possible.

However, Jup, after having given them serious anxiety for several days, began to recover. His constitution brought him through, the fever gradually subsided, and Gideon Spilett, who was a bit of a doctor, pronounced him quite out of danger. On the 16th of August, Jup began to eat. Neb made him nice little sweet dishes, which the invalid devoured with great relish, for if he had a pet failing it was that of being somewhat of a gourmend, and Neb had never done anything to cure him of this fault.

'What would you have?' said he to Gideon Spilett, who sometimes expostulated with him for spoiling the ape. 'Poor Jup has no other pleasure than that of the palate, and I am only too glad to be able to reward his services in this way!'

Ten days after taking to his bed, on the 21st of August, Master Jup arose. His wounds were healed, and it was evident that he would not be long in regaining his usual strength and agility. Like all convalescents, he was tremendously hungry, and the reporter allowed him to eat as much as he liked, for he trusted to that instinct, which is too often wanting in reasoning beings, to keep the orang from any excess. Neb was delighted to see his pupil's appetite returning.

'Eat away, my Jup,' said he, 'and don't spare anything; you have shed your blood for us, and it is the least I can do to make you strong again!'

On the 25th of August Neb's voice was heard calling to his companions.

'Captain, Mr. Spilett, Mr. Herbert, Pencroft, come! come!'

The colonists, who were together in the dining room, rose at Neb's call, who was then in Jup's room.

'What's the matter?' asked the reporter.

'Look,' replied Neb, with a shout of laughter. And what did they see? Master Jup smoking calmly and seriously, sitting crosslegged like a Turk at the entrance to Granite House!

'My pipe,' cried Pencroft. 'He has taken my pipe! Hello, my honest Jup, I make you a present of it! Smoke away, old boy, smoke away!'

And Jup gravely puffed out clouds of smoke which seemed to give him great satisfaction. Harding did not appear to be much astonished at this incident, and he cited several examples of tame apes, to whom the use of tobacco had become quite familiar.

But from this day Master Jup had a pipe of his own, the sailor's ex-pipe, which was hung in his room near his store of tobacco. He filled it himself, lighted it with a glowing coal, and appeared to be the happiest of quadrumana. It may readily be understood that this similarity of tastes of Jup and Pencroft served to tighten the bonds of friendship which already existed between the honest ape and the worthy sailor.

'Perhaps he is really a man,' said Pencroft sometimes to Neb. 'Should you be surprised to hear him beginning to speak to us some day?'

'My word, no,' replied Neb. 'What astonishes me is that he hasn't spoken to us before, for now he wants nothing but speech!'

'It would amuse me all the same,' resumed the sailor, 'if some fine day he said to me, 'Suppose we change pipes, Pencroft.'

'Yes,' replied Neb, 'what a pity he was born dumb!'

With the month of September the winter ended, and the works were again eagerly commenced. The building of the vessel advanced rapidly, she was already completely decked over, and all the inside parts of the hull were firmly united with ribs bent by means of steam, which answered all the purposes of a mould.

As there was no want of wood, Pencroft proposed to the engineer to give a double lining to the hull, to insure the strength of the vessel.

Harding, not knowing what the future might have in store for them, approved the sailor's idea of making the craft as strong as possible. The interior and deck of the vessel was entirely finished towards the 15th of September. For calking the seams they made oakum of dry seaweed, which was hammered in between the planks; then these seams were covered with boiling tar, which was obtained in great abundance from the pines in the forest.

The management of the vessel was very simple. She had from the first been ballasted with heavy blocks of granite walled up, in a bed of lime, twelve thousand pounds of which they stowed away.

A deck was placed over this ballast, and the interior was divided into two cabins; two benches extended along them and served also as lockers. The foot of the mast supported the partition which separated the two cabins, which were reached by two hatchways let into the deck.

Pencroft had no trouble in finding a tree suitable for the mast. He chose a straight young fir, with no knots, and which he had only to square at the step, and round off at the top. The ironwork of the mast, the rudder and the hull had been roughly but strongly forged at the Chimneys. Lastly, yards, masts, boom, spars, oars, etc., were all furnished by the first week in October, and it was agreed that a trial trip should be taken round the island, so as to ascertain how the vessel would behave at sea, and how far they might depend upon her.

During all this time the necessary works had not been neglected. The corral was enlarged, for the flock of musmons and goats had been increased by a number of young ones, who had to be housed and fed. The colonists had paid visits also to the oyster bed, the warren, the coal and iron mines, and to the till then unexplored districts of the Far West forest, which abounded in game. Certain indigenous plants were discovered, and those fit for immediate use contributed to vary the vegetable stores of Granite House.

They were a species of ficoide, some similar to those of the Cape, with eatable fleshy leaves, others bearing seeds containing a sort of flour.

On the 10th of October the vessel was launched. Pencroft was radiant with joy, the operation was perfectly successful; the boat completely rigged, having been pushed on rollers to the water's edge, was floated by the rising tide, amid the cheers of the colonists, particularly of Pencroft, who showed no modesty on this occasion. Besides his importance was to last beyond the finishing of the vessel, since, after having built her, he was to command her. The grade of captain was bestowed upon him with the approbation of all. To satisfy Captain Pencroft, it was now necessary to give a name to the vessel, and, after many propositions had been discussed, the votes were all in favour of the 'Bonadventure.' As soon as the 'Bonadventure' had been lifted by the rising tide, it was seen that she lay evenly in the water, and would be easily navigated. However, the trial trip was to be made that very day, by an excursion off the coast. The weather was fine, the breeze fresh, and the sea smooth, especially towards the south coast, for the wind was blowing from the northwest.

'All hands on board,' shouted Pencroft; but breakfast was first necessary, and it was thought best to take provisions on board, in the event of their excursion being prolonged until the evening.

Cyrus Harding was equally anxious to try the vessel, the model of which had originated with him, although on the sailor's advice he had altered some parts of it, but he did not share Pencroft's confidence in her, and as the latter had not again spoken of the voyage to Tabor Island, Harding hoped he had given it up. He would have indeed great reluctance in letting two or three of his companions venture so far in so small a boat, which was not of more than fifteen tons' burden.

At half-past ten everybody was on hoard, even Top and Jup, and Herbert weighed the anchor, which was fast in the sand near the mouth of the Mercy. The sail was hoisted, the Lincolnian flag floated from the masthead, and the 'Bonadventure,' steered by Pencroft, stood out to sea.

The wind blowing out of Union Bay she ran before it, and thus showed her owners, much to their satisfaction, that she possessed a remarkably fast pair of heels, according to Pencroft's mode of speaking. After having doubled Flotsam Point and Claw Cape, the captain kept her close hauled, so as to sail along the southern coast of the island, when it was found she sailed admirably within five points of the wind. All hands were enchanted, they had a good vessel, which, in case of need, would be of great service to them, and with fine weather and a fresh breeze the voyage promised to be charming.

Pencroft now stood off the shore, three or four miles across from Port Balloon. The island then appeared in all its extent and under a new aspect, with the varied panorama of its shore from Claw Cape to Reptile End, the forests in which dark firs contrasted with the young foliage of other trees and overlooked the whole, and Mount Franklin whose lofty head was still whitened with snow.

'How beautiful it is!' cried Herbert.

'Yes, our island is beautiful and good,' replied Pencroft. 'I love it as I loved my poor mother. It received us poor and destitute, and now what is wanting to us five fellows who fell on it from the sky?'

'Nothing,' replied Neb; 'nothing, captain.'

And the two brave men gave three tremendous cheers in honour of their island!

During all this time Gideon Spilett, leaning against the mast, sketched the panorama which was developed before his eyes.

Cyrus Harding gazed on it in silence.

'Well, Captain Harding,' asked Pencroft, 'what do you think of our vessel?'

'She appears to behave well,' replied the engineer.

'Good! And do you think now that she could undertake a voyage of some extent?'

'What voyage, Pencroft?'

'One to Tabor Island, for instance.'

'My friend,' replied Harding, 'I think that in any pressing emergency we need not hesitate to trust ourselves to the 'Bonadventure' even for a longer voyage; but you know I should see you set off to Tabor Island with great uneasiness, since nothing obliges you to go there.'

'One likes to know one's neighbours,' returned the sailor, who was obstinate in his idea. 'Tabor Island is our neighbour, and the only one! Politeness requires us to go at least to pay a visit.'

'By Jove,' said Spilett, 'our friend Pencroft has become very particular about the proprieties all at once!'

'I am not particular about anything at all,' retorted the sailor, who was rather vexed by the engineer's opposition, but who did not wish to cause him anxiety.

'Consider, Pencroft,' resumed Harding, 'you cannot go alone to Tabor Island.'

'One companion will be enough for me.

'Even so,' replied the engineer, 'you will risk depriving the colony of Lincoln Island of two settlers out of five.'

'Out of six,' answered Pencroft; 'you forget Jup.'

'Out of seven,' added Neb; 'Top is quite worth another.'

'There is no risk at all in it, captain,' replied Pencroft.

'That is possible, Pencroft; but I repeat it is to expose ourselves uselessly.'

The obstinate sailor did not reply, and let the conversation drop, quite determined to resume it again. But he did not suspect that an incident would come to his aid and change into an act of humanity that which was at first only a doubtful whim.

After standing off the shore the 'Bonadventure' again approached it in the direction of Port Balloon. It was important to ascertain the channels between the sandbanks and reefs, that buoys might be laid down since this little creek was to be the harbour.

They were not more than half a mile from the coast, and it was necessary to tack to beat against the wind. The 'Bonadventure' was then going at a very moderate rate, as the breeze, partly intercepted by the high land, scarcely swelled her sails, and the sea, smooth as glass, was only rippled now and then by passing gusts.

Herbert had stationed himself in the bows that he might indicate the course to be followed among the channels, when all at once he shouted,—

'Luff, Pencroft, luff!'

'What's the matter,' replied the sailor; 'a rock?'

'No—wait,' said Herbert; 'I don't quite see. Luff again—right—now.'

So saying, Herbert, leaning over the side, plunged his arm into the water, and pulled it out, exclaiming,—

'A bottle!'

He held in his hand a corked bottle which he had just seized a few cables' length from the shore.

Cyrus Harding took the bottle. Without uttering a single word he drew the cork, and took from it a damp paper, on which were written these words:—

'Castaway.... Tabor island: 153°W. long., 37° 11' S. lat.'

Chapter 13

'A castaway!' exclaimed Pencroft; 'left on this Tabor Island not two hundred miles from us! Ah, Captain Harding, you won't now oppose my going.'

'No, Pencroft,' replied Cyrus Harding; 'and you shall set out as soon as possible.'

'Tomorrow?'

'Tomorrow!'

The engineer still held in his hand the paper which he had taken from the bottle. He contemplated it for some instants, then resumed,

'From this document, my friends, from the way in which it is worded, we may conclude this: first, that the castaway on Tabor Island is a man possessing a considerable knowledge of navigation, since he gives the latitude and longitude of the island exactly as we ourselves found it, and to a second of approximation; secondly, that he is either English or American, as the document is written in the English language.'

'That is perfectly logical,' answered Spilett; 'and the presence of this castaway explains the arrival of the case on the shores of our island. There must have been a wreck, since there is a castaway. As to the latter, whoever he may be, it is lucky for him that Pencroft thought of building this boat and of trying her this very day, for a day later and this bottle might have been broken on the rocks.'

'Indeed,' said Herbert, 'it is a fortunate chance that the 'Bonadventure' passed exactly where the bottle was still floating!'

'Does not this appear strange to you?' asked Harding of Pencroft.

'It appears fortunate, that's all,' answered the sailor. 'Do you see anything extraordinary in it, captain? The bottle must go somewhere, and why not here as well as anywhere else?'

'Perhaps you are right, Pencroft,' replied the engineer; 'and yet—'

'But,' observed Herbert, 'there's nothing to prove that this bottle has been floating long in the sea.'

'Nothing,' replied Gideon Spilett, 'and the document appears even to have been recently written. What do you think about it, Cyrus?'

During this conversation Pencroft had not remained inactive. He had put the vessel about, and the 'Bonadventure,' all sails set, was running rapidly towards Claw Cape.

Every one was thinking of the castaway on Tabor Island. Should they be in time to save him? This was a great event in the life of the colonists! They themselves were but castaways, but it was to be feared that another might not have been so fortunate, and their duty was to go to his succour.

Claw Cape was doubled, and about four o'clock the 'Bonadventure' dropped her anchor at the mouth of the Mercy.

That same evening the arrangements for the new expedition were made. It appeared best that Pencroft and Herbert, who knew how to work the vessel, should undertake the voyage alone. By setting out the next day, the 10th of October, they would arrive on the 13th, for with the present wind it would not take more than forty-eight hours to make this passage of a hundred and fifty miles. One day in the island, three or four to return, they might hope therefore that on the 17th they would again reach Lincoln Island. The weather was fine, the barometer was rising, the wind appeared settled, everything then was in favour of these brave men whom an act of humanity was taking far from their island.

Thus it had been agreed that Cyrus Harding, Neb, and Gideon Spilett should remain at Granite House, but an objection was raised, and Spilett, who had not forgotten his business as reporter to the New York Herald, having declared that he would go by swimming rather than lose such an opportunity, he was admitted to take a part in the voyage.

The evening was occupied in transporting on board the 'Bonadventure,' articles of bedding, utensils, arms, ammunition, a compass, provisions for a week; this being rapidly done, the colonists ascended to Granite House.

The next day, at five o'clock in the morning, the farewells were said, not without some emotion on both sides, and Pencroft setting sail made towards Claw Cape, which had to be doubled in order to proceed to the southwest.

The 'Bonadventure' was already a quarter of a mile from the coast when the passengers perceived on the heights of Granite House two men waving their farewells; they were Cyrus Harding and Neb.

'Our friends,' exclaimed Spilett, 'this is our first separation in fifteen months.'

Pencroft, the reporter and Herbert waved in return, and Granite House soon disappeared behind the high rocks of the Cape.

During the first part of the day the 'Bonadventure' was still in sight of the southern coast of Lincoln Island, which soon appeared just like a green basket, with Mount Franklin rising from the centre. The heights, diminished by distance, did not present an appearance likely to tempt vessels to touch there. Reptile End was passed in about an hour, though at a distance of about ten miles.

At this distance it was no longer possible to distinguish anything of the Western Coast, which stretched away to the ridges of Mount Franklin, and three hours after the last of Lincoln Island sank below the horizon.

The 'Bonadventure' behaved capitally. Bounding over the waves she proceeded rapidly on her course. Pencroft had hoisted the foresail, and steering by the compass followed a rectilinear direction. From time to time Herbert relieved him at the helm, and the lad's hand was so firm that the sailor had not a point to find fault with.

Gideon Spilett chatted sometimes with one, sometimes with the other, if wanted he lent a hand with the ropes, and Captain Pencroft was perfectly satisfied with his crew.

In the evening the crescent moon, which would not be in its first quarter until the 16th, appeared in the twilight and soon set again. The night was dark but starry, and the next day again promised to be fine.

Pencroft prudently lowered the foresail, not wishing to be caught by a sudden gust while carrying too much canvas; it was perhaps an unnecessary precaution on such a calm night, but Pencroft was a prudent sailor and cannot be blamed for it.

The reporter slept part of the night. Pencroft and Herbert took turns for a spell of two hours each at the helm. The sailor trusted Herbert as he would himself, and his confidence was justified by the coolness and judgment of the lad. Pencroft gave him his directions as a commander to his steersman, and Herbert never allowed the 'Bonadventure' to swerve even a point. The night passed quickly, as did the day of the 12th of October. A south-easterly direction was strictly maintained. Unless the 'Bonadventure' fell in with some unknown current she would come exactly within sight of Tabor Island.

As to the sea over which the vessel was then sailing, it was absolutely deserted. Now and then a great albatross or frigate bird passed within gunshot, and Gideon Spilett wondered if it was to one of them that he had confided his last letter addressed to the New York Herald. These birds were the only beings that appeared to frequent this part of the ocean between Tabor and Lincoln Islands.

'And yet,' observed Herbert, 'this is the time that whalers usually proceed towards the southern part of the Pacific. Indeed I do not think there could be a more deserted sea than this.'

'It is not quite so deserted as all that,' replied Pencroft.

'What do you mean?' asked the reporter.

'We are on it. Do you take our vessel for a wreck and us for porpoises?'

And Pencroft laughed at his joke.

By the evening, according to calculation, it was thought that the 'Bonadventure' had accomplished a distance of a hundred and twenty miles since her departure from Lincoln Island, that is to say in thirty-six hours, which would give her a speed of between three and four knots an hour. The breeze was very slight and might soon drop altogether. However, it was hoped that the next morning by break of day, if the calculation had been correct and the course true, they would sight Tabor Island.

Neither Gideon Spilett, Herbert, nor Pencroft slept that night. In the expectation of the next day they could not but feel some emotion. There was so much uncertainty in their enterprise! Were they near Tabor Island? Was the island still inhabited by the castaway to whose succour they had come? Who was this man? Would not his presence disturb the little colony till then so united? Besides, would he be content to exchange his prison for another? All these questions, which would no doubt be answered the next day, kept them in suspense, and at the dawn of day they all fixed their gaze on the western horizon.

'Land!' shouted Pencroft at about six o'clock in the morning.

And it was impossible that Pencroft should be mistaken, it was evident that land was there. Imagine the joy of the little crew of the 'Bonadventure.' In a few hours they would land on the beach of the island!

The low coast of Tabor Island, scarcely emerging from the sea, was not more than fifteen miles distant.

The head of the 'Bonadventure,' which was a little to the south of the island, was set directly towards it, and as the sun mounted in the east, its rays fell upon one or two headlands.

'This is a much less important isle than Lincoln Island,' observed Herbert, 'and is probably due like ours to some submarine convulsion.'

At eleven o'clock the 'Bonadventure' was not more than two miles off, and Pencroft, while looking for a suitable place at which to land, proceeded very cautiously through the unknown waters. The whole of the island could now be surveyed, and on it could be seen groups of gum and other large trees, of the same species as those growing on Lincoln Island. But the astonishing thing was that no smoke arose to show that the island was inhabited, no signal whatever appeared on the shore!

And yet the document was clear enough; there was a castaway, and this castaway should have been on the watch.

In the meanwhile the 'Bonadventure' entered the winding channels among the reefs, and Pencroft observed every turn with extreme care. He had put Herbert at the helm, posting himself in the bows, inspecting the water, while he held the halliard in his hand, ready to lower the sail at a moment's notice. Gideon Spilett with his glass eagerly scanned the shore, though without perceiving anything.

However, at about twelve o'clock the keel of the 'Bonadventure' grated on the bottom. The anchor was let go, the sails furled, and the crew of the little vessel landed.

And there was no reason to doubt that this was Tabor Island, since according to the most recent charts there was no island in this part of the Pacific between New Zealand and the American Coast.

The vessel was securely moored, so that there should be no danger of her being carried away by the receding tide; then Pencroft and his companions, well armed, ascended the shore, so as to gain an elevation of about two hundred and fifty or three hundred feet which rose at a distance of half a mile.

'From the summit of that hill,' said Spilett, 'we can no doubt obtain a complete view of the island, which will greatly facilitate our search.'

'So as to do here,' replied Herbert, 'that which Captain Harding did the very first thing on Lincoln Island, by climbing Mount Franklin.'

'Exactly so,' answered the reporter, 'and it is the best plan.'

While thus talking the explorers had advanced along a clearing which terminated at the foot of the hill. Flocks of rock-pigeons and sea-swallows, similar to those of Lincoln Island, fluttered around them. Under the woods which skirted the glade on the left they could hear the bushes rustling and see the grass waving, which indicated the presence of timid animals, but still nothing to show that the island was inhabited.

Arrived at the foot of the hill, Pencroft, Spilett, and Herbert climbed it in a few minutes, and gazed anxiously round the horizon.

They were on an islet, which did not measure more than six miles in circumference, its shape not much bordered by capes or promontories, bays or creeks, being a lengthened oval. All around, the lonely sea extended to the limits of the horizon. No land nor even a sail was in sight.

This woody islet did not offer the varied aspects of Lincoln Island, arid and wild in one part, but fertile and rich in the other. On the contrary this was a uniform mass of verdure, out of which rose two or three hills of no great height. Obliquely to the oval of the island ran a stream through a wide meadow falling into the sea on the west by a narrow mouth.

'The domain is limited,' said Herbert.

'Yes,' rejoined Pencroft: 'It would have been too small for us.'

'And moreover,' said the reporter, 'it appears to be uninhabited.'

'Indeed,' answered Herbert, 'nothing here betrays the presence of man.'

'Let us go down,' said Pencroft, 'and search.'

The sailor and his two companions returned to the shore, to the place where they had left the 'Bonadventure.'

They had decided to make the tour of the island on foot, before exploring the interior; so that not a spot should escape their investigations. The beach was easy to follow, and only in some places was their way barred by large rocks, which, however, they easily passed round. The explorers proceeded towards the south, disturbing numerous flocks of sea-birds and herds of seals, which threw themselves into the sea as soon as they saw the strangers at a distance.

'Those beasts yonder,' observed the reporter, 'do not see men for the first time. They fear them, therefore they must know them.'

An hour after their departure they arrived on the southern point of the islet, terminated by a sharp cape, and proceeded towards the north along the western coast, equally formed by sand and rocks, the background bordered with thick woods.

There was not a trace of a habitation in any part, not the print of a human foot on the shore of the island, which after four hours' walking had been gone completely round.

It was to say the least very extraordinary, and they were compelled to believe that Tabor Island was not or was no longer inhabited. Perhaps, after all the document was already several months or several years old, and it was possible in this case, either that the castaway had been enabled to return to his country, or that he had died of misery.

Pencroft, Spilett, and Herbert, forming more or less probable conjectures, dined rapidly on board the 'Bonadventure' so as to be able to continue their excursion until nightfall. This was done at five o'clock in the evening, at which hour they entered the wood.

Numerous animals fled at their approach, being principally, one might say, only goats and pigs, which were obviously European species.

Doubtless some whaler had landed them on the island, where they had rapidly increased. Herbert resolved to catch one or two living, and take them back to Lincoln Island.

It was no longer doubtful that men at some period or other had visited this islet, and this became still more evident when paths appeared trodden through the forest, felled trees, and everywhere traces of the hand of man; but the trees were becoming rotten, and had been felled many years ago; the marks of the axe were velveted with moss, and the grass grew long and thick on the paths, so that it was difficult to find them.

'But,' observed Gideon Spilett, 'this not only proves that men have landed on the island, but also that they lived on it for some time. Now, who were these men? How many of them remain?'

'The document,' said Herbert, 'only spoke of one castaway.'

'Well, if he is still on the island,' replied Pencroft, 'it is impossible but that we shall find him.'

The exploration was continued. The sailor and his companions naturally followed the route which cut diagonally across the island, and they were thus obliged to follow the stream which flowed towards the sea.

If the animals of European origin, if works due to a human hand, showed incontestably that men had already visited the island, several specimens of the vegetable kingdom did not prove it less. In some places, in the midst of clearings, it was evident that the soil had been planted with culinary plants, at probably the same distant period.

What, then, was Herbert's joy, when he recognized potatoes, chicory, sorrel, carrots, cabbages, and turnips, of which it was sufficient to collect the seed to enrich the soil of Lincoln Island.

'Capital, jolly!' exclaimed Pencroft. 'That will suit Neb as well as us. Even if we do not find the castaway, at least our voyage will not have been useless, and God will have rewarded us.'

'Doubtless,' replied Gideon Spilett, 'but to see the state in which we find these plantations, it is to be feared that the island has not been inhabited for some time.'

'Indeed,' answered Herbert, 'an inhabitant, whoever he was, could not have neglected such an important culture!'

'Yes,' said Pencroft, 'the castaway has gone.'

'We must suppose so.'

'It must then be admitted that the document has already a distant date?'

'Evidently.'

'And that the bottle only arrived at Lincoln Island after having floated in the sea a long time.'

'Why not?' returned Pencroft. 'But night is coming on,' added he, 'and I think that it will be best to give up the search for the present.'

'Let us go on board, and tomorrow we will begin again,' said the reporter.

This was the wisest course, and it was about to be followed when Herbert, pointing to a confused mass among the trees, exclaimed,—

'A hut!'

All three immediately ran towards the dwelling. In the twilight it was just possible to see that it was built of planks and covered with a thick tarpaulin.

The half-closed door was pushed open by Pencroft, who entered with a rapid step.

The hut was empty!

Chapter 14

Pencroft, Herbert, and Gideon Spilett remained silent in the midst of the darkness.

Pencroft shouted loudly.

No reply was made.

The sailor then struck a light and set fire to a twig. This lighted for a minute a small room, which appeared perfectly empty. At the back was a rude fireplace, with a few cold cinders, supporting an armful of dry wood. Pencroft threw the blazing twig on it, the wood crackled and gave forth a bright light.

The sailor and his two companions then perceived a disordered bed, of which the damp and yellow coverlets proved that it had not been used for a long time. In the corner of the fireplace were two kettles, covered with rust, and an overthrown pot. A cupboard, with a few mouldy sailor's clothes; on the table a tin plate and a Bible, eaten away by damp; in a corner a few tools, a spade, pickaxe, two fowling-pieces, one of which was broken; on a plank, forming a shelf, stood a barrel of powder, still untouched, a barrel of shot, and several boxes of caps, all thickly covered with dust, accumulated, perhaps, by many long years.

'There is no one here,' said the reporter.

'No one,' replied Pencroft.

'It is a long time since this room has been inhabited,' observed Herbert.

'Yes, a very long time!' answered the reporter.

'Mr. Spilett,' then said Pencroft, 'instead of returning on board, I think that it would be well to pass the night in this hut.'

'You are right, Pencroft,' answered Gideon Spilett, 'and if its owner returns, well! perhaps he will not be sorry to find the place taken possession of.'

'He will not return,' said the sailor, shaking his head.

'You think that he has quilted the island?' asked the reporter.

'If he had quilted the island he would have taken away his weapons and his tools,' replied Pencroft. 'You know the value which castaways set on such articles as these the last remains of a wreck. No! no!' repeated the sailor, in a tone of conviction; 'no, he has not left the island! If he had escaped in a boat made by himself, he would still less have left these indispensable and necessary articles. No! he is on the island!'

'Living?' asked Herbert.

'Living or dead. But if he is dead, I suppose he has not buried himself, and so we shall at least find his remains!'

It was then agreed that the night should be passed in the deserted dwelling, and a store of wood found in a corner was sufficient to warm it. The door closed, Pencroft, Herbert and Spilett remained there, seated on a bench, talking little but wondering much. They were in a frame of mind to imagine anything or expect anything. They listened eagerly for sounds outside. The door might have opened suddenly, and a man presented himself to them without their being in the least surprised, notwithstanding all that the hut revealed of abandonment, and they had their hands ready to press the hands of this man, this castaway, this unknown friend, for whom friends were waiting.

But no voice was heard, the door did not open. The hours thus passed away.

How long the night appeared to the sailor and his companions!

Herbert alone slept for two hours, for at his age sleep is a necessity. They were all three anxious to continue their exploration of the day before, and to search the most secret recesses of the islet! The inferences deduced by Pencroft were perfectly reasonable, and it was nearly certain that, as the hut was deserted, and the tools, utensils, and weapons were still there, the owner had succumbed. It was agreed, therefore, that they should search for his remains, and give them at least Christian burial.

Day dawned; Pencroft and his companions immediately proceeded to survey the dwelling. It had certainly been built in a favourable situation, at the back of a little hill, sheltered by five or six magnificent gum-trees. Before its front and through the trees the axe had prepared a wide clearing, which allowed the view to extend to the sea. Beyond a lawn, surrounded by a wooden fence falling to pieces, was the shore, on the left of which was the mouth of the stream.

The hut had been built of planks, and it was easy to see that these planks had been obtained from the hull or deck of a ship. It was probable that a disabled vessel had been cast on the coast of the island, that one at least of the crew had been saved, and that by means of the wreck this man, having tools at his disposal, had built the dwelling.

And this became still more evident when Gideon Spilett, after having walked around the hut, saw on a plank, probably one of those which had formed the armour of the wrecked vessel, these letters already half effaced:

BR—TAN—A

'Britannia,' exclaimed Pencroft, whom the reporter had called; 'it is a common name for ships, and I could not say if she was English or American!'

'It matters very little, Pencroft!'

'Very little indeed,' answered the sailor, 'and we will save the survivor of her crew if he is still living, to whatever country he may belong. But before beginning our search again let us go on board the 'Bonadventure'.'

A sort of uneasiness had seized Pencroft upon the subject of his vessel. Should the island be inhabited after all, and should some one have taken possession of her? But he shrugged his shoulders at such an unreasonable supposition. At any rate the sailor was not sorry to go to breakfast on board. The road already trodden was not long, scarcely a mile. They set out on their walk, gazing into the wood and thickets through which goats and pigs fled in hundreds.

Twenty minutes after leaving the hut Pencroft and his companions reached the western coast of the island, and saw the 'Bonadventure' held fast by her anchor, which was buried deep in the sand.

Pencroft could not restrain a sigh of satisfaction. After all this vessel was his child, and it is the right of fathers to be often uneasy when there is no occasion for it.

They returned on board, breakfasted, so that it should not be necessary to dine until very late; then the repast being ended, the exploration was continued and conducted with the most minute care. Indeed, it was very probable that the only inhabitant of the island had perished. It was therefore more for the traces of a dead than of a living man that Pencroft and his companions searched. But their searches were vain, and during the half of that day they sought to no purpose among the thickets of trees which covered the islet. There was then scarcely any doubt that, if the castaway was dead, no trace of his body now remained, but that some wild beast had probably devoured it to the last bone.

'We will set off tomorrow at daybreak,' said Pencroft to his two companions, as about two o'clock they were resting for a few minutes under the shade of a clump of firs.

'I should think that we might without scruple take the utensils which belonged to the castaway,' added Herbert.

'I think so, too,' returned Gideon Spilett, 'and these arms and tools will make up the stores of Granite House. The supply of powder and shot is also most important.'

'Yes,' replied Pencroft, 'but we must not forget to capture a couple or two of those pigs, of which Lincoln Island is destitute.'

'Nor to gather those seeds,' added Herbert, 'which will give us all the vegetables of the Old and the New Worlds.'

'Then perhaps it would be best,' said the reporter, 'to remain a day longer on Tabor Island, so as to collect all that may be useful to us.'

'No, Mr. Spilett,' answered Pencroft, 'I will ask you to set off tomorrow at daybreak. The wind seems to me to be likely to shift to the west, and after having had a fair wind for coming we shall have a fair wind for going back.'

'Then do not let us lose time,' said Herbert, rising.

'We won't waste time,' returned Pencroft. 'You, Herbert, go and gather the seeds, which you know better than we do. While you do that, Mr. Spilett and I will go and have a pig hunt, and even without Top I hope we shall manage to catch a few!'

Herbert accordingly took the path which led towards the cultivated part of the islet, while the sailor and the reporter entered the forest.

Many specimens of the porcine race fled before them, and these animals, which were singularly active, did not appear to be in a humour to allow themselves to be approached.

However, after an hour's chase, the hunters had just managed to get hold of a couple lying in a thicket, when cries were heard resounding from the north part of the island, With the cries were mingled terrible yells, in which there was nothing human.

Pencroft and Gideon Spilett were at once on their feet, and the pigs by this movement began to run away, at the moment when the sailor was getting ready the rope to bind them.

'That's Herbert's voice,' said the reporter.

'Run!' exclaimed Pencroft.

And the sailor and Spilett immediately ran at full speed towards the spot from whence the cries proceeded.

They did well to hasten, for at a turn of the path near a clearing they saw the lad thrown on the ground and in the grasp of a savage being, apparently a gigantic ape, who was about to do him some great harm.

To rush on this monster, throw him on the ground in his turn, snatch Herbert from him, then bind him securely, was the work of a minute for Pencroft and Gideon Spilett. The sailor was of Herculean strength, the reporter also very powerful, and in spite of the monster's resistance he was firmly tied so that he could not even move.

'You are not hurt, Herbert?' asked Spilett.

'No, no!'

'Oh, if this ape had wounded him!' exclaimed Pencroft.

'But he is not an ape,' answered Herbert.

At these words Pencroft and Gideon Spilett looked at the singular being who lay on the ground. Indeed it was not an ape; it was a human being, a man. But what a man! A savage in all the horrible acceptation of the word, and so much the more frightful that he seemed fallen to the lowest degree of brutishness!

Shaggy hair, untrimmed beard descending to the chest, the body almost naked except a rag round the waist, wild eyes, enormous hands with immensely long nails, skin the colour of mahogany, feet as hard as if made of horn, such was the miserable creature who yet had a claim to be called a man. But it might justly be asked if there were yet a soul in this body, or if the brute instinct alone survived in it!

'Are you quite sure that this is a man, or that he has ever been one?' said Pencroft to the reporter.

'Alas! there is no doubt about it,' replied Spilett.

'Then this must be the castaway?' asked Herbert.

'Yes,' replied Gideon Spilett, 'but the unfortunate man has no longer anything human about him!'

The reporter spoke the truth. It was evident that if the castaway had ever been a civilized being, solitude had made him a savage, or worse, perhaps a regular man of the woods. Hoarse sounds issued from his throat between his teeth, which were sharp as the teeth of a wild beast made to tear raw flesh.

Memory must have deserted him long before, and for a long time also he had forgotten how to use his gun and tools, and he no longer knew how to make a fire! It could be seen that he was active and powerful, but the physical qualities had been developed in him to the injury of the moral qualities. Gideon Spilett spoke to him. He did not appear to understand or even to hear. And yet on looking into his eyes, the reporter thought he could see that all reason was not extinguished in him. However, the prisoner did not struggle, nor even attempt to break his bonds. Was he overwhelmed by the presence of men whose fellow he had once been? Had he found in some corner of his brain a fleeting remembrance which recalled him to humanity? If free, would he attempt to fly, or would he remain? They could not tell, but they did not make the experiment; and after gazing attentively at the miserable creature,—

'Whoever he may be,' remarked Gideon Spilett, 'whoever he may have been, and whatever he may become, it is our duty to take him with us to Lincoln Island.'

'Yes, yes!' replied Herbert, 'and perhaps with care we may arouse in him same gleam of intelligence.'

'The soul does not die,' said the reporter, 'and it would be a great satisfaction to rescue one of God's creatures from brutishness.'

Pencroft shook his head doubtfully.

'We must try at any rate,' returned the reporter; 'humanity commands us.'

It was indeed their duty as Christians and civilized beings. All three felt this, and they well knew that Cyrus Harding would approve of their acting thus.

'Shall we leave him bound?' asked the sailor.

'Perhaps he would walk if his feet were unfastened,' said Herbert.

'Let us try,' replied Pencroft.

The cords which shackled the prisoner's feet were cut off, but his arms remained securely fastened. He got up by himself and did not manifest any desire to run away. His hard eyes darted a piercing glance at the three men, who walked near him, but nothing denoted that he recollected being their fellow, or at least having been so. A continual hissing sound issued from his lips, his aspect was wild, but he did not attempt to resist.

By the reporter's advice the unfortunate man was taken to the hut. Perhaps the sight of the things that belonged to him would make some impression on him! Perhaps a spark would be sufficient to revive his obscured intellect, to rekindle his dulled soul. The dwelling was not far off. In a few minutes they arrived there, but the prisoner remembered nothing, and it appeared that he had lost consciousness of everything.

What could they think of the degree of brutishness into which this miserable being had fallen, unless that his imprisonment on the islet dated from a very distant period and after having arrived there a rational being solitude had reduced him to this condition.

The reporter then thought that perhaps the sight of fire would have some effect on him, and in a moment one of those beautiful flames, that attract even animals, blazed up on the hearth. The sight of the flame seemed at first to fix the attention of the unhappy object, but soon he turned away and the look of intelligence faded. Evidently there was nothing to be done, for the time at least, but to take him on board the 'Bonadventure.' This was done, and he remained there in Pencroft's charge.

Herbert and Spilett returned to finish their work; and some hours after they came back to the shore, carrying the utensils and guns, a store of vegetables, of seeds, some game, and two couple of pigs.

All was embarked, and the 'Bonadventure' was ready to weigh anchor and sail with the morning tide.

The prisoner had been placed in the fore-cabin, where he remained quiet, silent, apparently deaf and dumb.

Pencroft offered him something to eat, but he pushed away the cooked meat that was presented to him and which doubtless did not suit him. But on the sailor showing him one of the ducks which Herbert had killed, he pounced on it like a wild beast, and devoured it greedily.

'You think that he will recover his senses?' asked Pencroft. 'It is not impossible that our care will have an effect upon him, for it is solitude that has made him what he is, and from this time forward he will be no longer alone.'

'The poor man must no doubt have been in this state for a long time,' said Herbert.

'Perhaps,' answered Gideon Spilett.

'About what age is he?' asked the lad.

'It is difficult to say,' replied the reporter, 'for it is impossible to see his features under the thick beard which covers his face, but he is no longer young, and I suppose he might be about fifty.'

'Have you noticed, Mr. Spilett, how deeply sunk his eyes are?' asked Herbert.

'Yes, Herbert, but I must add that they are more human than one could expect from his appearance.'

'However, we shall see,' replied Pencroft, 'and I am anxious to know what opinion Captain Harding will have of our savage. We went to look for a human creature, and we are bringing back a monster! After all, we did what we could.'

The night passed, and whether the prisoner slept or not could not be known, but at any rate, although he had been unbound, he did not move. He was like a wild animal, which appears stunned at first by its capture, and becomes wild again afterwards.

At daybreak the next morning, the 15th of October, the change of weather predicted by Pencroft occurred. The wind having shifted to the northwest favoured the return of the 'Bonadventure,' but at the same time it freshened, which might render navigation more difficult.

At five o'clock in the morning the anchor was weighed. Pencroft took a reef in the mainsail, and steered towards the north-east, so as to sail straight for Lincoln Island.

The first day of the voyage was not marked by any incident. The prisoner remained quiet in the fore-cabin, and as he had been a sailor it appeared that the motion of the vessel might produce on him a salutary reaction. Did some recollection of his former calling return to him? However that might be, he remained tranquil, astonished rather than depressed.

The next day the wind increased, blowing more from the north, consequently in a less favourable direction for the 'Bonadventure.' Pencroft was soon obliged to sail close-hauled, and without saying anything about it he began to be uneasy at the state of the sea, which frequently broke over the bows. Certainly, if the wind did not moderate, it would take a longer time to reach Lincoln Island than it had taken to make Tabor Island.

Indeed, on the morning of the 17th, the 'Bonadventure' had been forty- eight hours at sea, and nothing showed that she was near the island. It was impossible, besides, to estimate the distance traversed, or to trust to the reckoning for the direction, as the speed had been very irregular.

Twenty-four hours after there was yet no land in sight. The wind was right ahead and the sea very heavy. The sails were close-reeved, and they tacked frequently. On the 18th, a wave swept completely over the 'Bonadventure'; and if the crew had not taken the precaution of lashing themselves to the deck, they would have been carried away.

On this occasion Pencroft and his companions, who were occupied with loosing themselves, received unexpected aid from the prisoner, who emerged from the hatchway as if his sailor's instinct had suddenly returned, broke a piece out of the bulwarks with a spar so as to let the water which filled the deck escape. Then the vessel being clear, he descended to his cabin without having uttered a word. Pencroft, Gideon Spilett, and Herbert, greatly astonished, let him proceed.

Their situation was truly serious, and the sailor had reason to fear that he was lost on the wide sea without any possibility of recovering his course.

The night was dark and cold. However, about eleven o'clock, the wind fell, the sea went down, and the speed of the vessel, as she laboured less, greatly increased.

Neither Pencroft, Spilett, nor Herbert thought of taking an hour's sleep. They kept a sharp lookout, for either Lincoln Island could not be far distant and would be sighted at daybreak, or the 'Bonadventure,' carried away by currents, had drifted so much that it would be impossible to rectify her course. Pencroft, uneasy to the last degree, yet did not despair, for he had a gallant heart, and grasping the tiller he anxiously endeavoured to pierce the darkness which surrounded them.

About two o'clock in the morning he started forward,—

'A light! a light!' he shouted.

Indeed, a bright light appeared twenty miles to the northeast. Lincoln Island was there, and this fire, evidently lighted by Cyrus Harding, showed them the course to be followed. Pencroft, who was bearing too much to the north, altered his course and steered towards the fire, which burned brightly above the horizon like a star of the first magnitude.

Chapter 15

The next day, the 20th of October, at seven o'clock in the morning, after a voyage of four days, the 'Bonadventure' gently glided up to the beach at the mouth of the Mercy.

Cyrus Harding and Neb, who had become very uneasy at the bad weather and the prolonged absence of their companions, had climbed at daybreak to the plateau of Prospect Heights, and they had at last caught sight of the vessel which had been so long in returning.

'God be praised! there they are!' exclaimed Cyrus Harding.

As to Neb in his joy, he began to dance, to twirl round, clapping his hands and shouting, 'Oh! my master!' A more touching pantomime than the finest discourse.

The engineer's first idea, on counting the people on the deck of the 'Bonadventure,' was that Pencroft had not found the castaway of Tabor Island, or at any rate that the unfortunate man had refused to leave his island and change one prison for another.

Indeed Pencroft, Gideon Spilett, and Herbert were alone on the deck of the 'Bonadventure.'

The moment the vessel touched, the engineer and Neb were waiting on the beach, and before the passengers had time to leap on to the sand, Harding said: 'We have been very uneasy at your delay, my friends! Did you meet with any accident?'

'No,' replied Gideon Spilett; 'on the contrary, everything went wonderfully well. We will tell you all about it.'

'However,' returned the engineer, 'your search has been unsuccessful, since you are only three, just as you went!'

'Excuse me, captain,' replied the sailor, 'we are four.'

'You have found the castaway?'

'Yes.'

'And you have brought him?'

'Yes.'

'Living?'

'Yes.'

'Where is he? Who is he?'

'He is,' replied the reporter, 'or rather he was a man! There, Cyrus, that is all we can tell you!'

The engineer was then informed of all that had passed during the voyage, and under what conditions the search had been conducted; how the only dwelling in the island had long been abandoned; how at last a castaway had been captured, who appeared no longer to belong to the human species.

'And that's just the point,' added Pencroft, 'I don't know if we have done right to bring him here.'

'Certainly you have, Pencroft,' replied the engineer quickly.

'But the wretched creature has no sense!'

'That is possible at present,' replied Cyrus Harding, 'but only a few months ago the wretched creature was a man like you and me. And who knows what will become of the survivor of us after a long solitude on this island? It is a great misfortune to be alone, my friends; and it must be believed that solitude can quickly destroy reason, since you have found this poor creature in such a state!'

'But, captain,' asked Herbert, 'what leads you to think that the brutishness of the unfortunate man began only a few months back?'

'Because the document we found had been recently written,' answered the engineer, 'and the castaway alone can have written it.'

'Always supposing,' observed Gideon Spilett, 'that it had not been written by a companion of this man, since dead.'

'That is impossible, my dear Spilett.'

'Why so?' asked the reporter.

'Because the document would then have spoken of two castaways,' replied Harding, 'and it mentioned only one.'

Herbert then in a few words related the incidents of the voyage, and dwelt on the curious fact of the sort of passing gleam in the prisoner's mind, when for an instant in the height of the storm he had become a sailor.

'Well, Herbert,' replied the engineer, 'you are right to attach great importance to this fact. The unfortunate man cannot be incurable, and despair has made him what he is; but here he will find his fellow-men, and since there is still a soul in him, this soul we shall save!'

The castaway of Tabor Island, to the great pity of the engineer and the great astonishment of Neb, was then brought from the cabin which he occupied in the fore part of the 'Bonadventure'; when once on land he manifested a wish to run away.

But Cyrus Harding approaching, placed his hand on his shoulder with a gesture full of authority, and looked at him with infinite tenderness. Immediately the unhappy man, submitting to a superior will, gradually became calm, his eyes fell, his head bent, and he made no more resistance.

'Poor fellow!' murmured the engineer.

Cyrus Harding had attentively observed him. To judge by his appearance this miserable being had no longer anything human about him, and yet Harding, as had the reporter already, observed in his look an indefinable trace of intelligence.

It was decided that the castaway, or rather the stranger as he was thenceforth termed by his companions, should live in one of the rooms of Granite House, from which, however, he could not escape. He was led there without difficulty, and with careful attention, it might, perhaps, be hoped that some day he would be a companion to the settlers in Lincoln Island.

Cyrus Harding, during breakfast, which Neb had hastened to prepare, as the reporter, Herbert, and Pencroft were dying of hunger, heard in detail all the incidents which had marked the voyage of exploration to the islet. He agreed with his friends on this point, that the stranger must be either English or American, the name Britannia leading them to suppose this, and, besides, through the bushy beard, and under the shaggy, matted hair, the engineer thought he could recognize the characteristic features of the Anglo-Saxon.

'But, by the bye,' said Gideon Spilett, addressing Herbert, 'you never told us how you met this savage, and we know nothing, except that you would have been strangled, if we had not happened to come up in time to help you!'

'Upon my word,' answered Herbert, 'it is rather difficult to say how it happened. I was, I think, occupied in collecting my plants, when I heard a noise like an avalanche falling from a very tall tree. I scarcely had time to look round. This unfortunate man, who was without doubt concealed in a tree, rushed upon me in less time than I take to tell you about it, and unless Mr. Spilett and Pencroft—'

'My boy!' said Cyrus Harding, 'you ran a great danger, but, perhaps, without that, the poor creature would have still hidden himself from your search, and we should not have had a new companion.'

'You hope, then, Cyrus, to succeed in reforming the man?' asked the reporter.

'Yes,' replied the engineer.

Breakfast over, Harding and his companions left Granite House and returned to the beach. They there occupied themselves in unloading the 'Bonadventure,' and the engineer, having examined the arms and tools, saw nothing which could help them to establish the identity of the stranger.

The capture of pigs, made on the islet, was looked upon as being very profitable to Lincoln Island, and the animals were led to the sty, where they soon became at home.

The two barrels, containing the powder and shot, as well as the box of caps, were very welcome. It was agreed to establish a small powder-magazine, either outside Granite House or in the Upper Cavern, where there would be no fear of explosion. However, the use of pyroxyle was to be continued, for this substance giving excellent results, there was no reason for substituting ordinary powder.

When the unloading of the vessel was finished,—

'Captain,' said Pencroft, 'I think it would be prudent to put our 'Bonadventure' in a safe place.'

'Is she not safe at the mouth of the Mercy?' asked Cyrus Harding.

'No, captain,' replied the sailor. 'Half of the time she is stranded on the sand, and that works her. She is a famous craft, you see, and she behaved admirably during the squall which struck us on our return.'

'Could she not float in the river?'

'No doubt, captain, she could; but there is no shelter there, and in the east winds, I think that the 'Bonadventure' would suffer much from the surf.'

'Well, where would you put her, Pencroft?'

'In Port Balloon,' replied the sailor. 'That little creek, shut in by rocks, seems to me to be just the harbour we want.'

'Is it not rather far?'

'Pooh! it is not more than three miles from Granite House, and we have a fine straight road to take us there!'

'Do it then, Pencroft, and take your 'Bonadventure' there,' replied the engineer, 'and yet I would rather have her under our more immediate protection. When we have time, we must make a little harbour for her.'

'Famous!' exclaimed Pencroft. 'A harbour with a lighthouse, a pier, and dock! Ah! really with you, captain, everything becomes easy.'

'Yes, my brave Pencroft,' answered the engineer, 'but on condition, however, that you help me, for you do as much as three men in all our work.'

Herbert and the sailor then re-embarked on board the 'Bonadventure,' the anchor was weighed, the sail hoisted, and the wind drove her rapidly towards Claw Cape. Two hours after, she was reposing on the tranquil waters of Port Balloon.

During the first days passed by the stranger in Granite House, had he already given them reason to think that his savage nature was becoming tamed? Did a brighter light burn in the depths of that obscured mind? In short, was the soul returning to the body?

Yes, to a certainty, and to such a degree, that Cyrus Harding and the reporter wondered if the reason of the unfortunate man had ever been totally extinguished. At first, accustomed to the open air, to the unrestrained liberty which he had enjoyed on Tabor Island, the stranger manifested a sullen fury, and it was feared that he might throw himself onto the beach, out of one of the windows of Granite House. But gradually he became calmer, and more freedom was allowed to his movements.

They had reason to hope, and to hope much. Already, forgetting his carnivorous instincts, the stranger accepted a less bestial nourishment than that on which he fed on the islet, and cooked meat did not produce in him the same sentiment of repulsion which he had showed on board the 'Bonadventure.' Cyrus Harding had profited by a moment when he was sleeping, to cut his hair and matted beard, which formed a sort of mane and gave him such a savage aspect. He had also been clothed more suitably, after having got rid of the rag which covered him. The result was that, thanks to these attentions, the stranger resumed a more human appearance, and it even seemed as if his eyes had become milder. Certainly, when formerly lighted up by intelligence, this man's face must have had a sort of beauty.

Every day, Harding imposed on himself the task of passing some hours in his company. He came and worked near him, and occupied himself in different things, so as to fix his attention. A spark, indeed, would be sufficient to reillumine that soul, a recollection crossing that brain to recall reason. That had been seen, during the storm, on board the 'Bonadventure!' The engineer did not neglect either to speak aloud, so as to penetrate at the same time by the organs of hearing and sight the depths of that torpid intelligence. Sometimes one of his companions, sometimes another, sometimes all joined him. They spoke most often of things belonging to the navy, which must interest a sailor.

At times, the stranger gave some slight attention to what was said, and the settlers were soon convinced that he partly understood them. Sometimes the expression of his countenance was deeply sorrowful, a proof that he suffered mentally, for his face could not be mistaken; but he did not speak, although at different times, however, they almost thought that words were about to issue from his lips. At all events, the poor creature was quite quiet and sad!

But was not his calm only apparent? Was not his sadness only the result of his seclusion? Nothing could yet be ascertained. Seeing only certain objects and in a limited space, always in contact with the colonists, to whom he would soon become accustomed, having no desires to satisfy, better fed, better clothed, it was natural that his physical nature should gradually improve; but was he penetrated with the sense of a new life? or rather, to employ a word which would be exactly applicable to him, was he not becoming tamed, like an animal in company with his master? This was an important question, which Cyrus Harding was anxious to answer, and yet he did not wish to treat his invalid roughly! Would he ever be a convalescent?

How the engineer observed him every moment! How he was on the watch for his soul, if one may use the expression! How he was ready to grasp it! The settlers followed with real sympathy all the phases of the cure undertaken by Harding. They aided him also in this work of humanity, and all, except perhaps the incredulous Pencroft, soon shared both his hope and his faith.

The calm of the stranger was deep, as has been said, and he even showed a sort of attachment for the engineer, whose influence he evidently felt. Cyrus Harding resolved then to try him, by transporting him to another scene, from that ocean which formerly his eyes had been accustomed to contemplate, to the border of the forest, which might perhaps recall those where so many years of his life had been passed!

'But,' said Gideon Spilett, 'can we hope that he will not escape, if once set at liberty?'

'The experiment must be tried,' replied the engineer.

'Well!' said Pencroft. 'When that fellow is outside, and feels the fresh air, he will be off as fast as his legs can carry him!'

'I do not think so,' returned Harding.

'Let us try,,' said Spilett.

'We will try,' replied the engineer.

This was on the 30th of October, and consequently the castaway of Tabor Island had been a prisoner in Granite House for nine days. It was warm, and a bright sun darted its rays on the island. Cyrus Harding and Pencroft went to the room occupied by the stranger, who was found lying near the window and gazing at the sky.

'Come, my friend,' said the engineer to him.

The stranger rose immediately. His eyes were fixed on Cyrus Harding, and he followed him, while the sailor marched behind them, little confident as to the result of the experiment.

Arrived at the door, Harding and Pencroft made him take his place in the lift, while Neb, Herbert, and Gideon Spilett waited for them before Granite House. The lift descended, and in a few moments all were united on the beach.

The settlers went a short distance from the stranger, so as to leave him at liberty.

He then made a few steps toward the sea, and his look brightened with extreme animation, but he did not make the slightest attempt to escape. He was gazing at the little waves which, broken by the islet, rippled on the sand.

'This is only the sea,' observed Gideon Spilett, 'and possibly it does not inspire him with any wish to escape!'

'Yes,' replied Harding, 'we must take him to the plateau, on the border of the forest. There the experiment will be more conclusive.'

'Besides, he could not run away,' said Neb, 'since the bridge is raised.'

'Oh!' said Pencroft, 'that isn't a man to be troubled by a stream like Creek Glycerine! He could cross it directly, at a single bound!'

'We shall soon see,' Harding contented himself with replying, his eyes not quitting those of his patient.

The latter was then led towards the mouth of the Mercy, and all climbing the left bank of the river, reached Prospect Heights.

Arrived at the spot on which grew the first beautiful trees of the forest, their foliage slightly agitated by the breeze, the stranger appeared greedily to drink in the penetrating odour which filled the atmosphere, and a long sigh escaped from his chest.

The settlers kept behind him, ready to seize him if he made any movement to escape!

And, indeed, the poor creature was on the point of springing into the creek which separated him from the forest, and his legs were bent for an instant as if for a spring, but almost immediately he stepped back, half sank down, and a large tear fell from his eyes.

'Ah!' exclaimed Cyrus Harding, 'you have become a man again, for you can weep!'

Chapter 16

Yes! the unfortunate man had wept! Some recollection doubtless had flashed across his brain, and to use Cyrus Harding's expression, by those tears he was once more a man.

The colonists left him for some time on the plateau, and withdrew themselves to a short distance, so that he might feel himself free; but he did not think of profiting by this liberty, and Harding soon brought him back to Granite House. Two days after this occurrence, the stranger appeared to wish gradually to mingle with their common life. He evidently heard and understood, but no less evidently was he strangely determined not to speak to the colonists; for one evening, Pencroft, listening at the door of his room, heard these words escape from his lips:—

'No! here! I! never!'

The sailor reported these words to his companions.

'There is some painful mystery there!' said Harding.

The stranger had begun to use the labouring tools, and he worked in the garden. When he stopped in his work, as was often the case, he remained retired within himself, but on the engineer's recommendation, they respected the reserve which he apparently wished to keep. If one of the settlers approached him, he drew back, and his chest heaved with sobs, as if overburdened!

Was it remorse that overwhelmed him thus? They were compelled to believe so, and Gideon Spilett could not help one day making this observation,—

'If he does not speak it is because he has, I fear, things too serious to be told!'

They must be patient and wait.

A few days later, on the 3rd of November, the stranger, working on the plateau, had stopped, letting his spade drop to the ground, and

Harding, who was observing him from a little distance, saw that tears were again flowing from his eyes. A sort of irresistible pity led him towards the unfortunate man, and he touched his arm lightly.

'My friend!' said he.

The stranger tried to avoid his look, and Cyrus Harding having endeavoured to take his hand, he drew back quickly.

'My friend,' said Harding in a firmer voice, 'look at me, I wish it!'

The stranger looked at the engineer, and seemed to be under his power, as a subject under the influence of a mesmerist. He wished to run away. But then his countenance suddenly underwent a transformation. His eyes flashed. Words struggled to escape from his lips. He could no longer contain himself! At last he folded his arms; then, in a hollow voice,—'Who are you?' he asked Cyrus Harding.

'Castaways, like you,' replied the engineer, whose emotion was deep. 'We have brought you here, among your fellow-men.'

'My fellow-men!... I have none!'

'You are in the midst of friends.'

'Friends!—for me! friends!' exclaimed the stranger, hiding his face in his hands. 'No—never—leave me! leave me!'

Then he rushed to the side of the plateau which overlooked the sea, and remained there a long time motionless.

Harding rejoined his companions and related to them what had just happened.

'Yes! there is some mystery in that man's life,' said Gideon Spilett, 'and it appears as if he had only re-entered society by the path of remorse.'

'I don't know what sort of a man we have brought here,' said the sailor. 'He has secrets—'

'Which we will respect,' interrupted Cyrus Harding quickly. 'If he has committed any crime, he has most fearfully expiated it, and in our eyes he is absolved.'

For two hours the stranger remained alone on the shore, evidently under the influence of recollections which recalled all his past life—a melancholy life doubtless—and the colonists, without losing sight of him, did not attempt to disturb his solitude. However, after two hours, appearing to have formed a resolution, he came to find Cyrus Harding. His eyes were red with the tears he had shed, but he wept no longer. His countenance expressed deep humility. He appeared anxious, timorous, ashamed, and his eyes were constantly fixed on the ground.

'Sir,' said he to Harding, 'your companions and you, are you English?'

'No,' answered the engineer, 'we are Americans.'

'Ah!' said the stranger, and he murmured, 'I prefer that!'

'And you, my friend?' asked the engineer.

'English,' replied he hastily.

And as if these few words had been difficult to say, he retreated to the beach, where he walked up and down between the cascade and the mouth of the Mercy, in a state of extreme agitation.

Then, passing one moment close to Herbert, he stopped and in a stifled voice,—

'What month?' he asked.

'December,' replied Herbert.

'What year?'

'1866.'

'Twelve years! twelve years!' he exclaimed.

Then he left him abruptly.

Herbert reported to the colonists the questions and answers which had been made.

'This unfortunate man,' observed Gideon Spilett, 'was no longer acquainted with either months or years!'

'Yes!' added Herbert, 'and he had been twelve years already on the islet when we found him there!'

'Twelve years!' rejoined Harding. 'Ah! twelve years of solitude, after a wicked life, perhaps, may well impair a man's reason!'

'I am induced to think,' said Pencroft, 'that this man was not wrecked on Tabor Island, but that in consequence of some crime he was left there.'

'You must be right, Pencroft,' replied the reporter, 'and if it is so it is not impossible that those who left him on the island may return to fetch him some day!'

'And they will no longer find him,' said Herbert.

'But then,' added Pencroft, 'they must return, and—'

'My friends,' said Cyrus Harding, 'do not let us discuss this question until we know more about it. I believe that the unhappy man has suffered, that he has severely expiated his faults, whatever they may have been, and that the wish to unburden himself stifles him. Do not let us press him to tell us his history! He will tell it to us doubtless, and when we know it, we shall see what course it will be best to follow. He alone besides can tell us, if he has more than a hope, a certainty, of returning some day to his country, but I doubt it!'

'And why?' asked the reporter.

'Because that, in the event of his being sure of being delivered at a certain time, he would have waited the hour of his deliverance and would not have thrown this document into the sea. No, it is more probable that he was condemned to die on that islet, and that he never expected to see his fellow-creatures again!'

'But,' observed the sailor, 'there is one thing which I cannot explain.'

'What is it?'

'If this man had been left for twelve years on Tabor Island, one may well suppose that he had been several years already in the wild state in which we found him!'

'That is probable,' replied Cyrus Harding.

'It must then be many years since he wrote that document!'

'No doubt,' and yet the document appears to have been recently written!

'Besides, how do you know that the bottle which enclosed the document may not have taken several years to come from Tabor Island to Lincoln Island?'

'That is not absolutely impossible,' replied the reporter.

'Might it not have been a long time already on the coast of the island?'

'No,' answered Pencroft, 'for it was still floating. We could not even suppose that after it had stayed for any length of time on the shore, it would have been swept off by the sea, for the south coast is all rocks, and it would certainly have been smashed to pieces there!'

'That is true,' rejoined Cyrus Harding thoughtfully.

'And then,' continued the sailor, 'if the document was several years old, if it had been shut up in that bottle for several years, it would have been injured by damp. Now, there is nothing of the kind, and it was found in a perfect state of preservation.'

The sailor's reasoning was very just, and pointed out an incomprehensible fact, for the document appeared to have been recently written, when the colonists found it in the bottle. Moreover, it gave the latitude and longitude of Tabor Island correctly, which implied that its author had a more complete knowledge of hydrography than could be expected of a common sailor.

'There is in this, again, something unaccountable,' said the engineer, 'but we will not urge our companions to speak. When he likes, my friends, then we shall be ready to hear him!'

During the following days the stranger did not speak a word, and did not once leave the precincts of the plateau. He worked away, without losing a moment, without taking a minute's rest, but always in a retired place. At meal times he never came to Granite House, although invited several times to do so, but contented himself with eating a few raw vegetables. At nightfall he did not return to the room assigned to him, but remained under some clump of trees, or when the weather was bad crouched in some cleft of the rocks. Thus he lived in the same manner as when he had no other shelter than the forests of Tabor Island, and as all persuasion to induce him to improve his life was in vain, the colonists waited patiently. And the time was near, when, as it seemed, almost involuntarily urged by his conscience, a terrible confession escaped him.

On the 10th of November, about eight o'clock in the evening, as night was coming on, the stranger appeared unexpectedly before the settlers, who were assembled under the veranda. His eyes burned strangely, and he had quite resumed the wild aspect of his worst days.

Cyrus Harding and his companions were astounded on seeing that, overcome by some terrible emotion, his teeth chattered like those of a person in a fever. What was the matter with him? Was the sight of his fellow-creatures insupportable to him? Was he weary of this return to a civilized mode of existence? Was he pining for his former savage life? It appeared so, as soon he was heard to express himself in these incoherent sentences:—

'Why am I here?.... By what right have you dragged me from my islet?.... Do you think there could be any tie between you and me?.... Do you know who I am—what I have done—why I was there—alone? And who told you that I was not abandoned there—that I was not condemned to die there?.... Do you know my past?.... How do you know that I have not stolen, murdered—that I am not a wretch—an accursed being—only fit to live like a wild beast, far from all—speak—do you know it?'

The colonists listened without interrupting the miserable creature, from whom these broken confessions escaped, as it were, in spite of himself. Harding wishing to calm him, approached him, but he hastily drew back.

'No! no!' he exclaimed; 'one word only—am I free?'

'You are free,' answered the engineer.

'Farewell, then!' he cried, and fled like a madman.

Neb, Pencroft, and Herbert ran also towards the edge of the wood—but they returned alone.

'We must let him alone!' said Cyrus Harding.

'He will never come back!' exclaimed Pencroft.

'He will come back,' replied the engineer.

Many days passed; but Harding—was it a sort of presentiment?—persisted in the fixed idea that sooner or later the unhappy man would return.

'It is the last revolt of his wild nature,' said he, 'which remorse has touched, and which renewed solitude will terrify.'

In the meanwhile, works of all sorts were continued, as well on Prospect Heights as at the corral, where Harding intended to build a farm. It is unnecessary to say that the seeds collected by Herbert on Tabor Island had been carefully sown. The plateau thus formed one immense kitchen-garden, well laid out and carefully tended, so that the arms of the settlers were never in want of work. There was always something to be done. As the esculents increased in number, it became necessary to enlarge the simple beds, which threatened to grow into regular fields and replace the meadows. But grass abounded in other parts of the island, and there was no fear of the onagers being obliged to go on short allowance. It was well worth while, besides, to turn Prospect Heights into a kitchen-garden, defended by its deep belt of creeks, and to remove them to the meadows, which had no need of protection against the depredations of quadrumana and quadrapeds.

On the 15th of November, the third harvest was gathered in. How wonderfully had the field increased in extent, since eighteen months ago, when the first grain of wheat was sown! The second crop of six hundred thousand grains produced this time four thousand bushels, or five hundred millions of grains!

The colony was rich in corn, for ten bushels alone were sufficient for sowing every year to produce an ample crop for the food both of men and beasts. The harvest was completed, and the last fortnight of the month of November was devoted to the work of converting it into food for man. In fact, they had corn, but not flour, and the establishment of a mill was necessary. Cyrus Harding could have utilized the second fall which flowed into the Mercy to establish his motive power, the first being already occupied with moving the felting mill, but, after some consultation, it was decided that a simple windmill should be built on Prospect Heights. The building of this presented no more difficulty than the building of the former, and it was moreover certain that there would be no want of wind on the plateau, exposed as it was to the sea breezes.

'Not to mention,' said Pencroft, 'that the windmill will be more lively and will have a good effect in the landscape!'

They set to work by choosing timber for the frame and machinery of the mill. Some large stones, found at the north of the lake, could be easily transformed into millstones, and as to the sails, the inexhaustible case of the balloon furnished the necessary material.

Cyrus Harding made his model, and the site of the mill was chosen a little to the right of the poultry-yard, near the shore of the lake. The frame was to rest on a pivot supported with strong timbers, so that it could turn with all the machinery it contained according as the wind required it. The work advanced rapidly. Neb and Pencroft had become very skilful carpenters, and had nothing to do but to copy the models provided by the engineer.

Soon a sort of cylindrical box, in shape like a pepper-pot, with a pointed roof, rose on the spot chosen. The four frames which formed the sails had been firmly fixed in the centre beam, so as to form a certain angle with it, and secured with iron clamps. As to the different parts of the internal mechanism, the box destined to contain the two millstones, the fixed stone and the moving stone, the hopper, a sort of large square trough, wide at the top, narrow at the bottom, which would allow the grain to fall on the stones, the oscillating spout intended to regulate the passing of the grain, and lastly the bolting machine, which by the operation of sifting, separates the bran from the flour, were made without difficulty. The tools were good, and the work not difficult, for in reality, the machinery of a mill is very simple. This was only a question of time.

Every one had worked at the construction of the mill, and on the 1st of December it was finished. As usual, Pencroft was delighted with his work, and had no doubt that the apparatus was perfect.

'Now for a good wind,' said he, 'and we shall grind our first harvest splendidly!'

'A good wind, certainly,' answered the engineer, 'but not too much, Pencroft.'

'Pooh! our mill would only go the faster!'

'There is no need for it to go so very fast,' replied Cyrus Harding. 'It is known by experience that the greatest quantity of work is performed by a mill when the number of turns made by the sails in a minute is six times the number of feet traversed by the wind in a second. A moderate breeze, which passes over twenty-four feet to the second, will give sixteen turns to the sails during a minute, and there is no need of more.'

'Exactly!' cried Herbert, 'a fine breeze is blowing from the northeast, which will soon do our business for us.'

There was no reason for delaying the inauguration of the mill, for the settlers were eager to taste the first piece of bread in Lincoln Island. On this morning two or three bushels of wheat were ground, and the next day at breakfast a magnificent loaf, a little heavy perhaps, although raised with yeast, appeared on the table at Granite House. Every one munched away at it with a pleasure which may be easily understood.

In the meanwhile, the stranger had not reappeared. Several times Gideon Spilett and Herbert searched the forest in the neighbourhood of Granite House, without meeting or finding any trace of him. They became seriously uneasy at this prolonged absence. Certainly, the former savage of Tabor island could not be perplexed how to live in the forest, abounding in game, but was it not to be feared that he had resumed his habits, and that this freedom would revive in him his wild instincts? However, Harding, by a sort of presentiment, doubtless, always persisted in saying that the fugitive would return.

'Yes, he will return!' he repeated with a confidence which his companions could not share. 'When this unfortunate man was on Tabor Island, he knew himself to be alone! Here, he knows that fellow-men are awaiting him! Since he has partially spoken of his past life, the poor penitent will return to tell the whole, and from that day he will belong to us!'

The event justified Cyrus Harding's predictions. On the 3rd of December, Herbert had left the plateau to go and fish on the southern bank of the lake. He was unarmed, and till then had never taken any precautions for defence, as dangerous animals had not shown themselves on that part of the island.

Meanwhile, Pencroft and Neb were working in the poultry-yard, while Harding and the reporter were occupied at the Chimneys in making soda, the store of soap being exhausted.

Suddenly cries resounded,—

'Help! help!'

Cyrus Harding and the reporter, being at too great a distance, had not been able to hear the shouts. Pencroft and Neb, leaving the poultry-yard in all haste, rushed towards the lake.

But before then, the stranger, whose presence at this place no one had suspected, crossed Creek Glycerine, which separated the plateau from the forest, and bounded up the opposite bank.

Herbert was there face to face with a fierce jaguar, similar to the one which had been killed on Reptile End. Suddenly surprised, he was standing with his back against a tree, while the animal gathering itself together was about to spring.

But the stranger, with no other weapon than a knife, rushed on the formidable animal, who turned to meet this new adversary.

The struggle was short. The stranger possessed immense strength and activity. He seized the jaguar's throat with one powerful hand, holding it as in a vice, without heeding the beast's claws which tore his flesh, and with the other he plunged his knife into its heart.

The jaguar fell. The stranger kicked away the body, and was about to fly at the moment when the settlers arrived on the field of battle, but Herbert, clinging to him, cried,—

'No, no! you shall not go!'

Harding advanced towards the stranger, who frowned when he saw him approaching. The blood flowed from his shoulder under his torn shirt, but he took no notice of it.

'My friend,' said Cyrus Harding, 'we have just contracted a debt of gratitude to you. To save our boy you have risked your life!'

'My life!' murmured the stranger. 'What is that worth? Less than nothing!'

'You are wounded?'

'It is no matter.'

'Will you give me your hand?'

And as Herbert endeavoured to. seize the hand which had just saved him, the stranger folded his arms, his chest heaved, his look darkened, and he appeared to wish to escape, but making a violent effort over himself, and in an abrupt tone,—

'Who are you?' he asked, 'and what do you claim to be to me?'

It was the colonists' history which he thus demanded, and for the first time. Perhaps this history recounted, he would tell his own.

In a few words Harding related all that had happened since their departure from Richmond; how they had managed, and what resources they now had at their disposal.

The stranger listened with extreme attention.

Then the engineer told who they all were, Gideon Spilett, Herbert, Pencroft, Neb, himself, and, he added, that the greatest happiness they had felt since their arrival in Lincoln Island was on the return of the vessel from Tabor Island, when they had been able to include among them a new companion.

At these words the stranger's face flushed, his head sunk on his breast, and confusion was depicted on his countenance.

'And now that you know us,' added Cyrus Harding, 'will you give us your hand?'

'No,' replied the, stranger in a hoarse voice; 'no! You are honest men! And I—'

Chapter 17

These last words justified the colonists' presentiment. There had been some mournful past, perhaps expiated in the sight of men, but from which his conscience had not yet absolved him. At any rate the guilty man felt remorse, he repented, and his new friends would have cordially pressed the hand which they sought; but he did not feel himself worthy to extend it to honest men! However, alter the scene with the jaguar, he did not return to the forest, and from that day did not go beyond the enclosure of Granite House.

What was the mystery of his life? Would the stranger one day speak of it? Time alone could show. At any rate, it was agreed that his secret should never be asked from him, and that they would live with him as if they suspected nothing.

For some days their life continued as before. Cyrus Harding and Gideon Spilett worked together, sometimes chemists, sometimes experimentalists. The reporter never left the engineer except to hunt with Herbert, for it would not have been prudent to allow the lad to ramble alone in the forest; and it was very necessary to be on their guard. As to Neb and Pencroft, one day at the stables and poultry-yard, another at the corral, without reckoning work in Granite House, they were never in want of employment.

The stranger worked alone, and he had resumed his usual life, never appearing at meals, sleeping under the trees in the plateau, never mingling with his companions. It really seemed as if the society of those who had saved him was insupportable to him!

'But then,' observed Pencroft, 'why did he entreat the help of his fellow-creatures? Why did he throw that paper into the sea?'

'He will tell us why,' invariably replied Cyrus Harding.

'When?'

'Perhaps sooner than you think, Pencroft.'

And, indeed, the day of confession was near.

On the 10th of December, a week after his return to Granite House, Harding saw the stranger approaching, who, in a calm voice and humble tone, said to him: 'Sir, I have a request to make of you.'

'Speak,' answered the engineer, 'but first let me ask you a question.'

At these words the stranger reddened, and was on the point of withdrawing. Cyrus Harding understood what was passing in the mind of the guilty man, who doubtless feared that the engineer would interrogate him on his past life.

Harding held him back.

'Comrade,' said he, 'we are not only your companions but your friends. I wish you to believe that, and now I will listen to you.'

The stranger pressed his hand over his eyes. He was seized with a sort of trembling, and remained a few moments without being able to articulate a word.

'Sir,' said he at last, 'I have come to beg you to grant me a favour.'

'What is it?'

'You have, four or five miles from here, a corral for your domesticated animals. These animals need to be taken care of. Will you allow me to live there with them?'

Cyrus Harding gazed at the unfortunate man for a few moments with a feeling of deep commiseration; then,—

'My friend,' said he, 'the corral has only stables hardly fit for animals.'

'It will be good enough for me, sir.'

'My friend,' answered Harding, 'we will not constrain you in anything. You wish to live at the corral, so be it. You will, however, be always welcome at Granite House. But since you wish to live at the corral we will make the necessary arrangements for your being comfortably established there.'

'Never mind that, I shall do very well.'

'My friend,' answered Harding, who always intentionally made use of this cordial appellation, 'you must let us judge what it will be best to do in this respect.'

'Thank you, sir,' replied the stranger as he withdrew.

The engineer then made known to his companions the proposal which had been made to him, and it was agreed that they should build a wooden house at the corral, which they would make as comfortable as possible.

That very day the colonists repaired to the corral with the necessary tools, and a week had not passed before the house was ready to receive its tenant. It was built about twenty feet from the sheds, and from there it was easy to overlook the flock of sheep, which then numbered more than eighty. Some furniture, a bed, table, bench, cupboard, and chest were manufactured, and a gun, ammunition, and tools were carried to the corral.

The stranger, however, had seen nothing of his new dwelling, and he had allowed the settlers to work there without him, while he occupied himself on the plateau, wishing, doubtless, to put the finishing stroke to his work. Indeed, thanks to him, all the ground was dug up and ready to he sowed when the time came.

It was on the 20th of December that all the arrangements at the corral were completed. The engineer announced to the stranger that his dwelling was ready to receive him, and the latter replied that he would go and sleep there that very evening.

On this evening the colonists were gathered in the diningroom of Granite House. It was then eight o'clock, the hour at which their companion was to leave them. Not wishing to trouble him by their presence, and thus imposing on him the necessity of saying farewells which might perhaps be painful to him, they had left him alone and ascended to Granite House.

Now, they had been talking in the room for a few minutes, when a light knock was heard at the door. Almost immediately the stranger entered, and without any preamble,—

'Gentlemen,' said he, 'before I leave you, it is right that you should know my history. I will tell it you.'

These simple words profoundly impressed Cyrus Harding and his companions. The engineer rose.

'We ask you nothing, my friend,' said he; 'it is your right to be silent.'

'It is my duty to speak.'

'Sit down, then.'

'No, I will stand.'

'We are ready to hear you,' replied Harding.

The stranger remained standing in a corner of the room, a little in the shade. He was bareheaded, his arms folded across his chest, and it was in this posture that in a hoarse voice, speaking like some one who obliges himself to speak, he gave the following recital, which his auditors did not once interrupt:—

'On the 20th of December, 1854, a steam-yacht, belonging to a Scotch nobleman, Lord Glenarvan, anchored off Cape Bernouilli, on the western coast of Australia, in the thirty-seventh parallel. On board this yacht were Lord Glenarvan and his wife, a major in the English army, a French geographer, a young girl, and a young boy. These two last were the children of Captain Grant, whose ship, the 'Britannia,' had been lost, crew and cargo, a year before. The 'Duncan' was commanded by Captain John Mangles, and manned by a crew of fifteen men.

'This is the reason the yacht at this time lay off the coast of Australia. Six months before, a bottle, enclosing a document written in English, German, and French, had been found in the Irish Sea, and picked up by the 'Duncan.' This document stated in substance that there still existed three survivors from the wreck of the 'Britannia,' that these survivors were Captain Grant and two of his men, and that they had found refuge on some land, of which the document gave the latitude, but of which the longitude, effaced by the sea, was no longer legible.

'This latitude was 37ø 11' south; therefore, the longitude being unknown, if they followed the thirty-seventh parallel over continents and seas, they would be certain to reach the spot inhabited by Captain Grant and his two companions. The English Admiralty having hesitated to undertake this search, Lord Glenarvan resolved to attempt everything to find the captain. He communicated with Mary and Robert Grant, who joined him. The 'Duncan' yacht was equipped for the distant voyage, in which the nobleman's family and the captain's children wished to take part, and the 'Duncan,' leaving Glasgow, proceeded towards the Atlantic, passed through the Straits of Magellan, and ascended the Pacific as far as Patagonia, where, according to a previous interpretation of the document, they supposed that Captain Grant was a prisoner among the Indians.

'The 'Duncan' disembarked her passengers on the western coast of Patagonia, and sailed to pick them up again on the eastern coast at Cape Corrientes. Lord Glenarvan traversed Patagonia, following the thirty-seventh parallel, and having found no trace of the captain, he re-embarked on the 13th of November, so as to pursue his search through the Ocean.

'After having unsuccessfully visited the islands of Tristan d'Acunha and Amsterdam, situated in her course, the 'Duncan,' as I have said, arrived at Cape Bernouilli, on the Australian coast, on the 20th of December, 1854.

'It was Lord Glenarvan's intention to traverse Australia as he had traversed America, and he disembarked. A few miles from the coast was established a farm, belonging to an Irishman, who offered hospitality to the travellers. Lord Glenarvan made known to the Irishman the cause which had brought him to these parts, and asked if he knew whether a three-masted English vessel, the 'Britannia,' had been lost less than two years before on the west coast of Australia.

'The Irishman had never heard of this wreck, but, to the great surprise of the bystanders, one of his servants came forward and said,—

"My lord, praise and thank God! If Captain Grant is still living, he is living on the Australian shores.'

"Who are you?' asked Lord Glenarvan.

"A Scotchman like yourself, my lord,' replied the man; 'I am one of Captain Grant's crew—one of the castaways of the 'Britannia."

'This man was called Ayrton. He was, in fact, the boatswain's mate of the 'Britannia,' as his papers showed. But, separated from Captain Grant at the moment when the ship struck upon the rocks, he had till then believed that the captain with all his crew had perished, and that he, Ayrton, was the sole survivor of the 'Britannia.'

"Only,' he added, 'it was not on the west coast, but on the east coast of Australia that the vessel was lost, and if Captain Grant is still living, as his document indicates, he is a prisoner among the natives, and it is on the other coast that he must be looked for.'

'This man spoke in a frank voice and with a confident look; his words could not be doubted. The Irishman, in whose service he had been for more than a year, answered for his trustworthiness. Lord Glenarvan, therefore, believed in the fidelity of this man and, by his advice, resolved to cross Australia, following the thirty-seventh parallel. Lord Glenarvan, his wife, the two children, the major, the Frenchman, Captain Mangles, and a few sailors composed the little band under the command of Ayrton, while the 'Duncan,' under charge of the mate, Tom Austin, proceeded to Melbourne, there to await Lord Glenarvan's instructions.

'They set out on the 23rd of December, 1854.

'It is time to say that Ayrton was a traitor. He was, indeed, the boatswain's mate of the 'Britannia,' but, after some dispute with his captain, he endeavoured to incite the crew to mutiny and seize the ship, and Captain Grant had landed him, on the 8th of April, 1852, on the west coast of Australia, and then sailed, leaving him there, as was only just.

'Therefore this wretched man knew nothing of the wreck of the 'Britannia'; he had just heard of it from Glenarvan's account. Since his abandonment, he had become, under the name of Ben Joyce, the leader of the escaped convicts; and if he boldly maintained that the wreck had taken place on the east coast, and led Lord Glenarvan to proceed in that direction, it was that he hoped to separate him from his ship, seize the 'Duncan,' and make the yacht a pirate in the Pacific.'

Here the stranger stopped for a moment. His voice trembled, but he continued,—

'The expedition set out and proceeded across Australia. It was inevitably unfortunate, since Ayrton, or Ben Joyce, as he may be called, guided it, sometimes preceded, sometimes followed by his band of convicts, who had been told what they had to do.

'Meanwhile, the 'Duncan' had been sent to Melbourne for repairs. It was necessary, then, to get Lord Glenarvan to order her to leave Melbourne and go to the east coast of Australia, where it would be easy to seize her. After having led the expedition near enough to the coast, in the midst of vast forests with no resources, Ayrton obtained a letter, which he was charged to carry to the mate of the 'Duncan'—a letter which ordered the yacht to repair immediately to the east coast, to Twofold Bay, that is to say a few days' journey from the place where the expedition had stopped. It was there that Ayrton had agreed to meet his accomplices, and two days after gaining possession of the letter, he arrived at Melbourne.

'So far the villain had succeeded in his wicked design. He would be able to take the 'Duncan' into Twofold Bay, where it would be easy for the convicts to seize her, and her crew massacred, Ben Joyce would become master of the seas. But it pleased God to prevent the accomplishment of these terrible projects.

'Ayrton, arrived at Melbourne, delivered the letter to the mate, Tom Austin, who read it and immediately set sail, but judge of Ayrton's rage and disappointment, when the next day he found that the mate was taking the vessel, not to the east coast of Australia, to Twofold Bay, but to the east coast of New Zealand. He wished to stop him, but Austin showed him the letter!... And indeed, by a providential error of the French geographer, who had written the letter, the east coast of New Zealand was mentioned as the place of destination.

'All Ayrton's plans were frustrated! He became outrageous. They put him in irons. He was then taken to the coast of New Zealand, not knowing what would become of his accomplices, or what would become of Lord Glenarvan.

'The 'Duncan' cruised about on this coast until the 3rd of March. On that day Ayrton heard the report of guns. The guns on the 'Duncan' were being fired, and soon Lord Glenarvan and his companions came on board.

'This is what had happened.

'After a thousand hardships, a thousand dangers, Lord Glenarvan had accomplished his journey, and arrived on the east coast of Australia, at Twofold Bay. 'No 'Duncan!' ' He telegraphed to Melbourne. They answered, ''Duncan' sailed on the 18th instant. Destination unknown.'

'Lord Glenarvan could only arrive at one conclusion; that his honest yacht had fallen into the hands of Ben Joyce, and had become a pirate vessel!

'However, Lord Glenarvan would not give up. He was a bold and generous man. He embarked in a merchant vessel, sailed to the west coast of New Zealand, traversed it along the thirty-seventh parallel, without finding any trace of Captain Grant; but on the other side, to his great surprise, and by the will of Heaven, he found the 'Duncan,' under command of the mate, who had been waiting for him for five weeks!

'This was on the 3rd of March, 1855. Lord Glenarvan was now on board the 'Duncan,' but Ayrton was there also. He appeared before the nobleman, who wished to extract from him all that the villain knew about Captain Grant. Ayrton refused to speak. Lord Glenarvan then told him, that at the first port they put into, he would be delivered up to the English authorities. Ayrton remained mute.

'The 'Duncan' continued her voyage along the thirty-seventh parallel. In the meanwhile, Lady Glenarvan undertook to vanquish the resistance of the ruffian.

'At last, her influence prevailed, and Ayrton, in exchange for what he could tell, proposed that Lord Glenarvan should leave him on some island in the Pacific, instead of giving him up to the English authorities. Lord Glenarvan, resolving to do anything to obtain information about Captain Grant, consented.

'Ayrton then related all his life, and it was certain that he knew nothing from the day on which Captain Grant had landed him on the Australian coast.

'Nevertheless, Lord Glenarvan kept the promise which he had given. The 'Duncan' continued her voyage and arrived at Tabor Island. It was there that Ayrton was to be landed, and it was there also that, by a veritable miracle, they found Captain Grant and two men, exactly on the thirty- seventh parallel.

'The convict, then, went to take their place on this desert islet, and at the moment he left the yacht these words were pronounced by Lord Glenarvan:—

"Here, Ayrton, you will be far from any land, and without any possible communication with your fellow-creatures. You can not escape from this islet on which the 'Duncan' leaves you. You will be alone, under the eye of a God who reads the depths of the heart, but you will be neither lost nor forgotten, as was Captain Grant. Unworthy as you are to be remembered by men, men will remember you. I know where you are Ayrton, and I know where to find you. I will never forget it!

'And the 'Duncan,' making sail, soon disappeared. This was 18th of March, 1855.

(The events which have just been briefly related are taken from a work which some of our readers have no doubt read, and which is entitled, 'Captain Grant's children.' They will remark on this occasion, as well as later, some discrepancy in the dates; but later again, they will understand why the real dates were not at first given.)

'Ayrton was alone, but he had no want of either ammunition, weapons, tools, or seeds.

'At his, the convict's disposal, was the house built by honest Captain Grant. He had only to live and expiate in solitude the crimes which he had committed.

'Gentlemen, he repented, he was ashamed of his crimes and was very miserable! He said to himself, that if men came some day to take him from that islet, he must be worthy to return among them! How he suffered, that wretched man! How he laboured to recover himself by work! How he prayed to be reformed by prayer! For two years, three years, this went on, but Ayrton, humbled by solitude, always looking for some ship to appear on the horizon, asking himself if the time of expiation would soon be complete, suffered as none other suffered! Oh! how dreadful was this solitude, to a heart tormented by remorse!

'But doubtless Heaven had not sufficiently punished this unhappy man, for he felt that he was gradually becoming a savage! He felt that brutishness was gradually gaining on him!

'He could not say if it was after two or three years of solitude, but at last he became the miserable creature you found!

'I have no need to tell you, gentlemen, that Ayrton, Ben Joyce, and I, are the same.'

Cyrus Harding and his companions rose at the end of this account. It is impossible to say how much they were moved! What misery, grief, and despair lay revealed before them!

'Ayrton,' said Harding, rising, 'you have been a great criminal, but Heaven must certainly think that you have expiated your crimes! That has been proved by your having been brought again among your fellow-creatures. Ayrton, you are forgiven! And now you will be our companion?'

Ayrton drew back.

'Here is my hand!' said the engineer.

Ayrton grasped the hand which Harding extended to him, and great tears fell from his eyes.

'Will you live with us?' asked Cyrus Harding.

'Captain Harding, leave me some time longer,' replied Ayrton, 'leave me alone in the hut in the corral!'

'As you like, Ayrton,' answered Cyrus Harding. Ayrton was going to withdraw, when the engineer addressed one more question to him:—

'One word more, my friend. Since it was your intention to live alone, why did you throw into the sea the document which put us on your track?'

'A document?' repeated Ayrton, who did not appear to know what he meant.

'Yes, the document which we found enclosed in a bottle, giving us the exact position of Tabor Island!'

Ayrton passed his hand over his brow, then after having thought, 'I never threw any document into the sea!' he answered.

'Never?' exclaimed Pencroft.

'Never!'

And Ayrton, bowing, reached the door and departed.

Chapter 18

'Poor man!' said Herbert, who had rushed to the door, but returned, having seen Ayrton slide down the rope on the lift and disappear in the darkness.

'He will come back,' said Cyrus Harding.

'Come, now, captain,' exclaimed Pencroft, 'what does that mean? What! wasn't it Ayrton who threw that bottle into the sea? Who was it then?'

Certainly, if ever a question was necessary to be made, it was that one!

'It was he,' answered Neb, 'only the unhappy man was half-mad.'

'Yes!' said Herbert, 'and he was no longer conscious of what he was doing.'

'It can only be explained in that way, my friends,' replied Harding quickly, 'and I understand now how Ayrton was able to point out exactly the situation of Tabor Island, since the events which had preceded his being left on the island had made it known to him.'

'However,' observed Pencroft, 'if he was not yet a brute when he wrote that document, and if he threw it into the sea seven or eight years ago, how is it that the paper has not been injured by damp?'

'That proves,' answered Cyrus Harding, 'that Ayrton was deprived of intelligence at a more recent time than he thinks.'

'Of course it must be so,' replied Pencroft, 'without that the fact would be unaccountable.'

'Unaccountable indeed,' answered the engineer, who did not appear desirous to prolong the conversation.

'But has Ayrton told the truth?' asked the sailor.

'Yes,' replied the reporter. 'The story which he has told is true in every point. I remember quite well the account in the newspapers of the yacht expedition undertaken by Lord Glenarvan, and its result.'

'Ayrton has told the truth,' added Harding. 'Do not doubt it, Pencroft, for it was painful to him. People tell the truth when they accuse themselves like that!'

The next day—the 21st of December—the colonists descended to the beach, and having climbed the plateau they found nothing of Ayrton. He had reached his house in the corral during the night and the settlers judged it best not to agitate him by their presence. Time would doubtless perform what sympathy had been unable to accomplish.

Herbert, Pencroft, and Neb resumed their ordinary occupations. On this day the same work brought Harding and the reporter to the workshop at the Chimneys.

'Do you know, my dear Cyrus,' said Gideon Spilett, 'that the explanation you gave yesterday on the subject of the bottle has not satisfied me at all! How can it be supposed that the unfortunate man was able to write that document and throw the bottle into the sea without having the slightest recollection of it?'

'Nor was it he who threw it in, my dear Spilett.'

'You think then—'

'I think nothing, I know nothing!' interrupted Cyrus Harding. 'I am content to rank this incident among those which I have not been able to explain to this day!'

'Indeed, Cyrus,' said Spilett, 'these things are incredible! Your rescue, the case stranded on the sand, Top's adventure, and lastly this bottle... Shall we never have the answer to these enigmas?'

'Yes!' replied the engineer quickly, 'yes, even if I have to penetrate into the bowels of this island!'

'Chance will perhaps give us the key to this mystery!'

'Chance! Spilett! I do not believe in chance, any more than I believe in mysteries in this world. There is a reason for everything unaccountable which has happened here, and that reason I shall discover. But in the meantime we must work and observe.'

The month of January arrived. The year 1867 commenced. The summer occupations were assiduously continued. During the days which followed, Herbert and Spilett having gone in the direction of the corral, ascertained that Ayrton had taken possession of the habitation which had been prepared for him. He busied himself with the numerous flock confided to his care, and spared his companions the trouble of coming every two or three days to visit the corral. Nevertheless, in order not to leave Ayrton in solitude for too long a time, the settlers often paid him a visit.

It was not unimportant either, in consequence of some suspicions entertained by the engineer and Gideon Spilett, that this part of the island should be subject to a surveillance of some sort, and that Ayrton, if any incident occurred unexpectedly, should not neglect to inform the inhabitants of Granite House of it.

Nevertheless it might happen that something would occur which it would be necessary to bring rapidly to the engineer's knowledge. Independently of facts bearing on the mystery of Lincoln Island, many others might happen, which would call for the prompt interference of the colonists,—such as the sighting of a vessel, a wreck on the western coast, the possible arrival of pirates, etc.

Therefore Cyrus Harding resolved to put the corral in instantaneous communication with Granite House.

It was on the 10th of January that he made known his project to his companions.

'Why! how are you going to manage that, captain?' asked Pencroft. 'Do you by chance happen to think of establishing a telegraph?'

'Exactly so,' answered the engineer.

'Electric?' cried Herbert.

'Electric,' replied Cyrus Harding. 'We have all the necessary materials for making a battery, and the most difficult thing will be to stretch the wires, but by means of a drawplate I think we shall manage it.'

'Well, after that,' returned the sailor, 'I shall never despair of seeing ourselves some day rolling along on a railway!'

They then set to work, beginning with the most difficult thing, for, if they failed in that, it would be useless to manufacture the battery and other accessories.

The iron of Lincoln Island, as has been said, was of excellent quality, and consequently very fit for being drawn out. Harding commenced by manufacturing a drawplate, that is to say, a plate of steel, pierced with conical holes of different sizes, which would successively bring the wire to the wished-for tenacity. This piece of steel, after having been tempered, was fixed in as firm a way as possible in a solid framework planted in the ground, only a few feet from the great fall, the motive power of which the engineer intended to utilize. In fact as the fulling- mill was there, although not then in use, its beam moved with extreme power would serve to stretch out the wire by rolling it round itself. It was a delicate operation, and required much care. The iron, prepared previously in long thin rods, the ends of which were sharpened with the file, having been introduced into the largest hole of the drawplate, was drawn out by the beam which wound it round itself, to a length of twenty-five or thirty feet, then unrolled, and the same operation was performed successively through the holes of a less size. Finally, the engineer obtained wires from forty to fifty feet long, which could be easily fastened together and stretched over the distance of five miles, which separated the corral from the bounds of Granite House.

It did not take more than a few days to perform this work, and indeed as soon as the machine had been commenced, Cyrus Harding left his companions to follow the trade of wiredrawers, and occupied himself with manufacturing his battery.

It was necessary to obtain a battery with a constant current. It is known that the elements of modern batteries are generally composed of retort coal, zinc, and copper. Copper was absolutely wanting to the engineer, who, notwithstanding all his researches, had never been able to find any trace of it in Lincoln Island, and was therefore obliged to do without it. Retort coal, that is to say, the hard graphite which is found in the retorts of gas manufactories, after the coal has been dehydrogenized, could have been obtained, but it would have been necessary to establish a special apparatus, involving great labour. As to zinc, it may be remembered that the case found at Flotsam Point was lined with this metal, which could not be better utilized than for this purpose.

Cyrus Harding, after mature consideration, decided to manufacture a very simple battery, resembling as nearly as possible that invented by Becquerel in 1820, and in which zinc only is employed. The other substances, azotic acid and potash, were all at his disposal.

The way in which the battery was composed was as follows, and the results were to be attained by the reaction of acid and potash on each other. A number of glass bottles were made and filled with azotic acid. The engineer corked them by means of a stopper through which passed a glass tube, bored at its lower extremity, and intended to be plunged into the acid by means of a clay stopper secured by a rag. Into this tube, through its upper extremity, he poured a solution of potash, previously obtained by burning and reducing to ashes various plants, and in this way the acid and potash could act on each other through the clay.

Cyrus Harding then took two slips of zinc, one of which was plunged into azotic acid, the other into a solution of potash. A current was immediately produced, which was transmitted from the slip of zinc in the bottle to that in the tube, and the two slips having been connected by a metallic wire the slip in the tube became the positive pole, and that in the bottle the negative pole of the apparatus. Each bottle, therefore, produced as many currents as united would be sufficient to produce all the phenomena of the electric telegraph. Such was the ingenious and very simple apparatus constructed by Cyrus Harding, an apparatus which would allow them to establish a telegraphic communication between Granite House and the corral.

On the 6th of February was commenced the planting along the road to the corral, of posts furnished with glass insulators, and intended to support the wire. A few days after, the wire was extended, ready to produce the electric current at a rate of twenty thousand miles a second.

Two batteries had been manufactured, one for Granite House, the other for the corral; for if it was necessary the corral should be able to communicate with Granite House it might also be useful that Granite House should be able to communicate with the corral.

As to the receiver and manipulator, they were very simple. At the two stations the wire was wound round a magnet, that is to say, round a piece of soft iron surrounded with a wire. The communication was thus established between the two poles; the current, starting from the positive pole, traversed the wire, passed through the magnet which was temporarily magnetized, and returned through the earth to the negative pole. If the current was interrupted, the magnet immediately became unmagnetized. It was sufficient to place a plate of soft iron before the magnet, which, attracted during the passage of the current, would fall back when the current was interrupted. This movement of the plate thus obtained, Harding could easily fasten to it a needle arranged on a dial, bearing the letters of the alphabet, and in this way communicate from one station to the other.

All was completely arranged by the 12th of February. On this day, Harding, having sent the current through the wire, asked if all was going on well at the corral, and received in a few moments a satisfactory reply from Ayrton. Pencroft was wild with joy, and every morning and evening he sent a telegram to the corral, which always received an answer.

This mode of communication presented two very real advantages: firstly, because it enabled them to ascertain that Ayrton was at the corral; and secondly, that he was thus not left completely isolated. Besides, Cyrus Harding never allowed a week to pass without going to see him, and Ayrton came from time to time to Granite House, where he always found a cordial welcome.

The fine season passed away in the midst of the usual work. The resources of the colony, particularly in vegetables and corn, increased from day to day, and the plants brought from Tabor Island had succeeded perfectly.

The plateau of Prospect Heights presented an encouraging aspect. The fourth harvest had been admirable and it may be supposed that no one thought of counting whether the four hundred thousand millions of grains duly appeared in the crop. However, Pencroft had thought of doing so, but Cyrus Harding having told him that even if he managed to count three hundred grains a minute, or nine thousand an hour, it would take him nearly five thousand five-hundred years to finish his task, the honest sailor considered it best to give up the idea.

The weather was splendid, the temperature very warm in the day time, but in the evening the sea-breezes tempered the heat of the atmosphere and procured cool nights for the inhabitants of Granite House. There were, however, a few storms, which, although they were not of long duration, swept over Lincoln Island with extraordinary fury. The lightning blazed and the thunder continued to roll for some hours.

At this period the little colony was extremely prosperous.

The tenants of the poultry-yard swarmed, and they lived on the surplus, but it became necessary to reduce the population to a more moderate number. The pigs had already produced young, and it may be understood that their care for these animals absorbed a great part of Neb and Pencroft's time. The onagers, who had two pretty colts, were most often mounted by Gideon Spilett and Herbert, who had become an excellent rider under the reporter's instruction, and they also harnessed them to the cart either for carrying wood and coal to Granite House, or different mineral productions required by the engineer.

Several expeditions were made about this time into the depths of the Far West Forests. The explorers could venture there without having anything to fear from the heat, for the sun's rays scarcely penetrated through the thick foliage spreading above their heads. They thus visited all the left bank of the Mercy, along which ran the road from the corral to the mouth of Falls River.

But in these excursions the settlers took care to be well armed, for they met with savage wild boars, with which they often had a tussle. They also, during this season, made fierce war against the jaguars. Gideon Spilett had vowed a special hatred against them, and his pupil Herbert seconded him well. Armed as they were, they no longer feared to meet one of those beasts. Herbert's courage was superb, and the reporter's sang-froid astonishing. Already twenty magnificent skins ornamented the dining room of Granite House, and if this continued, the jaguar race would soon be extinct in the island, the object aimed at by the hunters.

The engineer sometimes took part in the expeditions made to the unknown parts of the island, which he surveyed with great attention. It was for other traces than those of animals that he searched the thickets of the vast forest, but nothing suspicious ever appeared. Neither Top nor Jup, who accompanied him, ever betrayed by their behaviour that there was anything strange there, and yet more than once again the dog barked at the mouth of the well, which the engineer had before explored without result.

At this time Gideon Spilett, aided by Herbert, took several views of the most picturesque parts of the island, by means of the photographic apparatus found in the cases, and of which they had not as yet made any use.

This apparatus, provided with a powerful object-glass, was very complete. Substances necessary for the photographic reproduction, collodion for preparing the glass plate, nitrate of silver to render it sensitive, hyposulfate of soda to fix the prints obtained, chloride of ammonium in which to soak the paper destined to give the positive proof, acetate of soda and chloride of gold in which to immerse the paper, nothing was wanting. Even the papers were there, all prepared, and before laying in the printing-frame upon the negatives, it was sufficient to soak them for a few minutes in the solution of nitrate of silver.

The reporter and his assistant became in a short time very skilful operators, and they obtained fine views of the country, such as the island, taken from Prospect Heights with Mount Franklin in the distance, the mouth of the Mercy, so picturesquely framed in high rocks, the glade and the corral, with the spurs of the mountain in the background, the curious development of Claw Cape, Flotsam Point, etc.

Nor did the photographers forget to take the portraits of all the inhabitants of the island, leaving out no one.

'It multiplies us,' said Pencroft.

And the sailor was enchanted to see his own countenance, faithfully reproduced, ornamenting the walls of Granite House, and he stopped as willingly before this exhibition as he would have done before the richest shop-windows in Broadway.

But it must be acknowledged that the most successful portrait was incontestably that of Master Jup. Master Jup had sat with a gravity not to be described, and his portrait was lifelike!

'He looks as if he was just going to grin!' exclaimed Pencroft.

And if Master Jup had not been satisfied, he would have been very difficult to please; but he was quite contented and contemplated his own countenance with a sentimental air which expressed some small amount of conceit.

The summer heat ended with the month of March. The weather was sometimes rainy, but still warm. The month of March, which corresponds to the September of northern latitudes, was not so fine as might have been hoped. Perhaps it announced an early and rigorous winter.

It might have been supposed one morning—the 21st—that the first snow had already made its appearance. In fact Herbert looking early from one of the windows of Granite House, exclaimed,—

'Hallo! the islet is covered with snow!'

'Snow at this time?' answered the reporter, joining the boy.

Their companions were soon beside them, but could only ascertain one thing, that not only the islet but all the beach below Granite House was covered with one uniform sheet of white.

'It must be snow!' said Pencroft.

'Or rather it's very like it!' replied Neb.

'But the thermometer marks fifty-eight degrees!' observed Gideon Spilett.

Cyrus Harding gazed at the sheet of white without saying anything, for he really did not know how to explain this phenomenon, at this time of year and in such a temperature.

'By Jove!' exclaimed Pencroft, 'all our plants will be frozen!'

And the sailor was about to descend, when he was preceded by the nimble Jup, who slid down to the sand.

But the orang had not touched the ground, when the snowy sheet arose and dispersed in the air in such innumerable flakes that the light of the sun was obscured for some minutes.

'Birds!' cried Herbert.

They were indeed swarms of sea-birds, with dazzling white plumage. They had perched by thousands on the islet and on the shore, and they disappeared in the distance, leaving the colonists amazed as if they had been present at some transformation scene, in which summer succeeded winter at the touch of a fairy's wand. Unfortunately the change had been so sudden, that neither the reporter nor the lad had been able to bring down one of these birds, of which they could not recognize the species.

A few days after came the 26th of March, the day on which, two years before, the castaways from the air had been thrown upon Lincoln Island.

Chapter 19

Two years already! and for two years the colonists had had no communication with their fellow-creatures! They were without news from the civilized world, lost on this island, as completely as if they had been on the most minute star of the celestial hemisphere!

What was now happening in their country? The picture of their native land was always before their eyes, the land torn by civil war at the time they left it, and which the Southern rebellion was perhaps still staining with blood! It was a great sorrow to them, and they often talked together of these things, without ever doubting however that the cause of the North must triumph, for the honour of the American Confederation.

During these two years not a vessel had passed in sight of the island; or, at least, not a sail had been seen. It was evident that Lincoln Island was out of the usual track, and also that it was unknown,—as was besides proved by the maps,—for though there was no port, vessels might have visited it for the purpose of renewing their store of water. But the surrounding ocean was deserted as far as the eye could reach, and the colonists must rely on themselves for regaining their native land.

However, one chance of rescue existed, and this chance was discussed one day on the first week of April, when the colonists were gathered together in the dining room of Granite House.

They had been talking of America, of their native country, which they had so little hope of ever seeing again.

'Decidedly we have only one way, said Spilett, 'one single way for leaving Lincoln Island, and that is, to build a vessel large enough to sail several hundred miles. It appears to me, that when one has built a boat it is just as easy to build a ship!'

'And in which we might go to the Pomoutous,' added Herbert, 'just as easily as we went to Tabor Island.'

'I do not say no,' replied Pencroft, who had always the casting vote in maritime questions; 'I do not say no, although it is not exactly the same thing to make a long as a short voyage! If our little craft had been caught in any heavy gale of wind during the voyage to Tabor Island, we should have known that land was at no great distance either way; but twelve hundred miles is a pretty long way, and the nearest land is at least that distance!'

'Would you not, in that case, Pencroft, attempt the adventure?' asked the reporter.

'I will attempt anything that is desired, Mr. Spilett,' answered the sailor, 'and you know well that I am not a man to flinch!'

'Remember, besides, that we number another sailor amongst us now,' remarked Neb.

'Who is that?' asked Pencroft.

'Ayrton.'

'If he will consent to come,' said Pencroft.

'Nonsense!' returned the reporter; 'do you think that if Lord Glenarvan's yacht had appeared at Tabor Island, while he was still living there, Ayrton would have refused to depart?'

'You forget, my friends,' then said Cyrus Harding, 'that Ayrton was not in possession of his reason during the last years of his stay there. But that is not the question. The point is to know if we may count among our chances of being rescued, the return of the Scotch vessel. Now, Lord Glenarvan promised Ayrton that he would return to take him off from Tabor Island when he considered that his crimes were expiated, and I believe that he will return.'

'Yes,' said the reporter, 'and I will add that he will return soon, for it is twelve years since Ayrton was abandoned.'

'Well!' answered Pencroft, 'I agree with you that the nobleman will return, and soon too. But where will he touch? At Tabor Island, and not at Lincoln Island.'

'That is the more certain,' replied Herbert, 'as Lincoln Island is not even marked on the map.'

'Therefore, my friends,' said the engineer, 'we ought to take the necessary precautions for making our presence and that of Ayrton on Lincoln Island known at Tabor Island.'

'Certainly,' answered the reporter, 'and nothing is easier than to place in the hut, which was Captain Grant's and Ayrton's dwelling, a notice which Lord Glenarvan and his crew cannot help finding, giving the position of our island.'

'It is a pity,' remarked the sailor, 'that we forgot to take that precaution on our first visit to Tabor Island.'

'And why should we have done it?' asked Herbert. 'At that time we did not know Ayrton's history; we did not know that any one was likely to come some day to fetch him, and when we did know his history, the season was too advanced to allow us to return then to Tabor Island.'

'Yes,' replied Harding, 'it was too late, and we must put off the voyage until next spring.'

'But suppose the Scotch yacht comes before that,' said Pencroft.

'That is not probable,' replied the engineer, 'for Lord Glenarvan would not choose the winter season to venture into these seas. Either he has already returned to Tabor Island, since Ayrton has been with us, that is to say, during the last five months and has left again; or he will not come till later, and it will be time enough in the first fine October days to go to Tabor Island, and leave a notice there.'

'We must allow,' said Neb, 'that it will be very unfortunate if the 'Duncan' has returned to these parts only a few months ago!'

'I hope that it is not so,' replied Cyrus Harding, 'and that Heaven has not deprived us of the best chance which remains to us.'

'I think,' observed the reporter, 'that at any rate we shall know what we have to depend on when we have been to Tabor Island, for if the yacht has returned there, they will necessarily have left some traces of their visit.'

'That is evident,' answered the engineer. 'So then, my friends, since we have this chance of returning to our country, we must wait patiently, and if it is taken from us we shall see what will be best to do.'

'At any rate,' remarked Pencroft, 'it is well understood that if we do leave Lincoln Island, it will not be because we were uncomfortable there!'

'No, Pencroft,' replied the engineer, 'it will be because we are far from all that a man holds dearest in the world, his family, his friends, his native land!'

Matters being thus decided, the building of a vessel large enough to sail either to the Archipelagoes in the north, or to New Zealand in the west, was no longer talked of, and they busied themselves in their accustomed occupations, with a view to wintering a third time in Granite House.

However, it was agreed that before the stormy weather came on, their little vessel should be employed in making a voyage round the island. A complete survey of the coast had not yet been made, and the colonists had but an imperfect idea of the shore to the west and north, from the mouth of Falls River to the Mandible Capes, as well as of the narrow bay between them, which opened like a shark's jaws.

The plan of this excursion was proposed by Pencroft, and Cyrus Harding fully acquiesced in it, for he himself wished to see this part of his domain.

The weather was variable, but the barometer did not fluctuate by sudden movements, and they could therefore count on tolerable weather. However, during the first week of April, after a sudden barometrical fall, a renewed rise was marked by a heavy gale of wind, lasting five or six days; then the needle of the instrument remained stationary at a height of twenty-nine inches and nine-tenths, and the weather appeared propitious for an excursion.

The departure was fixed for the 16th of April, and the 'Bonadventure,' anchored in Port Balloon, was provisioned for a voyage which might be of some duration.

Cyrus Harding informed Ayrton of the projected expedition, and proposed that he should take part in it, but Ayrton preferring to remain on shore, it was decided that he should come to Granite House during the absence of his companions. Master Jup was ordered to keep him company, and made no remonstrance.

On the morning of the 16th of April all the colonists, including Top, embarked. A fine breeze blew from the south-west, and the 'Bonadventure' tacked on leaving Port Balloon so as to reach Reptile End. Of the ninety miles which the perimeter of the island measured, twenty included the south coast between the port and the promontory. The wind being right ahead it was necessary to hug the shore.

It took the whole day to reach the promontory, for the vessel on leaving pon had only two hours of ebb tide and had therefore to make way for six hours against the flood. It was nightfall before the promontory was doubled.

The sailor then proposed to the engineer that they should continue sailing slowly with two reefs in the sail. But Harding preferred to anchor a few cable-lengths from the shore, so as to survey that part of the coast during the day. It was agreed also that as they were anxious for a minute exploration of the coast they should not sail during the night, but would always, when the weather permitted it, be at anchor near the shore.

The night was passed under the promontory, and the wind having fallen, nothing disturbed the silence. The passengers, with the exception of the sailor, scarcely slept as well on board the 'Bonadventure' as they would have done in their rooms at Granite House, but they did sleep however. Pencroft set sail at break of day, and by going on the larboard tack they could keep close to the shore.

The colonists knew this beautiful wooded coast, since they had already explored it on foot, and yet it again excited their admiration. They coasted along as close in as possible, so as to notice everything, avoiding always the trunks of trees which floated here and there. Several times also they anchored, and Gideon Spilett took photographs of the superb scenery.

About noon the 'Bonadventure' arrived at the mouth of Falls River. Beyond, on the left bank, a few scattered trees appeared, and three miles further even these dwindled into solitary groups among the western spurs of the mountain, whose arid ridge sloped down to the shore.

What a contrast between the northern and southern part of the coast! In proportion as one was woody and fertile so was the other rugged and barren! It might have been designated as one of those iron coasts, as they are called in some countries, and its wild confusion appeared to indicate that a sudden crystallization had been produced in the yet liquid basalt of some distant geological sea. These stupendous masses would have terrified the settlers if they had been cast at first on this part of the island! They had not been able to perceive the sinister aspect of this shore from the summit of Mount Franklin, for they overlooked it from too great a height, but viewed from the sea it presented a wild appearance which could not perhaps be equalled in any corner of the globe.

The 'Bonadventure' sailed along this coast for the distance of half a mile. It was easy to see that it was composed of blocks of all sizes, from twenty to three hundred feet in height, and of all shapes, round like towers, prismatic like steeples, pyramidal like obelisks, conical like factory chimneys. An iceberg of the Polar seas could not have been more capricious in its terrible sublimity! Here, bridges were thrown from one rock to another; there, arches like those of a wave, into the depths of which the eye could not penetrate; in one place, large vaulted excavations presented a monumental aspect; in another, a crowd of columns, spires, and arches, such as no Gothic cathedral ever possessed. Every caprice of nature, still more varied than those of the imagination, appeared on this grand coast, which extended over a length of eight or nine miles.

Cyrus Harding and his companions gazed, with a feeling of surprise bordering on stupefaction. But, although they remained silent, Top, not being troubled with feelings of this sort, uttered barks which were repeated by the thousand echoes of the basaltic cliff. The engineer even observed that these barks had something strange in them, like those which the dog had uttered at the mouth of the well in Granite House.

'Let us go close in,' said he.

And the 'Bonadventure' sailed as near as possible to the rocky shore. Perhaps some cave, which it would be advisable to explore, existed there? But Harding saw nothing, not a cavern, not a cleft which could serve as a retreat to any being whatever, for the foot of the cliff was washed by the surf. Soon Top's barks ceased, and the vessel continued her course at a few cables-length from the coast.

In the northwest part of the island the shore became again flat and sandy. A few trees here and there rose above a low, marshy ground, which the colonists had already surveyed, and in violent contrast to the other desert shore, life was again manifested by the presence of myriads of water-fowl. That evening the 'Bonadventure' anchored in a small bay to the north of the island, near the land, such was the depth of water there. The night passed quietly, for the breeze died away with the last light of day, and only rose again with the first streaks of dawn.

As it was easy to land, the usual hunters of the colony, that is to say, Herbert and Gideon Spilett, went for a ramble of two hours or so, and returned with several strings of wild duck and snipe. Top had done wonders, and not a bird had been lost, thanks to his zeal and cleverness.

At eight o'clock in the morning the 'Bonadventure' set sail, and ran rapidly towards North Mandible Cape, for the wind was right astern and freshening rapidly.

'However,' observed Pencroft, 'I should not be surprised if a gale came up from the west. Yesterday the sun set in a very red-looking horizon, and now, this morning, those mares-tails don't forbode anything good.'

These mares-tails are cirrus clouds, scattered in the zenith, their height from the sea being less than five thousand feet. They look like light pieces of cotton wool, and their presence usually announces some sudden change in the weather.

'Well,' said Harding, 'let us carry as much sail as possible, and run for shelter into Shark Gulf. I think that the 'Bonadventure' will be safe there.'

'Perfectly,' replied Pencroft, 'and besides, the north coast is merely sand, very uninteresting to look at.'

'I shall not be sorry,' resumed the engineer, 'to pass not only tonight but tomorrow in that bay, which is worth being carefully explored.'

'I think that we shall be obliged to do so, whether we like it or not,' answered Pencroft, 'for the sky looks very threatening towards the west. Dirty weather is coming on!'

'At any rate we have a favourable wind for reaching Cape Mandible,' observed the reporter.

'A very fine wind,' replied the sailor; 'but we must tack to enter the gulf, and I should like to see my way clear in these unknown quarters.'

'Quarters which appear to be filled with rocks,' added Herbert, 'if we judge by what we saw on the south coast of Shark Gulf.'

'Pencroft,' said Cyrus Harding, 'do as you think best, we will leave it to you.'

'Don't make your mind uneasy, captain,' replied the sailor, 'I shall not expose myself needlessly! I would rather a knife were run into my ribs than a sharp rock into those of my 'Bonadventure!''

That which Pencroft called ribs was the pan of his vessel under water, and he valued it more than his own skin.

'What o'clock is it?' asked Pencroft.

'Ten o'clock,' replied Gideon Spilett.

'And what distance is it to the Cape, captain?'

'About fifteen miles,' replied the engineer.

'That's a matter of two hours and a half,' said the sailor, 'and we shall be off the Cape between twelve and one o'clock. Unluckily, the tide will be turning at that moment, and will be ebbing out of the gulf. I am afraid that it will be very difficult to get in, having both wind and tide against us.'

'And the more so that it is a full moon today,' remarked Herbert, 'and these April tides are very strong.'

'Well, Pencroft,' asked Harding, 'can you not anchor off the Cape?'

'Anchor near land, with bad weather coming on!' exclaimed the sailor. 'What are you thinking of, captain? We should run aground, of a certainty!'

'What will you do then?'

'I shall try to keep in the offing until the flood, that is to say, till about seven in the evening, and if there is still light enough I will try to enter the gulf; if not, we must stand off and on during the night, and we will enter tomorrow at sunrise.'

'As I told you, Pencroft, we will leave it to you,' answered Harding.

'Ah!' said Pencroft, 'if there was only a lighthouse on the coast, it would be much more convenient for sailors.'

'Yes,' replied Herbert, 'and this time we shall have no obliging engineer to light a fire to guide us into port!'

'Why, indeed, my dear Cyrus,' said Spilett, 'we have never thanked you; but frankly, without that fire we should never have been able—'

'A fire?' asked Harding, much astonished at the reporter's words.

'We mean, captain,' answered Pencroft, 'that on board the 'Bonadventure' we were very anxious during the few hours before our return, and we should have passed to windward of the island, if it had not been for the precaution you took of lighting a fire the night of the 19th of October, on Prospect Heights.

'Yes, yes! That was a lucky idea of mine!' replied the engineer.

'And this time,' continued the sailor. 'unless the idea occurs to Ayrton, there will be no one to do us that little service!'

'No! No one!' answered Cyrus Harding.

A few minutes after, finding himself alone in the bows of the vessel, with the reporter, the engineer bent down and whispered,—

'If there is one thing certain in this world, Spilett, it is that I never lighted any fire during the night of the 19th of October, neither on Prospect Heights nor on any other part of the island!'

Chapter 20

Things happened as Pencroft had predicted, he being seldom mistaken in his prognostications. The wind rose, and from a fresh breeze it soon increased to a regular gale; that is to say, it acquired a speed of from forty to forty-five miles an hour, before which a ship in the open sea would have run under close-reeved topsails. Now, as it was nearly six o'clock when the 'Bonadventure' reached the gulf, and as at that moment the tide turned, it was impossible to enter. They were therefore compelled to stand off, for even if he had wished to do so, Pencroft could not have gained the mouth of the Mercy. Hoisting the jib to the mainmast by way of a storm-sail, he hove to, putting the head of the vessel towards the land.

Fortunately, although the wind was strong the sea, being sheltered by the land, did not run very high. They had then little to fear from the waves, which always endanger small craft. The 'Bonadventure' would doubtlessly not have capsized, for she was well ballasted, but enormous masses of water falling on the deck might injure her if her timbers could not sustain them. Pencroft, as a good sailor, was prepared for anything. Certainly, he had great confidence in his vessel, but nevertheless he awaited the return of day with some anxiety.

During the night, Cyrus Harding and Gideon Spilett had no opportunity for talking together, and yet the words pronounced in the reporter's ear by the engineer were well worth being discussed, together with the mysterious influence which appeared to reign over Lincoln Island. Gideon Spilett did not cease from pondering over this new and inexplicable incident, the appearance of a fire on the coast of the island. The fire had actually been seen! His companions, Herbert and Pencroft, had seen it with him! The fire had served to signalize the position of the island during that dark night, and they had not doubted that it was lighted by the engineer's hand; and here was Cyrus Harding expressly declaring that he had never done anything of the sort! Spilett resolved to recur to this incident as soon as the 'Bonadventure' returned, and to urge Cyrus Harding to acquaint their companions with these strange facts. Perhaps it would be decided to make in common a complete investigation of every part of Lincoln Island.

However that might be, on this evening no fire was lighted on these yet unknown shores, which formed the entrance to the gulf, and the little vessel stood off during the night.

When the first streaks of dawn appeared in the western horizon, the wind, which had slightly fallen, shifted two points, and enabled Pencroft to enter the narrow gulf with greater ease. Towards seven o'clock in the morning, the 'Bonadventure,' weathering the North Mandible Cape, entered the strait and glided on to the waters, so strangely enclosed in the frame of lava.

'Well,' said Pencroft, 'this bay would make admirable roads, in which a whole fleet could lie at their ease!'

'What is especially curious,' observed Harding, 'is that the gulf has been formed by two rivers of lava, thrown out by the volcano, and accumulated by successive eruptions. The result is that the gulf is completely sheltered on all sides, and I believe that even in the stormiest weather, the sea here must be as calm as a lake.'

'No doubt,' returned the sailor, 'since the wind has only that narrow entrance between the two capes to get in by, and, besides, the north cape protects that of the south in a way which would make the entrance of gusts very difficult. I declare our 'Bonadventure' could stay here from one end of the year to the other, without even dragging at her anchor!'

'It is rather large for her!' observed the reporter.

'Well! Mr. Spilett,' replied the sailor, 'I agree that it is too large for the 'Bonadventure,' but if the fleets of the Union were in want of a harbour in the Pacific, I don't think they would ever find a better place than this!'

'We are in the shark's mouth,' remarked Nab, alluding to the form of the gulf.

'Right into its mouth, my honest Nab!' replied Herbert, 'but you are not afraid that it will shut upon us, are you?'

'No, Mr. Herbert,' answered Neb, 'and yet this gulf here doesn't please me much! It has a wicked look!'

'Hallo!' cried Pencroft, 'here is Neb turning up his nose at my gulf, just as I was thinking of presenting it to America!'

'But, at any rate, is the water deep enough?' asked the engineer, 'for a depth sufficient for the keel of the 'Bonadventure' would not be enough for those of our iron-clads.'

'That is easily found out,' replied Pencroft.

And the sailor sounded with a long cord, which served him as a lead-line, and to which was fastened a lump of iron. This cord measured nearly fifty fathoms, and its entire length was unrolled without finding any bottom.

'There,' exclaimed Pencroft, 'our iron-dads can come here after all! They would not run aground!'

'Indeed,' said Gideon Spilett, 'this gulf is a regular abyss, but, taking into consideration the volcanic origin of the island, it is not astonishing that the sea should offer similar depressions.'

'One would say too,' observed Herbert, 'that these cliffs were perfectly perpendicular; and I believe that at their foot, even with a line five or six times longer, Pencroft would not find bottom.'

'That is all very well,' then said the reporter, 'but I must point out to Pencroft that his harbour is wanting in one very important respect!'

'And what is that, Mr. Spilett?'

'An opening, a cutting of some sort, to give access to the interior of the island. I do not see a spot on which we could land.' And, in fact, the steep lava cliffs did not afford a single place suitable for landing. They formed an insuperable barrier, recalling, but with more wildness, the fiords of Norway. The 'Bonadventure,' coasting as close as possible along the cliffs, did not discover even a projection which would allow the passengers to leave the deck.

Pencroft consoled himself by saying that with the help of a mine they could soon open out the cliff when that was necessary, and then, as there was evidently nothing to be done in the gulf, he steered his vessel towards the strait and passed out at about two o'clock in the afternoon.

'Ah!' said Nab, uttering a sigh of satisfaction.

One might really say that the honest Negro did not feel at his ease in those enormous jaws.

The distance from Mandible Cape to the mouth of the Mercy was not more than eight miles. The head of the 'Bonadventure' was put towards Granite House, and a fair wind filling her sails, she ran rapidly along the coast.

To the enormous lava rocks succeeded soon those capricious sand dunes, among which the engineer had been so singularly recovered, and which seabirds frequented in thousands.

About four o'clock, Pencroft leaving the point of the islet on his left, entered the channel which separated it from the coast, and at five o'clock the anchor of the 'Bonadventure' was buried in the sand at the mouth of the Mercy.

The colonists had been absent three days from their dwelling. Ayrton was waiting for them on the beach, and Jup came joyously to meet them, giving vent to deep grunts of satisfaction.

A complete exploration of the coast of the island had now been made, and no suspicious appearances had been observed. If any mysterious being resided on it, it could only be under cover of the impenetrable forest of the Serpentine Peninsula, to which the colonists had not yet directed their investigations.

Gideon Spilett discussed these things with the engineer, and it was agreed that they should direct the attention of their companions to the strange character of certain incidents which had occurred on the island, and of which the last was the most unaccountable.

However, Harding, returning to the fact of a fire having been kindled on the shore by an unknown hand, could not refrain from repeating for the twentieth time to the reporter,—

'But are you quite sure of having seen it? Was it not a partial eruption of the volcano, or perhaps some meteor?'

'No, Cyrus,' answered the reporter, 'it was certainly a fire lighted by the hand of man. Besides; question Pencroft and Herbert. They saw it as I saw it myself, and they will confirm my words.'

In consequence, therefore, a few days after, on the 25th of April, in the evening, when the settlers were all collected on Prospect Heights, Cyrus Harding began by saying,—

'My friends, I think it my duty to call your attention to certain incidents which have occurred in the island, on the subject of which I shall be happy to have your advice. These incidents are, so to speak, supernatural—'

'Supernatural!' exclaimed the sailor, emitting a volume of smoke from his mouth. 'Can it be possible that our island is supernatural?'

'No, Pencroft, but mysterious, most certainly,' replied the engineer; 'unless you can explain that which Spilett and I have until now failed to understand.'

'Speak away, captain,' answered the sailor.

'Well, have you understood,' then said the engineer, 'how was it that after falling into the sea, I was found a quarter of a mile into the interior of the island, and that, without my having any consciousness of my removal there?'

'Unless, being unconscious—' said Pencroft.

'That is not admissible,' replied the engineer. 'But to continue. Have you understood how Top was able to discover your retreat five miles from the cave in which I was lying?'

'The dog's instinct—' observed Herbert.

'Singular instinct!' returned the reporter, 'since notwithstanding the storm of rain and wind which was raging during that night, Top arrived at the Chimneys, dry and without a speck of mud!'

'Let us continue,' resumed the engineer. 'Have you understood how our dog was so strangely thrown up out of the water of the lake, after his struggle with the dugong?'

'No! I confess, not at all,' replied Pencroft, 'and the wound which the dugong had in its side, a wound which seemed to have been made with a sharp instrument; that can't be understood, either.'

'Let us continue again,' said Harding. 'Have you understood, my friends, how that bullet got into the body of the young peccary; how that case happened to be so fortunately stranded, without there being any trace of a wreck; how that bottle containing the document presented itself so opportunely, during our first sea-excursion; how our canoe, having broken its moorings, floated down the current of the Mercy and rejoined us at the very moment we needed it; how after the ape invasion the ladder was so obligingly thrown down from Granite House; and lastly, how the document, which Ayrton asserts was never written by him, fell into our hands?'

As Cyrus Harding thus enumerated, without forgetting one, the singular incidents which had occurred in the island, Herbert, Neb, and Pencroft stared at each other, not knowing what to reply, for this succession of incidents, grouped thus for the first time, could not but excite their surprise to the highest degree.

''Pon my word,' said Pencroft at last, 'you are right, captain, and it is difficult to explain all these things!'

'Well, my friends,' resumed the engineer, 'a last fact has just been added to these, and it is no less incomprehensible than the others!'

'What is it, captain?' asked Herbert quickly.

'When you were returning from Tabor Island, Pencroft,' continued the engineer, 'you said that a fire appeared on Lincoln Island?'

'Certainly,' answered the sailor.

'And you are quite certain of having seen this fire?'

'As sure as I see you now.'

'You also, Herbert?'

'Why, captain,' cried Herbert, 'that fire was blazing like a star of the first magnitude!'

'But was it not a star?' urged the engineer.

'No,' replied Pencroft, 'for the sky was covered with thick clouds, and at any rate a star would not have been so low on the horizon. But Mr. Spilett saw it as well as we, and he will confirm our words.'

'I will add,' said the reporter, 'that the fire was very bright, and that it shot up like a sheet of lightning.'

'Yes, yes! exactly,' added Herbert, 'and it was certainly placed on the heights of Granite House.'

'Well, my friends,' replied Cyrus Harding, 'during the night of the 19th of October, neither Neb nor I lighted any fire on the coast.'

'You did not!' exclaimed Pencroft, in the height of his astonishment, not being able to finish his sentence.

'We did not leave Granite House,' answered Cyrus Harding, 'and if a fire appeared on the coast, it was lighted by another hand than ours!'

Pencroft, Herbert, and Neb were stupefied. No illusion could be possible, and a fire had actually met their eyes during the night of the 19th of October. Yes! they had to acknowledge it, a mystery existed! An inexplicable influence, evidently favourable to the colonists, but very irritating to their curiosity, was executed always in the nick of time on Lincoln Island. Could there be some being hidden in its profoundest recesses? It was necessary at any cost to ascertain this.

Harding also reminded his companions of the singular behaviour of Top and Jup when they prowled round the mouth of the well, which placed Granite House in communication with the sea, and he told them that he had explored the well, without discovering anything suspicious. The final resolve taken, in consequence of this conversation, by all the members of the colony, was that as soon as the fine season returned they would thoroughly search the whole of the island.

But from that day Pencroft appeared to be anxious. He felt as if the island which he had made his own personal property belonged to him entirely no longer, and that he shared it with another master, to whom, willing or not, he felt subject. Neb and he often talked of those unaccountable things, and both, their natures inclining them to the marvellous, were not far from believing that Lincoln Island was under the dominion of some supernatural power.

In the meanwhile, the bad weather came with the month of May, the November of the northern zones. It appeared that the winter would be severe and forward. The preparations for the winter season were therefore commenced without delay.

Nevertheless, the colonists were well prepared to meet the winter, however hard it might be. They had plenty of felt clothing, and the musmons, very numerous by this time, had furnished an abundance of wool necessary for the manufacture of this warm material.

It is unnecessary to say that Ayrton had been provided with this comfortable clothing. Cyrus Harding proposed that he should come to spend the bad season with them in Granite House, where he would be better lodged than at the corral, and Ayrton promised to do so, as soon as the last work at the corral was finished. He did this towards the middle of April. From that time Ayrton shared the common life, and made himself useful on all occasions; but still humble and sad, he never took part in the pleasures of his companions.

For the greater part of this, the third winter which the settlers passed in Lincoln Island, they were confined to Granite House. There were many violent storms and frightful tempests, which appeared to shake the rocks to their very foundations. Immense waves threatened to overwhelm the island, and certainly any vessel anchored near the shore would have been dashed to pieces. Twice, during one of these hurricanes, the Mercy swelled to such a degree as to give reason to fear that the bridges would be swept away, and it was necessary to strengthen those on the shore, which disappeared under the foaming waters, when the sea beat against the beach.

It may well be supposed that such storms, comparable to water-spouts in which were mingled rain and snow, would cause great havoc on the plateau of Prospect Heights. The mill and the poultry-yard particularly suffered. The colonists were often obliged to make immediate repairs, without which the safety of the birds would have been seriously threatened.

During the worst weather, several jaguars and troops of quadrumana ventured to the edge of the plateau, and it was always to be feared that the most active and audacious would, urged by hunger, manage to cross the stream, which besides, when frozen, offered them an easy passage. Plantations and domestic animals would then have been infallibly destroyed, without a constant watch, and it was often necessary to make use of the guns to keep those dangerous visitors at a respectful distance. Occupation was not wanting to the colonists, for without reckoning their outdoor cares, they had always a thousand plans for the fitting up of Granite House.

They had also some fine sporting excursions, which were made during the frost in the vast Tadorn Marsh. Gideon Spilett and Herbert, aided by Jup and Top, did not miss a shot in the midst of myriads of wild-duck, snipe, teal, and others. The access to these hunting-grounds was easy; besides, whether they reached them by the road to Port Balloon, after having passed the Mercy Bridge, or by turning the rocks from Flotsam Point, the hunters were never distant from Granite House more than two or three miles.

Thus passed the four winter months, which were really rigorous, that is to say, June, July, August, and September. But, in short, Granite House did not suffer much from the inclemency of the weather, and it was the same with the corral, which, less exposed than the plateau, and sheltered partly by Mount Franklin, only received the remains of the hurricanes, already broken by the forests and the high rocks of the shore. The damages there were consequently of small importance, and the activity and skill of Ayrton promptly repaired them, when some time in October he returned to pass a few days in the corral.

During this winter, no fresh inexplicable incident occurred. Nothing strange happened, although Pencroft and Neb were on the watch for the most insignificant facts to which they attached any mysterious cause. Top and Jup themselves no longer growled round the well or gave any signs of uneasiness. It appeared, therefore, as if the series of supernatural incidents was interrupted, although they often talked of them during the evenings in Granite House, and they remained thoroughly resolved that the island should be searched, even in those parts the most difficult to explore. But an event of the highest importance, and of which the consequences might be terrible, momentarily diverted from their projects Cyrus Harding and his companions.

It was the month of October. The fine season was swiftly returning. Nature was reviving; and among the evergreen foliage of the coniferae which formed the border of the wood, already appeared the young leaves of the banksias, deodars, and other trees.

It may be remembered that Gideon Spilett and Herbert had, at different times, taken photographic views of Lincoln Island.

Now, on the 17th of this month of October, towards three o'clock in the afternoon, Herbert, enticed by the charms of the sky, thought of reproducing Union Bay, which was opposite to Prospect Heights, from Cape Mandible to Claw Cape.

The horizon was beautifully clear, and the sea, undulating under a soft breeze, was as calm as the waters of a lake, sparkling here and there under the sun's rays.

The apparatus had been placed at one of the windows of the dining room at Granite House, and consequently overlooked the shore and the bay. Herbert proceeded as he was accustomed to do, and the negative obtained, he went away to fix it by means of the chemicals deposited in a dark nook of Granite House.

Returning to the bright light, and examining it well, Herbert perceived on his negative an almost imperceptible little spot on the sea horizon. He endeavoured to make it disappear by reiterated washing, but could not accomplish it.

'It is a flaw in the glass,' he thought.

And then he had the curiosity to examine this flaw with a strong magnifier which he unscrewed from one of the telescopes.

But he had scarcely looked at it, when he uttered a cry, and the glass almost fell from his hands.

Immediately running to the room in which Cyrus Harding then was, he extended the negative and magnifier towards the engineer, pointing out the little spot.

Harding examined it; then seizing his telescope he rushed to the window.

The telescope, after having slowly swept the horizon, at last stopped on the looked-for spot, and Cyrus Harding, lowering it, pronounced one word only,—

'A vessel!'

And in fact a vessel was in sight, off Lincoln Island!

PART THREE

THE SECRET OF THE ISLAND

Chapter 1

It was now two years and a half since the castaways from the balloon had been thrown on Lincoln Island, and during that period there had been no communication between them and their fellow-creatures. Once the reporter had attempted to communicate with the inhabited world by confiding to a bird a letter which contained the secret of their situation, but that was a chance on which it was impossible to reckon seriously. Ayrton, alone, under the circumstances which have been related, had come to join the little colony. Now, suddenly, on this day, the 17th of October, other men had unexpectedly appeared in sight of the island, on that deserted sea!

There could be no doubt about it! A vessel was there! But would she pass on, or would she put into port? In a few hours the colonists would definitely know what to expect.

Cyrus Harding and Herbert having immediately called Gideon Spilett, Pencroft, and Neb into the dining room of Granite House, told them what had happened. Pencroft, seizing the telescope, rapidly swept the horizon, and stopping on the indicated point, that is to say, on that which had made the almost imperceptible spot on the photographic negative,—

'I'm blessed but it is really a vessel!' he exclaimed, in a voice which did not express any great amount of satisfaction.

'Is she coming here?' asked Gideon Spilett.

'Impossible to say anything yet,' answered Pencroft, 'for her rigging alone is above the horizon, and not a bit of her hull can be seen.'

'What is to be done?' asked the lad.

'Wait,' replied Harding.

And for a considerable time the settlers remained silent, given up to all the thoughts, and the emotions, all the fears, all the hopes, which were aroused by this incident—the most important which had occurred since their arrival in Lincoln Island. Certainly, the colonists were not in the situation of castaways abandoned on a sterile islet, constantly contending against a cruel nature for their miserable existence, and incessantly tormented by the longing to return to inhabited countries. Pencroft and

Neb, especially, who felt themselves at once so happy and so rich, would not have left their island without regret. They were accustomed, besides, to this new life in the midst of the domain which their intelligence had as it were civilized. But at any rate this ship brought news from the world, perhaps even from their native land. It was bringing fellow-creatures to them, and it may be conceived how deeply their hearts were moved at the sight!

From time to time Pencroft took the glass and rested himself at the window. From thence he very attentively examined the vessel, which was at a distance of twenty miles to the east. The colonists had as yet, therefore, no means of signalizing their presence. A flag would not have been perceived; a gun would not have been heard; a fire would not have been visible. However, it was certain that the island, overtopped by Mount Franklin, could not escape the notice of the vessel's lookout. But why was the ship coming there? Was it simple chance which brought it to that part of the Pacific, where the maps mentioned no land except Tabor Island, which itself was out of the route usually followed by vessels from the Polynesian Archipelagoes, from New Zealand, and from the American coast? To this question, which each one asked himself, a reply was suddenly made by Herbert.

'Can it be the 'Duncan'?' he cried.

The 'Duncan,' as has been said, was Lord Glenarvan's yacht, which had left Ayrton on the islet, and which was to return there someday to fetch him. Now, the islet was not so far distant from Lincoln Island, but that a vessel, standing for the one, could pass in sight of the other. A hundred and fifty miles only separated them in longitude, and seventy in latitude.

'We must tell Ayrton,' said Gideon Spilett, 'and send for him immediately. He alone can say if it is the 'Duncan."

This was the opinion of all, and the reporter, going to the telegraphic apparatus which placed the corral in communication with Granite House, sent this telegram:—'Come with all possible speed.'

In a few minutes the bell sounded.

'I am coming,' replied Ayrton.

Then the settlers continued to watch the vessel.

'If it is the 'Duncan,' ' said Herbert, 'Ayrton will recognize her without difficulty, since he sailed on board her for some time.'

'And if he recognizes her,' added Pencroft, 'it will agitate him exceedingly!'

'Yes,' answered Cyrus Harding; 'but now Ayrton is worthy to return on board the 'Duncan,' and pray Heaven that it is indeed Lord Glenarvan's yacht, for I should be suspicious of any other vessel. These are ill-famed seas, and I have always feared a visit from Malay pirates to our island.'

'We could defend it,', cried Herbert.

'No doubt, my boy,' answered the engineer smiling, 'but it would be better not to have to defend it.'

'A useless observation,' said Spilett. 'Lincoln Island is unknown to navigators, since it is not marked even on the most recent maps. Do you think, Cyrus, that that is a sufficient motive for a ship, finding herself unexpectedly in sight of new land, to try and visit rather than avoid it?'

'Certainly,' replied Pencroft.

'I think so too,' added the engineer. 'It may even be said that it is the duty of a captain to come and survey any land or island not yet known, and Lincoln Island is in this position.'

'Well,' said Pencroft, 'suppose this vessel comes and anchors there a few cables-lengths from our island, what shall we do?'

This sudden question remained at first without any reply. But Cyrus Harding, after some moments' thought, replied in the calm tone which was usual to him,—

'What we shall do, my friends? What we ought to do is this:—we will communicate with the ship, we will take our passage on board her, and we will leave our island, after having taken possession of it in the name of the United States. Then we will return with any who may wish to follow us to colonize it definitely, and endow the American Republic with a useful station in this part of the Pacific Ocean!'

'Hurrah!' exclaimed Pencroft, 'and that will be no small present which we shall make to our country! The colonization is already almost finished; names are given to every part of the island; there is a natural port, fresh water, roads, a telegraph, a dockyard, and manufactories; and there will be nothing to be done but to inscribe Lincoln Island on the maps!'

'But if anyone seizes it in our absence?' observed Gideon Spilett.

'Hang it!' cried the sailor. 'I would rather remain all alone to guard it: and trust to Pencroft, they shouldn't steal it from him, like a watch from the pocket of a swell!'

For an hour it was impossible to say with any certainty whether the vessel was or was not standing towards Lincoln Island. She was nearer, but in what direction was she sailing? This Pencroft could not determine. However, as the wind was blowing from the northeast, in all probability the vessel was sailing on the starboard tack. Besides, the wind was favourable for bringing her towards the island, and, the sea being calm, she would not be afraid to approach although the shallows were not marked on the chart.

Towards four o'clock—an hour after he had been sent for—Ayrton arrived at Granite House. He entered the dining room saying,—

'At your service, gentlemen.'

Cyrus Harding gave him his hand, as was his custom to do, and, leading him to the window,—

'Ayrton,' said he, 'we have begged you to come here for an important reason. A ship is in sight of the island.'

Ayrton at first paled slightly, and for a moment his eyes became dim; then, leaning out the window, he surveyed the horizon, but could see nothing.

'Take this telescope,' said Spilett, 'and look carefully, Ayrton, for it is possible that this ship may be the 'Duncan' come to these seas for the purpose of taking you home again.'

'The 'Duncan!'' murmured Ayrton. 'Already?' This last word escaped Ayrton's lips as if involuntarily, and his head drooped upon his hands.

Did not twelve years' solitude on a desert island appear to him a sufficient expiation? Did not the penitent yet feel himself pardoned, either in his own eyes or in the eyes of others?

'No,' said he, 'no! it cannot be the 'Duncan'!'

'Look, Ayrton,' then said the engineer, 'for it is necessary that we should know beforehand what to expect.'

Ayrton took the glass and pointed it in the direction indicated. During some minutes he examined the horizon without moving, without uttering a word. Then,—

'It is indeed a vessel,' said he, 'but I do not think she is the 'Duncan.''

'Why do you not think so?' asked Gideon Spilett.

'Because the 'Duncan' is a steam-yacht, and I cannot perceive any trace of smoke either above or near that vessel.'

'Perhaps she is simply sailing,' observed Pencroft. 'The wind is favourable for the direction which she appears to be taking, and she may be anxious to economize her coal, being so far from land.'

'It is possible that you may be right, Mr. Pencroft,' answered Ayrton, 'and that the vessel has extinguished her fires. We must wait until she is nearer, and then we shall soon know what to expect.'

So saying, Ayrton sat down in a corner of the room and remained silent. The colonists again discussed the strange ship, but Ayrton took no part in the conversation. All were in such a mood that they found it impossible to continue their work. Gideon Spilett and Pencroft were particularly nervous, going, coming, not able to remain still in one place. Herbert felt more curiosity. Neb alone maintained his usual calm manner. Was not his country that where his master was? As to the engineer, he remained plunged in deep thought, and in his heart feared rather than desired the arrival of the ship. In the meanwhile, the vessel was a little nearer the island. With the aid of the glass, it was ascertained that she was a brig, and not one of those Malay proas, which are generally used by the pirates of the Pacific. It was, therefore, reasonable to believe that the engineer's apprehensions would not be justified, and that the presence of this vessel in the vicinity of the island was fraught with no danger.

Pencroft, after a minute examination, was able positively to affirm that the vessel was rigged as a brig, and that she was standing obliquely towards the coast, on the starboard tack, under her topsails and top-gallant-sails. This was confirmed by Ayrton. But by continuing in this direction she must soon disappear behind Claw Cape, as the wind was from the southwest, and to watch her it would be then necessary to ascend the height of Washington Bay, near Port Balloon—a provoking circumstance, for it was already five o'clock in the evening, and the twilight would soon make any observation extremely difficult.

'What shall we do when night comes on?' asked Gideon Spilett. 'Shall we light a fire, so as to signal our presence on the coast?'

This was a serious question, and yet, although the engineer still retained some of his presentiments, it was answered in the affirmative. During the night the ship might disappear and leave for ever, and, this ship gone, would another ever return to the waters of Lincoln Island? Who could foresee what the future would then have in store for the colonists?

'Yes,' said the reporter, 'we ought to make known to that vessel, whoever she may be, that the island is inhabited. To neglect the opportunity which is offered to us might be to create everlasting regrets.'

It was therefore decided that Neb and Pencroft should go to Port Balloon, and that there, at nightfall, they should light an immense fire, the blaze of which would necessarily attract the attention of the brig.

But at the moment when Neb and the sailor were preparing to leave Granite House, the vessel suddenly altered her course, and stood directly for Union Bay. The brig was a good sailer, for she approached rapidly. Neb and Pencroft put off their departure, therefore, and the glass was put into Ayrton's hands, that he might ascertain for certain whether the ship was or was not the 'Duncan.' The Scotch yacht was also rigged as a brig. The question was, whether a chimney could be discerned between the two masts of the vessel, which was now at a distance of only five miles.

The horizon was still very clear. The examination was easy, and Ayrton soon let the glass fall again, saying—

'It is not the 'Duncan'! It could not be!'

Pencroft again brought the brig within the range of the telescope, and could see that she was of between three and four hundred tons burden, wonderfully narrow, well-masted, admirably built, and must be a very rapid sailer. But to what nation did she belong? That was difficult to say.

'And yet,' added the sailor, 'a flag is floating from her peak, but I cannot distinguish the colours of it.'

'In half an hour we shall be certain about that,' answered the reporter. 'Besides, it is very evident that the intention of the captain of this ship is to land, and, consequently, if not today, tomorrow at the latest, we shall make his acquaintance.'

'Never mind!' said Pencroft. 'It is best to know whom we have to deal with, and I shall not be sorry to recognize that fellow's colours!'

And, while thus speaking, the sailor never left the glass. The day began to fade, and with the day the breeze fell also. The brig's ensign hung in folds, and it became more and more difficult to observe it.

'It is not the American flag,' said Pencroft from time to time, 'nor the English, the red of which could be easily seen, nor the French or German colours, nor the white flag of Russia, nor the yellow of Spain. One would say it was all one colour. Let's see: in these seas, what do we generally meet with? The Chilean flag?—but that is tri-colour. Brazilian?—it is green. Japanese?—it is yellow and black, while this—'

At that moment the breeze blew out the unknown flag. Ayrton seizing the telescope which the sailor had put down, put it to his eye, and in a hoarse voice, —

'The black flag!' he exclaimed.

And indeed the somber bunting was floating from the mast of the brig, and they had now good reason for considering her to be a suspicious vessel!

Had the engineer, then, been right in his presentiments? Was this a pirate vessel? Did she scour the Pacific, competing with the Malay proas which still infest it? For what had she come to look at the shores of Lincoln Island? Was it to them an unknown island, ready to become a magazine for stolen cargoes? Had she come to find on the coast a sheltered port for the winter months? Was the settlers' honest domain destined to be transformed into an infamous refuge—the headquarters of the piracy of the Pacific?

All these ideas instinctively presented themselves to the colonists' imaginations. There was no doubt, besides, of the signification which must be attached to the colour of the hoisted flag. It was that of pirates! It was that which the 'Duncan' would have carried, had the convicts succeeded in their criminal design! No time was lost before discussing it.

'My friends,' said Cyrus Harding, 'perhaps this vessel only wishes to survey the coast of the island. Perhaps her crew will not land. There is a chance of it. However that may be, we ought to do everything we can to hide our presence here. The windmill on Prospect Heights is too easily seen. Let Ayrton and Neb go and take down the sails. We must also conceal the windows of Granite House with thick branches. All the fires must be extinguished, so that nothing may betray the presence of men on the island.'

'And our vessel?' said Herbert.

'Oh,' answered Pencroft, 'she is sheltered in Port Balloon, and I defy any of those rascals there to find her!'

The engineer's orders were immediately executed. Neb and Ayrton ascended the plateau, and took the necessary precautions to conceal any indication of a settlement. While they were thus occupied, their companions went to the border of Jacamar Wood, and brought back a large quantity of branches and creepers, which would at some distance appear as natural foliage, and thus disguise the windows in the granite cliff. At the same time, the ammunition and guns were placed ready so as to be at hand in case of an unexpected attack.

When all these precautions had been taken,—

'My friends,' said Harding, and his voice betrayed some emotion, 'if the wretches endeavour to seize Lincoln Island, we shall defend it—shall we not?'

'Yes, Cyrus,' replied the reporter, 'and if necessary we will die to defend it!'

The engineer extended his hand to his companions, who pressed it warmly. Ayrton remained in his corner, not joining the colonists. Perhaps he, the former convict, still felt himself unworthy to do so!

Cyrus Harding understood what was passing in Ayrton's mind, and going to him—

'And you, Ayrton,' he asked, 'what will you do?'

'My duty,' answered Ayrton.

He then took up his station near the window and gazed through the foliage.

It was now half-past seven. The sun had disappeared twenty minutes ago behind Granite House. Consequently the Eastern horizon was becoming obscured. In the meanwhile the brig continued to advance towards Union Bay. She was now not more than two miles off, and exactly opposite the plateau of Prospect Heights, for after having tacked off Claw Cape, she had drifted towards the north in the current of the rising tide. One might have said that at this distance she had already entered the vast bay, for a straight line drawn from Claw Cape to Cape Mandible would have rested on her starboard quarter.

Was the brig about to penetrate far into the bay? That was the first question. When once in the bay, would she anchor there? That was the second. Would she not content herself with only surveying the coast, and stand out to sea again without landing her crew? They would know this in an hour. The colonists could do nothing but wait.

Cyrus Harding had not seen the suspected vessel hoist the black flag without deep anxiety. Was it not a direct menace against the work which he and his companions had till now conducted so successfully? Had these pirates—for the sailors of the brig could be nothing else—already visited the island, since on approaching it they had hoisted their colours. Had they formerly invaded it, so that certain unaccountable peculiarities might be explained in this way? Did there exist in the as yet unexplored parts some accomplice ready to enter into communication with them?

To all these questions which he mentally asked himself, Harding knew not what to reply; but he felt that the safety of the colony could not but be seriously threatened by the arrival of the brig.

However, he and his companions were determined to fight to the last gasp. It would have been very important to know if the pirates were numerous and better armed than the colonists. But how was this information to he obtained?

Night fell. The new moon had disappeared. Profound darkness enveloped the island and the sea. No light could pierce through the heavy piles of clouds on the horizon. The wind had died away completely with the twilight. Not a leaf rustled on the trees, not a ripple murmured on the shore. Nothing could be seen of the ship, all her lights being extinguished, and if she was still in sight of the island, her whereabouts could not be discovered.

'Well! who knows?' said Pencroft. 'Perhaps that cursed craft will stand off during the night, and we shall see nothing of her at daybreak.'

As if in reply to the sailor's observation, a bright light flashed in the darkness, and a cannon-shot was heard.

The vessel was still there and had guns on board.

Six seconds elapsed between the flash and the report.

Therefore the brig was about a mile and a quarter from the coast.

At the same time, the chains were heard rattling through the hawse-holes.

The vessel had just anchored in sight of Granite House!

Chapter 2

There was no longer any doubt as to the pirates' intentions. They had dropped anchor at a short distance from the island, and it was evident that the next day by means of their boats they purposed to land on the beach!

Cyrus Harding and his companions were ready to act, but, determined though they were, they must not forget to be prudent. Perhaps their presence might still be concealed in the event of the pirates contenting themselves with landing on the shore without examining the interior of the island. It might be, indeed, that their only intention was to obtain fresh water from the Mercy, and it was not impossible that the bridge, thrown across a mile and a half from the mouth, and the manufactory at the Chimneys might escape their notice.

But why was that flag hoisted at the brig's peak? What was that shot fired for? Pure bravado doubtless, unless it was a sign of the act of taking possession. Harding knew now that the vessel was well armed. And what had the colonists of Lincoln Island to reply to the pirates' guns? A few muskets only.

'However,' observed Cyrus Harding, 'here we are in an impregnable position. The enemy cannot discover the mouth of the outlet, now that it is hidden under reeds and grass, and consequently it would be impossible for them to penetrate into Granite House.'

'But our plantations, our poultry-yard, our corral, all, everything!' exclaimed Pencroft, stamping his foot. 'They may spoil everything, destroy everything in a few hours!'

'Everything, Pencroft,' answered Harding, 'and we have no means of preventing them.'

'Are they numerous? that is the question,' said the reporter. 'If they are not more than a dozen, we shall be able to stop them, but forty, fifty, more perhaps!'

'Captain Harding,' then said Ayrton, advancing towards the engineer, 'will you give me leave?'

'For what, my friend?'

'To go to that vessel to find out the strength of her crew.'

'But Ayrton—' answered the engineer, hesitating, 'you will risk your life—'

'Why not, sir?'

'That is more than your duty.'

'I have more than my duty to do,' replied Ayrton.

'Will you go to the ship in the boat?' asked Gideon Spilett.

'No, sir, but I will swim. A boat would be seen where a man may glide between wind and water.'

'Do you know that the brig is a mile and a quarter from the shore?' said Herbert.

'I am a good swimmer, Mr. Herbert.'

'I tell you it is risking your life,' said the engineer.

'That is no matter,' answered Ayrton. 'Captain Harding, I ask this as a favour. Perhaps it will be a means of raising me in my own eyes!'

'Go, Ayrton,' replied the engineer, who felt sure that a refusal would have deeply wounded the former convict, now become an honest man.

'I will accompany you,' said Pencroft.

'You mistrust me!' said Ayrton quickly.

Then more humbly,—

'Alas!'

'No! no!' exclaimed Harding with animation, 'no, Ayrton, Pencroft does not mistrust you. You interpret his words wrongly.'

'Indeed,' returned the sailor, 'I only propose to accompany Ayrton as far as the islet. It may be, although it is scarcely possible, that one of these villains has landed, and in that case two men will not be too many to hinder him from giving the alarm. I will wait for Ayrton on the islet, and he shall go alone to the vessel, since he has proposed to do so.' These things agreed to, Ayrton made preparations for his departure. His plan was bold, but it might succeed, thanks to the darkness of the night. Once arrived at the vessel's side, Ayrton, holding on to the main chains, might reconnoitre the number and perhaps overhear the intentions of the pirates.

Ayrton and Pencroft, followed by their companions, descended to the beach. Ayrton undressed and rubbed himself with grease, so as to suffer less from the temperature of the water, which was still cold. He might, indeed, be obliged to remain in it for several hours.

Pencroft and Neb, during this time, had gone to fetch the boat, moored a few hundred feet higher up, on the bank of the Mercy, and by the time they returned, Ayrton was ready to start. A coat was thrown over his shoulders, and the settlers all came round him to press his hand.

Ayrton then shoved off with Pencroft in the boat.

It was half-past ten in the evening when the two adventurers disappeared in the darkness. Their companions returned to wait at the Chimneys.

The channel was easily traversed, and the boat touched the opposite shore of the islet. This was not done without precaution, for fear lest the pirates might be roaming about there. But after a careful survey, it was evident that the islet was deserted. Ayrton then, followed by Pencroft, crossed it with a rapid step, scaring the birds nestled in the holes of the rocks; then, without hesitating, he plunged into the sea, and swam noiselessly in the direction of the ship, in which a few lights had recently appeared, showing her exact situation. As to Pencroft, he crouched down in a cleft of the rock, and awaited the return of his companion.

In the meanwhile, Ayrton, swimming with a vigorous stroke, glided through the sheet of water without producing the slightest ripple. His head just emerged above it and his eyes were fixed on the dark hull of the brig, from which the lights were reflected in the water. He thought only of the duty which he had promised to accomplish, and nothing of the danger which he ran, not only on board the ship, but in the sea, often frequented by sharks. The current bore him along and he rapidly receded from the shore.

Half an hour afterwards, Ayrton, without having been either seen or heard, arrived at the ship and caught hold of the main-chains. He took breath, then, hoisting himself up, he managed to reach the extremity of the cutwater. There were drying several pairs of sailors' trousers. He put on a pair. Then settling himself firmly, he listened. They were not sleeping on board the brig. On the contrary, they were talking, singing, laughing. And these were the sentences, accompanied with oaths, which principally struck Ayrton:—

'Our brig is a famous acquisition.'

'She sails well, and merits her name of the 'Speedy."'

'She would show all the navy of Norfolk a clean pair of heels.'

'Hurrah for her captain!'

'Hurrah for Bob Harvey!'

What Ayrton felt when he overheard this fragment of conversation may be understood when it is known that in this Bob Harvey he recognized one of his old Australian companions, a daring sailor, who had continued his criminal career. Bob Harvey had seized, on the shores of Norfolk Island this brig, which was loaded with arms, ammunition, utensils, and tools of all sorts, destined for one of the Sandwich Islands. All his gang had gone on board, and pirates after having been convicts, these wretches, more ferocious than the Malays themselves, scoured the Pacific, destroying vessels, and massacring their crews.

The convicts spoke loudly, they recounted their deeds, drinking deeply at the same time, and this is what Ayrton gathered. The actual crew of the 'Speedy' was composed solely of English prisoners, escaped from Norfolk

Island.

Here it may be well to explain what this island was. In 29° 2' south latitude, and 165° 42' east longitude, to the east of Australia, is found a little island, six miles in circumference, overlooked by Mount Pitt, which rises to a height of 1,100 feet above the level of the sea. This is Norfolk Island, once the seat of an establishment in which were lodged the most intractable convicts from the English penitentiaries. They numbered 500, under an iron discipline, threatened with terrible punishments, and were guarded by 150 soldiers, and 150 employed under the orders of the governor. It would be difficult to imagine a collection of greater ruffians. Sometimes,—although very rarely,—notwithstanding the extreme surveillance of which they were the object, many managed to escape, and seizing vessels which they surprised, they infested the Polynesian Archipelagoes.

Thus had Bob Harvey and his companions done. Thus had Ayrton formerly wished to do. Bob Harvey had seized the brig 'Speedy,' anchored in sight of Norfolk Island; the crew had been massacred; and for a year this ship had scoured the Pacific, under the command of Harvey, now a pirate, and well known to Ayrton!

The convicts were, for the most part, assembled under the poop; but a few, stretched on the deck, were talking loudly.

The conversation still continued amid shouts and libations. Ayrton learned that chance alone had brought the 'Speedy' in sight of Lincoln Island; Bob Harvey had never yet set foot on it; but, as Cyrus Harding had conjectured, finding this unknown land in his course, its position being marked on no chart, he had formed the project of visiting it, and, if he found it suitable, of making it the brig's headquarters.

As to the black flag hoisted at the 'Speedy's' peak, and the gun which had been fired, in imitation of men-of-war when they lower their colours, it was pure piratical bravado. It was in no way a signal, and no communication yet existed between the convicts and Lincoln Island.

The settlers' domain was now menaced with terrible danger. Evidently the island, with its water, its harbour, its resources of all kinds so increased in value by the colonists, and the concealment afforded by Granite House, could not but be convenient for the convicts; in their hands it would become an excellent place of refuge, and, being unknown, it would assure them, for a long time perhaps, impunity and security. Evidently, also, the lives of the settlers would not be respected, and Bob Harvey and his accomplices' first care would be to massacre them without mercy. Harding and his companions had, therefore, not even the choice of flying and hiding themselves in the island, since the convicts intended to reside there, and since, in the event of the 'Speedy' departing on an expedition, it was probable that some of the crew would remain on shore, so as to settle themselves there. Therefore, it would be necessary to fight, to destroy every one of these scoundrels, unworthy of pity, and against whom any means would be right. So thought Ayrton, and he well knew that Cyrus Harding would be of his way of thinking.

But was resistance and, in the last place, victory possible? That would depend on the equipment of the brig, and the number of men which she carried.

This Ayrton resolved to learn at any cost, and as an hour after his arrival the vociferations had begun to die away, and as a large number of the convicts were already buried in a drunken sleep, Ayrton did not hesitate to venture onto the 'Speedy's' deck, which the extinguished lanterns now left in total darkness. He hoisted himself onto the cutwater, and by the bowsprit arrived at the forecastle. Then, gliding among the convicts stretched here and there, he made the round of the ship, and found that the 'Speedy' carried four guns, which would throw shot of from eight to ten pounds in weight. He found also, on touching them that these guns were breech-loaders. They were therefore, of modern make, easily used, and of terrible effect.

As to the men lying on the deck, they were about ten in number, but it was to be supposed that more were sleeping down below. Besides, by listening to them, Ayrton had understood that there were fifty on board. That was a large number for the six settlers of Lincoln Island to contend with! But now, thanks to Ayrton's devotion, Cyrus Harding would not be surprised, he would know the strength of his adversaries, and would make his arrangements accordingly.

There was nothing more for Ayrton to do but to return, and render to his companions an account of the mission with which he had charged himself, and he prepared to regain the bows of the brig, so that he might let himself down into the water. But to this man, whose wish was, as he had said, to do more than his duty, there came an heroic thought. This was to sacrifice his own life, but save the island and the colonists. Cyrus Harding evidently could not resist fifty ruffians, all well armed, who, either by penetrating by main force into Granite House, or by starving out the besieged, could obtain from them what they wanted. And then he thought of his preservers—those who had made him again a man, and an honest mm, those to whom he owed all—murdered without pity, their works destroyed, their island turned into a pirates' den! He said to himself that he, Ayrton, was the principal cause of so many disasters, since his old companion, Bob Harvey, had but realized his own plans, and a feeling of horror took possession of him. Then he was seized with an irresistible desire to blow up the brig and with her, all whom she had on board. He would perish in the explosion, but he would have done his duty.

Ayrton did not hesitate. To reach the powder-room, which is always situated in the after-part of a vessel, was easy. There would be no want of powder in a vessel which followed such a trade, and a spark would be enough to destroy it in an instant.

Ayrton stole carefully along the between-decks, strewn with numerous sleepers, overcome more by drunkenness than sleep. A lantern was lighted at the foot of the mainmast, round which was hung a gun-rack, furnished with weapons of all sorts.

Ayrton took a revolver from the rack, and assured himself that it was loaded and primed. Nothing more was needed to accomplish the work of destruction. He then glided towards the stern, so as to arrive under the brig's poop at the powder-magazine.

It was difficult to proceed along the dimly lighted deck without stumbling over some half-sleeping convict, who retorted by oaths and kicks. Ayrton was, therefore, more than once obliged to halt. But at last he arrived at the partition dividing the aftercabin, and found the door opening into the magazine itself.

Ayrton, compelled to force it open, set to work. It was a difficult operation to perform without noise, for he had to break a padlock. But under his vigorous hand, the padlock broke, and the door was open.

At that moment a hand was laid on Ayrton's shoulder.

'What are you doing here?' asked a tail man, in a harsh voice, who, standing in the shadow, quickly threw the light of a lantern in Ayrton's face.

Ayrton drew beck. In the rapid flash of the lantern, he had recognized his former accomplice, Bob Harvey, who could not have known him, as he must have thought Ayrton long since dead.

'What are you doing here?' again said Bob Harvey, seizing Ayrton by the waistband.

But Ayrton, without replying, wrenched himself from his grasp and attempted to rush into the magazine. A shot fired into the midst of the powder-casks, and all would be over!

'Help, lads!' shouted Bob Harvey.

At his shout two or three pirates awoke, jumped up, and, rushing on Ayrton, endeavoured to throw him down. He soon extricated himself from their grasp. He fired his revolver, and two of the convicts fell, but a blow from a knife which he could not ward off made a gash in his shoulder.

Ayrton perceived that he could no longer hope to carry out his project. Bob Harvey had reclosed the door of the powder-magazine, and a movement on the deck indicated a general awakening of the pirates. Ayrton must reserve himself to fight at the side of Cyrus Harding. There was nothing for him but flight!

But was flight still possible? It was doubtful, yet Ayrton resolved to dare everything in order to rejoin his companions.

Four barrels of the revolver were still undischarged. Two were fired— one, aimed at Bob Harvey, did not wound him, or at any rate only slightly, and Ayrton, profiting by the momentary retreat of his adversaries, rushed towards the companion-ladder to gain the deck. Passing before the lantern, he smashed it with a blow from the butt of his revolver. A profound darkness ensued, which favoured his flight. Two or three pirates, awakened by the noise, were descending the ladder at the same moment.

A fifth shot from Ayrton laid one low, and the others drew back, not understanding what was going on. Ayrton was on deck in two bounds, and three seconds later, having discharged his last barrel in the face of a pirate who was about to seize him by the throat, he leaped over the bulwarks into the sea.

Ayrton had not made six strokes before shots were splashing around him like hail.

What were Pencroft's feelings, sheltered under a rock on the islet! What were those of Harding, the reporter, Herbert, and Neb, crouched in the Chimneys, when they heard the reports on board the brig! They rushed out on to the beach, and, their guns shouldered, they stood ready to repel any attack.

They had no doubt about it themselves! Ayrton, surprised by the pirates, had been murdered, and, perhaps, the wretches would profit by the night to make a descent on the island!

Half an hour was passed in terrible anxiety. The firing had ceased, and yet neither Ayrton nor Pencroft had reappeared. Was the islet invaded? Ought they not to fly to the help of Ayrton and Pencroft? But how? The tide being high at that time, rendered the channel impassable. The boat was not there! We may imagine the horrible anxiety which took possession of Harding and his companions!

At last, towards half-past twelve, a boat, carrying two men, touched the beach. It was Ayrton, slightly wounded in the shoulder, and Pencroft, safe and sound, whom their friends received with open arms.

All immediately took refuge in the Chimneys. There Ayrton recounted all that had passed, even to his plan for blowing up the brig, which he had attempted to put into execution.

All hands were extended to Ayrton, who did not conceal from them that their situation was serious. The pirates had been alarmed. They knew that Lincoln Island was inhabited. They would land upon it in numbers and well armed. They would respect nothing. Should the settlers fall into their hands, they must expect no mercy!

'Well, we shall know how to die!' said the reporter.

'Let us go in and watch,' answered the engineer.

'Have we any chance of escape, captain?' asked the sailor.

'Yes, Pencroft.'

'Hum! six against fifty!'

'Yes! six! without counting—'

'Who?' asked Pencroft.

Cyrus did not reply, but pointed upwards.

Chapter 3

The night passed without incident. The colonists were on the Qui Vive, and did not leave their post at the Chimneys. The pirates, on their side, did not appear to have made any attempt to land. Since the last shots fired at Ayrton not a report, not even a sound, had betrayed the presence of the brig in the neighbourhood of the island. It might have been fancied that she had weighed anchor, thinking that she had to deal with her match, and had left the coast.

But it was no such thing, and when day began to dawn the settlers could see a confused mass through the morning mist. It was the 'Speedy.'

'These, my friends,' said the engineer, 'are the arrangements which appear to me best to make before the fog completely clears away. It hides us from the eyes of the pirates, and we can act without attracting their attention. The most important thing is, that the convicts should believe that the inhabitants of the island are numerous, and consequently capable of resisting them. I therefore propose that we divide into three parties. The first of which shall be posted at the Chimneys, the second at the mouth of the Mercy. As to the third, I think it would be best to place it on the islet, so as to prevent, or at all events delay, any attempt at landing. We have the use of two rifles and four muskets. Each of us will be armed, and, as we are amply provided with powder and shot, we need not spare our fire. We have nothing to fear from the muskets nor even from the guns of the brig. What can they do against these rocks? And, as we shall not fire from the windows of Granite House, the pirates will not think of causing irreparable damage by throwing shell against it. What is to be feared is, the necessity of meeting hand-to-hand, since the convicts have numbers on their side. We must therefore try to prevent them from landing, but without discovering ourselves. Therefore, do not economize the ammunition. Fire often, but with a sure aim. We have each eight or ten enemies to kill, and they must be killed!'

Cyrus Harding had clearly represented their situation, although he spoke in the calmest voice, as if it was a question of directing a piece of work and not ordering a battle. His companions approved these arrangements without even uttering a word. There was nothing more to be done but for each to take his place before the fog should be completely dissipated. Neb and Pencroft immediately ascended to Granite House and brought back a sufficient quantity of ammunition. Gideon Spilett and Ayrton, both very good marksmen, were armed with the two rifles, which carried nearly a mile. The four other muskets were divided among Harding, Neb, Pencroft, and Herbert.

The posts were arranged in the following manner:—

Cyrus Harding and Herbert remained in ambush at the Chimneys, thus commanding the shore to the foot of Granite House.

Gideon Spilett and Neb crouched among the rocks at the mouth of the Mercy, from which the drawbridges had been raised, so as to prevent any one from crossing in a boat or landing on the opposite shore.

As to Ayrton and Pencroft, they shoved off in the boat, and prepared to cross the channel and to take up two separate stations on the islet. In this way, shots being fired from four different points at once, the convicts would be led to believe that the island was both largely peopled and strongly defended.

In the event of a landing being effected without their having been able to prevent it, and also if they saw that they were on the point of being cut off by the brig's boat, Ayrton and Pencroft were to return in their boat to the shore and proceed towards the threatened spot.

Before starting to occupy their posts, the colonists for the last time wrung each other's hands.

Pencroft succeeded in controlling himself sufficiently to suppress his emotion when he embraced Herbert, his boy! and then they separated.

In a few moments Harding and Herbert on one side, the reporter and Neb on the other, had disappeared behind the rocks, and five minutes later Ayrton and Pencroft, having without difficulty crossed the channel, disembarked on the islet and concealed themselves in the clefts of its eastern shore.

None of them could have been seen, for they themselves could scarcely distinguish the brig in the fog.

It was half-past six in the morning.

Soon the fog began to clear away, and the topmasts of the brig issued from the vapour. For some minutes great masses rolled over the surface of the sea, then a breeze sprang up, which rapidly dispelled the mist.

The 'Speedy' now appeared in full view, with a spring on her cable, her head to the north, presenting her larboard side to the island. Just as Harding had calculated, she was not more than a mile and a quarter from the coast.

The sinister black flag floated from the peak.

The engineer, with his telescope, could see that the four guns on board were pointed at the island. They were evidently ready to fire at a moment's notice.

In the meanwhile the 'Speedy' remained silent. About thirty pirates could be seen moving on the deck. A few more on the poop; two others posted in the shrouds, and armed with spyglasses, were attentively surveying the island.

Certainly, Bob Harvey and his crew would not be able easily to give an account of what had happened during the night on board the brig. Had this half-naked man, who had forced the door of the powder-magazine, and with whom they had struggled, who had six times discharged his revolver at them, who had killed one and wounded two others, escaped their shot? Had he been able to swim to shore? Whence did he come? What had been his object? Had his design really been to blow up the brig, as Bob Harvey had thought? All this must be confused enough to the convicts' minds. But what they could no longer doubt was that the unknown island before which the 'Speedy' had cast anchor was inhabited, and that there was, perhaps, a numerous colony ready to defend it. And yet no one was to be seen, neither on the shore, nor on the heights. The beach appeared to be absolutely deserted. At any rate, there was no trace of dwellings. Had the inhabitants fled into the interior? Thus probably the pirate captain reasoned, and doubtless, like a prudent man, he wished to reconnoitre the locality before he allowed his men to venture there.

During an hour and a half, no indication of attack or landing could be observed on board the brig. Evidently Bob Harvey was hesitating. Even with his strongest telescopes he could not have perceived one of the settlers crouched among the rocks. It was not even probable that his attention had been awakened by the screen of green branches and creepers hiding the windows of Granite House, and showing rather conspicuously on the bare rock. Indeed, how could he imagine that a dwelling was hollowed out, at that height, in the solid granite? From Claw Cape to the Mandible

Capes, in all the extent of Union Bay, there was nothing to lead him to suppose that the island was or could be inhabited.

At eight o'clock, however, the colonists observed a movement on board the 'Speedy.' A boat was lowered, and seven men jumped into her. They were armed with muskets; one took the yoke-lines, four others the oars, and the two others, kneeling in the bows, ready to fire, reconnoitred the island. Their object was no doubt to make an examination but not to land, for in the latter case they would have come in larger numbers. The pirates from their lookout could have seen that the coast was sheltered by an islet, separated from it by a channel half a mile in width. However, it was soon evident to Cyrus Harding, on observing the direction followed by the boat, that they would not attempt to penetrate into the channel, but would land on the islet.

Pencroft and Ayrton, each hidden in a narrow cleft of the rock, saw them coming directly towards them, and waited till they were within range.

The boat advanced with extreme caution. The oars only dipped into the water at long intervals. It could now be seen that one of the convicts held a lead-line in his hand, and that he wished to fathom the depth of the channel hollowed out by the current of the Mercy. This showed that it was Bob Harvey's intention to bring his brig as near as possible to the coast. About thirty pirates, scattered in the rigging, followed every movement of the boat, and took the bearings of certain landmarks which would allow them to approach without danger. The boat was not more than two cables-lengths off the islet when she stopped. The man at the tiller stood up and looked for the best place at which to land.

At that moment two shots were heard. Smoke curled up from among the rocks of the islet. The man at the helm and the man with the lead-line fell backwards into the boat. Ayrton's and Pencroft's balls had struck them both at the same moment.

Almost immediately a louder report was heard, a cloud of smoke issued from the brig's side, and a ball, striking the summit of the rock which sheltered Ayrton and Pencroft, made it fly in splinters, but the two marksmen remained unhurt.

Horrible imprecations burst from the boat, which immediately continued its way. The man who had been at the tiller was replaced by one of his comrades, and the oars were rapidly plunged into the water. However, instead of returning on board as might have been expected, the boat coasted along the islet, so as to round its southern point. The pirates pulled vigorously at their oars that they might get out of range of the bullets.

They advanced to within five cables-lengths of that part of the shore terminated by Flotsam Point, and after having rounded it in a semicircular line, still protected by the brig's guns, they proceeded towards the mouth of the Mercy.

Their evident intention was to penetrate into the channel, and cut off the colonists posted on the islet, in such a way, that whatever their number might be, being placed between the fire from the boat and the fire from the brig, they would find themselves in a very disadvantageous position.

A quarter of an hour passed while the boat advanced in this direction. Absolute silence, perfect calm reigned in the air and on the water.

Pencroft and Ayrton, although they knew they ran the risk of being cut off, had not left their post, both that they did not wish to show themselves as yet to their assailants, and expose themselves to the 'Speedy's' guns, and that they relied on Neb and Gideon Spilett, watching at the mouth of the river, and on Cyrus Harding and Herbert, in ambush among the rocks at the Chimneys.

Twenty minutes after the first shots were fired, the boat was less than two cables-lengths off the Mercy. As the tide was beginning to rise with its accustomed violence, caused by the narrowness of the straits, the pirates were drawn towards the river, and it was only by dint of hard rowing that they were able to keep in the middle of the channel. But, as they were passing within good range of the mouth of the Mercy, two balls saluted them, and two more of their number were laid in the bottom of the boat. Neb and Spilett had not missed their aim.

The brig immediately sent a second ball on the post betrayed by the smoke, but without any other result than that of splintering the rock.

The boat now contained only three able men. Carried on by the current, it shot through the channel with the rapidity of an arrow, passed before Harding and Herbert, who, not thinking it within range, withheld their fire, then, rounding the northern point of the islet with the two remaining oars, they pulled towards the brig.

Hitherto the settlers had nothing to complain of. Their adversaries had certainly had the worst of it. The latter already counted four men seriously wounded if not dead; they, on the contrary, unwounded, had not missed a shot. If the pirates continued to attack them in this way, if they renewed their attempt to land by means of a boat, they could be destroyed one by one.

It was now seen how advantageous the engineer's arrangements had been. The pirates would think that they had to deal with numerous and well-armed adversaries, whom they could not easily get the better of.

Half an hour passed before the boat, having to pull against the current, could get alongside the 'Speedy.' Frightful cries were heard when they returned on board with the wounded, and two or three guns were fired with no results.

But now about a dozen other convicts, maddened with rage, and possibly by the effect of the evening's potations, threw themselves into the boat. A second boat was also lowered, in which eight men took their places, and while the first pulled straight for the islet, to dislodge the colonists from thence the second manoeuvred so as to force the entrance of the Mercy.

The situation was evidently becoming very dangerous for Pencroft and Ayrton, and they saw that they must regain the mainland.

However, they waited till the first boat was within range, when two well- directed balls threw its crew into disorder. Then, Pencroft and Ayrton, abandoning their posts, under fire from the dozen muskets, ran across the islet at full speed, jumped into their boat, crossed the channel at the moment the second boat reached the southern end, and ran to hide themselves in the Chimneys.

They had scarcely rejoined Cyrus Harding and Herbert, before the islet was overrun with pirates in every direction. Almost at the same moment, fresh reports resounded from the Mercy station, to which the second boat was rapidly approaching. Two, out of the eight men who manned her, were mortally wounded by Gideon Spilett and Neb, and the boat herself, carried irresistibly onto the reefs, was stove in at the mouth of the Mercy. But the six survivors, holding their muskets above their heads to preserve them from contact with the water, managed to land on the right bank of the river. Then, finding they were exposed to the fire of the ambush there, they fled in the direction of Flotsam Point, out of range of the balls.

The actual situation was this: on the islet were a dozen convicts, of whom some were no doubt wounded, but who had still a boat at their disposal; on the island were six, but who could not by any possibility reach Granite House, as they could not cross the river, all the bridges being raised.

'Hallo,' exclaimed Pencroft as he rushed into the Chimneys, 'hallo, captain! What do you think of it, now?'

'I think,' answered the engineer, 'that the combat will now take a new form, for it cannot be supposed that the convicts will be so foolish as to remain in a position so unfavourable for them!'

'They won't cross the channel,' said the sailor. 'Ayrton and Mr. Spilett's rifles are there to prevent them. You know that they carry more than a mile!'

'No doubt,' replied Herbert; 'but what can two rifles do against the brig's guns?'

'Well, the brig isn't in the channel yet, I fancy!' said Pencroft.

'But suppose she does come there?' said Harding.

'That's impossible, for she would risk running aground and being lost!'

'It is possible,' said Ayrton. 'The convicts might profit by the high tide to enter the channel, with the risk of grounding at low tide, it is true; but then, under the fire from her guns, our posts would be no longer tenable.'

'Confound them!' exclaimed Pencroft, 'it really seems as if the blackguards were preparing to weigh anchor.'

'Perhaps we shall be obliged to take refuge in Granite House!' observed Herbert.

'We must wait!' answered Cyrus Harding.

'But Mr. Spilett and Neb?' said Pencroft.

'They will know when it is best to rejoin us. Be ready, Ayrton. It is yours and Spilett's rifles which must speak now.'

It was only too true. The 'Speedy' was beginning to weigh her anchor, and her intention was evidently to approach the islet. The tide would be rising for an hour and a half, and the ebb current being already weakened, it would be easy for the brig to advance. But as to entering the channel, Pencroft, contrary to Ayrton's opinion, could not believe that she would dare to attempt it.

In the meanwhile, the pirates who occupied the islet had gradually advanced to the opposite shore, and were now only separated from the mainland by the channel.

Being armed with muskets alone, they could do no harm to the settlers, in ambush at the Chimneys and the mouth of the Mercy; but, not knowing the latter to be supplied with long-range rifles, they on their side did not believe themselves to be exposed. Quite uncovered, therefore, they surveyed the islet, and examined the shore.

Their illusion was of short duration. Ayrton's and Gideon Spilett's rifles then spoke, and no doubt imparted some very disagreeable intelligence to two of the convicts, for they fell backwards.

Then there was a general helter-skelter. The ten others, not even stopping to pick up their dead or wounded companions, fled to the other side of the islet, tumbled into the boat which had brought them, and pulled away with all their strength.

'Eight less!' exclaimed Pencroft. 'Really, one would have thought that Mr. Spilett and Ayrton had given the word to fire together!'

'Gentlemen,' said Ayrton, as he reloaded his gun, 'this is becoming more serious. The brig is making sail!'

'The anchor is weighed!' exclaimed Pencroft.

'Yes, and she is already moving.'

In fact, they could distinctly hear the creaking of the windlass. The 'Speedy' was at first held by her anchor; then, when that had been raised, she began to drift towards the shore. The wind was blowing from the sea; the jib and the foretopsail were hoisted, and the vessel gradually approached the island.

From the two posts of the Mercy and the Chimneys they watched her without giving a sign of life, but not without some emotion. What could be more terrible for the colonists than to be exposed, at a short distance, to the brig's guns, without being able to reply with any effect? How could they then prevent the pirates from landing?

Cyrus Harding felt this strongly, and he asked himself what it would be possible to do. Before long, he would be called upon for his determination. But what was it to be? To shut themselves up in Granite House, to be besieged there, to remain there for weeks, for months even, since they had an abundance of provisions? So far good! But after that? The pirates would not the less be masters of the island, which they would ravage at their pleasure, and in time, they would end by having their revenge on the prisoners in Granite House.

However, one chance yet remained; it was that Bob Harvey, after all, would not venture his ship into the channel, and that he would keep outside the islet. He would be still separated from the coast by half a mile, and at that distance his shot could not be very destructive.

'Never!' repeated Pencroft, 'Bob Harvey will never, if he is a good seaman, enter that channel! He knows well that it would risk the brig, if the sea got up ever so little! And what would become of him without his vessel?'

In the meanwhile the brig approached the islet, and it could be seen that she was endeavouring to make the lower end. The breeze was light, and as the current had then lost much of its force, Bob Harvey had absolute command over his vessel.

The route previously followed by the boats had allowed her to reconnoitre the channel, and she boldly entered it.

The pirate's design was now only too evident; he wished to bring her broadside to bear on the Chimneys and from there to reply with shell and ball to the shot which had till then decimated her crew.

Soon the 'Speedy' reached the point of the islet; she rounded it with ease; the mainsail was braced up, and the brig hugging the wind, stood across the mouth of the Mercy.

'The scoundrels! they are coming!' said Pencroft.

At that moment, Cyrus Harding, Ayrton, the sailor, and Herbert, were rejoined by Neb and Gideon Spilett.

The reporter and his companion had judged it best to abandon the post at the Mercy, from which they could do nothing against the ship, and they had acted wisely. It was better that the colonists should be together at the moment when they were about to engage in a decisive action. Gideon Spilett and Neb had arrived by dodging behind the rocks, though not without attracting a shower of bullets, which had not, however, reached them.

'Spilett! Neb!' cried the engineer. 'You are not wounded?'

'No,' answered the reporter, 'a few bruises only from the ricochet! But that cursed brig has entered the channel!'

'Yes,' replied Pencroft, 'and in ten minutes she will have anchored before Granite House!'

'Have you formed any plan, Cyrus?' asked the reporter.

'We must take refuge in Granite House while there is still time, and the convicts cannot see us.'

'That is, my opinion, too,' replied Gideon Spilett, 'but once shut up—'

'We must be guided by circumstances,' said the engineer.

'Let us be off, then, and make haste!' said the reporter.

'Would you not wish, captain, that Ayrton and I should remain here?' asked the sailor.

'What would be the use of that, Pencroft?' replied Harding. 'No. We will not separate!'

There was not a moment to be lost. The colonists left the Chimneys. A bend of the cliff prevented them from being seen by those in the brig, but two or three reports, and the crash of bullets on the rock, told them that the 'Speedy' was at no great distance.

To spring into the lift, hoist themselves up to the door of Granite House, where Top and Jup had been shut up since the evening before, to rush into the large room, was the work of a minute only.

It was quite time, for the settlers, through the branches, could see the 'Speedy,' surrounded with smoke, gliding up the channel. The firing was incessant, and shot from the four guns struck blindly, both on the Mercy post, although it was not occupied, and on the Chimneys. The rocks were splintered, and cheers accompanied each discharge. However, they were hoping that Granite House would be spared, thanks to Harding's precaution of concealing the windows when a shot, piercing the door, penetrated into the passage.

'We are discovered!' exclaimed Pencroft.

The colonists had not, perhaps, been seen, but it was certain that Bob Harvey had thought proper to send a ball through the suspected foliage which concealed that part of the cliff. Soon he redoubled his attack, when another ball having torn away the leafy screen, disclosed a gaping aperture in the granite.

The colonists' situation was desperate. Their retreat was discovered. They could not oppose any obstacle to these missiles, nor protect the stone, which flew in splinters around them. There was nothing to be done but to take refuge in the upper passage of Granite House, and leave their dwelling to be devastated, when a deep roar was heard, followed by frightful cries!

Cyrus Harding and his companions rushed to one of the windows—

The brig, irresistibly raised on a sort of water-spout, had just split in two, and in less than ten seconds she was swallowed up with all her criminal crew!

Chapter 4

'She has blown up!' cried Herbert.

'Yes! blown up, just as if Ayrton had set fire to the powder!' returned Pencroft, throwing himself into the lift together with Neb and the lad.

'But what has happened?' asked Gideon Spilett, quite stunned by this unexpected catastrophe.

'Oh! this time, we shall know—' answered the engineer quickly.

'What shall we know?—'

'Later! later! Come, Spilett. The main point is that these pirates have been exterminated!'

And Cyrus Harding, hurrying away the reporter and Ayrton, joined Pencroft, Neb, and Herbert on the beach.

Nothing could be seen of the brig, not even her masts. After having been raised by the water-spout, she had fallen on her side, and had sunk in that position, doubtless in consequence of some enormous leak. But as in that place the channel was not more than twenty feet in depth, it was certain that the sides of the submerged brig would reappear at low water.

A few things from the wreck floated on the surface of the water, a raft could be seen consisting of spare spars, coops of poultry with their occupants still living, boxes and barrels, which gradually came to the surface, after having escaped through the hatchways, but no pieces of the wreck appeared, neither planks from the deck, nor timber from the hull,—which rendered the sudden disappearance of the 'Speedy' perfectly inexplicable.

However, the two masts, which had been broken and escaped from the shrouds and stays came up, and with their sails, some furled and the others spread. But it was not necessary to wait for the tide to bring up these riches, and Ayrton and Pencroft jumped into the boat with the intention of towing the pieces of wreck either to the beach or to the islet. But just as they were shoving off, an observation from Gideon Spilett arrested them.

'What about those six convicts who disembarked on the right bank of the Mercy?' said he.

In fact, it would not do to forget that the six men whose boat had gone to pieces on the rocks had landed at Flotsam Point.

They looked in that direction. None of the fugitives were visible. It was probable that, having seen their vessel engulfed in the channel, they had fled into the interior of the island.

'We will deal with them later,' said Harding. 'As they are armed, they will still be dangerous; but as it is six against six, the chances are equal. To the most pressing business first.'

Ayrton and Pencroft pulled vigorously towards the wreck.

The sea was calm and the tide very high, as there had been a new moon but two days before. A whole hour at least would elapse before the hull of the brig could emerge from the water of the channel.

Ayrton and Pencroft were able to fasten the masts and spars by means of ropes, the ends of which were carried to the beach. There, by the united efforts of the settlers the pieces of wreck were hauled up. Then the boat picked up all that was floating, coops, barrels, and boxes, which were immediately carried to the Chimneys.

Several bodies floated also. Among them, Ayrton recognized that of Bob Harvey, which he pointed out to his companion, saying with some emotion,—

'That is what I have been, Pencroft.'

'But what you are no longer, brave Ayrton!' returned the sailor warmly.

It was singular enough that so few bodies floated. Only five or six were counted, which were already being carried by the current towards the open sea. Very probably the convicts had not had time to escape, and the ship lying over on her side, the greater number of them had remained below. Now the current, by carrying the bodies of these miserable men out to sea, would spare the colonists the sad task of burying them in some corner of their island.

For two hours, Cyrus Harding and his companions were solely occupied in hauling up the spars on to the sand, and then in spreading the sails which were perfectly uninjured, to dry. They spoke little, for they were absorbed in their work, but what thoughts occupied their minds!

The possession of this brig, or rather all that she contained, was a perfect mine of wealth. In fact, a ship is like a little world in miniature, and the stores of the colony would be increased by a large number of useful articles. It would be, on a large scale, equivalent to the chest found at Flotsam Point.

'And besides,' thought Pencroft, 'why should it be impossible to refloat the brig? If she has only a leak, that may be stopped up; a vessel from three to four hundred tons, why she is a regular ship compared to our 'Bonadventure'! And we could go a long distance in her! We could go anywhere we liked! Captain Harding, Ayrton and I must examine her! She would be well worth the trouble!'

In fact, if the brig was still fit to navigate, the colonists' chances of returning to their native land were singularly increased. But, to decide this important question, it was necessary to wait until the tide was quite low, so that every part of the brig's hull might be examined.

When their treasures had been safely conveyed on shore, Harding and his companions agreed to devote some minutes to breakfast. They were almost famished; fortunately, the larder was not far off, and Neb was noted for being an expeditious cook. They breakfasted, therefore, near the Chimneys, and during their repast, as may be supposed, nothing was talked of but the event which had so miraculously saved the colony.

'Miraculous is the word,' repeated Pencroft, 'for it must be acknowledged that those rascals blew up just at the right moment! Granite House was beginning to be uncomfortable as a habitation!'

'And can you guess, Pencroft,' asked the reporter, 'how it happened, or what can have occasioned the explosion?'

'Oh! Mr. Spilett, nothing is more simple,' answered Pencroft. 'A convict vessel is not disciplined like a man-of-war! Convicts are not sailors. Of course the powder-magazine was open, and as they were firing incessantly, some careless or clumsy fellow just blew up the vessel!'

'Captain Harding,' said Herbert, 'what astonishes me is that the explosion has not produced more effect. The report was not loud, and besides there are so few planks and timbers torn out. It seems as if the ship had rather foundered than blown up.'

'Does that astonish you, my boy?' asked the engineer.

'Yes, captain.'

'And it astonishes me also, Herbert,' replied he, 'but when we visit the hull of the brig, we shall no doubt find the explanation of the matter.'

'Why, captain,' said Pencroft, 'you don't suppose that the 'Speedy' simply foundered like a ship which has struck on a rock?'

'Why not,' observed Neb, 'if there are rocks in the channel?'

'Nonsense, Neb,' answered Pencroft, 'you did not look at the right moment. An instant before she sank, the brig, as I saw perfectly well, rose on an enormous wave, and fell back on her larboard side. Now, if she had only struck, she would have sunk quietly and gone to the bottom like an honest vessel.'

'It was just because she was not an honest vessel!' returned Neb.

'Well, we shall soon see, Pencroft,' said the engineer.

'We shall soon see,' rejoined the sailor, 'but I would wager my head there are no rocks in the channel. Look here, captain, to speak candidly, do you mean to say that there is anything marvellous in the occurrence?'

Cyrus Harding did not answer.

'At any rate,' said Gideon Spilett, 'whether rock or explosion, you will agree, Pencroft, that it occurred just in the nick of time!'

'Yes! yes!' replied the sailor, 'but that is not the question. I ask Captain Harding if he sees anything supernatural in all this.'

'I cannot say, Pencroft,' said the engineer. 'That is all the answer I can make.'

A reply which did not satisfy Pencroft at all. He stuck to 'an explosion,' and did not wish to give it up. He would never consent to admit that in that channel, with its fine sandy bed, just like the beach, which he had often crossed at low water, there could be an unknown rock.

And besides, at the time the brig foundered, it was high water, that is to say, there was enough water to carry the vessel clear over any rocks which would not be uncovered at low tide. Therefore, there could not have been a collision. Therefore, the vessel had not struck. So she had blown up.

And it must be confessed that the sailor's arguments were reasonable.

Towards half-past one, the colonists embarked in the boat to visit the wreck. It was to be regretted that the brig's two boats had not been saved; but one, as has been said, had gone to pieces at the mouth of the Mercy, and was absolutely useless; the other had disappeared when the brig went down, and had not again been seen, having doubtless been crushed.

The hull of the 'Speedy' was just beginning to issue from the water. The brig was lying right over on her side, for her masts being broken, pressed down by the weight of the ballast displaced by the shock, the keel was visible along her whole length. She had been regularly turned over by the inexplicable but frightful submarine action, which had been at the same time manifested by an enormous water-spout.

The settlers rowed round the hull, and in proportion as the tide went down, they could ascertain, if not the cause which had occasioned the catastrophe, at least the effect produced.

Towards the bows, on both sides of the keel, seven or eight feet from the beginning of the stem, the sides of the brig were frightfully torn. Over a length of at least twenty feet there opened two large leaks, which would be impossible to stop up. Not only had the copper sheathing and the planks disappeared, reduced, no doubt, to powder, but also the ribs, the iron bolts, and treenalls which united them. From the entire length of the hull to the stern the false keel had been separated with an unaccountable violence, and the keel itself, torn from the carline in several places, was split in all its length.

'I've a notion!' exclaimed Pencroft, 'that this vessel will be difficult to get afloat again.'

'It will be impossible,' said Ayrton.

'At any rate,' observed Gideon Spilett to the sailor, 'the explosion, if there has been one, has produced singular effects! It has split the lower part of the hull, instead of blowing up the deck and topsides! These great rents appear rather to have been made by a rock than by the explosion of a powder-magazine.'

'There is not a rock in the channel!' answered the sailor. 'I will admit anything you like, except the rock.'

'Let us try to penetrate into the interior of the brig,' said the engineer; 'perhaps we shall then know what to think of the cause of her destruction.'

This was the best thing to be done, and it was agreed, besides, to take an inventory of all the treasures on board, and to arrange their preservation.

Access to the interior of the brig was now easy. The tide was still going down and the deck was practicable. The ballast, composed of heavy masses of iron, had broken through in several places. The noise of the sea could be heard as it rushed out at the holes in the hull.

Cyrus Harding and his companions, hatchets in hand, advanced along the shattered deck. Cases of all sorts encumbered it, and, as they had been but a very short time in the water, their contents were perhaps uninjured.

They then busied themselves in placing all this cargo in safety. The water would not return for several hours, and these hours must be employed in the most profitable way. Ayrton and Pencroft had, at the entrance made in the hull, discovered tackle, which would serve to hoist up the barrels and chests. The boat received them and transported them to the shore. They took the articles as they came, intending to sort them afterwards.

At any rate, the settlers saw at once, with extreme satisfaction, that the brig possessed a very varied cargo—an assortment of all sorts of articles, utensils, manufactured goods, and tools—such as the ships which make the great coasting-trade of Polynesia are usually laden with. It was probable that they would find a little of everything, and they agreed that it was exactly what was necessary for the colony of Lincoln Island.

However-and Cyrus Harding observed it in silent astonishment-not only, as has been said, had the hull of the brig enormously suffered from the shock, whatever it was, that had occasioned the catastrophe, but the interior arrangements had been destroyed, especially towards the bows. Partitions and stanchions were smashed, as if some tremendous shell had burst in the interior of the brig. The colonists could easily go fore and aft, after having removed the cases as they were extricated. They were not heavy bales, which would have been difficult to remove, but simple packages, of which the stowage, besides, was no longer recognizable.

The colonists then reached the stern of the brig—the part formerly surmounted by the poop. It was there that, following Ayrton's directions, they must look for the powder-magazine. Cyrus Harding thought that it had not exploded; that it was possible some barrels might be saved, and that the powder, which is usually enclosed in metal coverings might not have suffered from contact with the water.

This, in fact, was just what had happened. They extricated from among a large number of shot twenty barrels, the insides of which were lined with copper. Pencroft was convinced by the evidence of his own eyes that the destruction of the 'Speedy' could not be attributed to an explosion. That part of the hull in which the magazine was situated was, moreover, that which had suffered least.

'It may be so,' said the obstinate sailor; 'but as to a rock, there is not one in the channel!'

'Then, how did it happen?' asked Herbert.

'I don't know,' answered Pencroft, 'Captain Harding doesn't know, and nobody knows or ever will know!'

Several hours had passed during these researches, and the tide began to flow. Work must be suspended for the present. There was no fear of the brig being carried away by the sea, for she was already fixed as firmly as if moored by her anchors.

They could, therefore, without inconvenience, wait until the next day to resume operations; but, as to the vessel itself, she was doomed, and it would be best to hasten to save the remains of her hull, as she would not be long in disappearing in the quicksands of the channel.

It was now five o'clock in the evening. It had been a hard day's work for the men. They ate with good appetite, and notwithstanding their fatigue, they could not resist, after dinner, their desire of inspecting the cases which composed the cargo of the 'Speedy.'

Most of them contained clothes, which, as may be believed, was well received. There were enough to clothe a whole colony—linen for every one's use, shoes for every one's feet.

'We are too rich!' exclaimed Pencroft, 'But what are we going to do with all this?'

And every moment burst forth the hurrahs of the delighted sailor when he caught sight of the barrels of gunpowder, firearms and sidearms, balls of cotton, implements of husbandry, carpenter's, joiner's, and blacksmith's tools, and boxes of all kinds of seeds, not in the least injured by their short sojourn in the water. Ah, two years before, how these things would have been prized! And now, even though the industrious colonists had provided themselves with tools, these treasures would find their use.

There was no want of space in the storerooms of Granite House, but that daytime would not allow them to stow away the whole. It would not do also to forget that the six survivors of the 'Speedy's' crew had landed on the island, for they were in all probability scoundrels of the deepest dye, and it was necessary that the colonists should be on their guard against them. Although the bridges over the Mercy were raised, the convicts would not be stopped by a river or a stream and, rendered desperate, these wretches would be capable of anything.

They would see later what plan it would be best to follow; but in the meantime it was necessary to mount guard over cases and packages heaped up near the Chimneys, and thus the settlers employed themselves in turn during the night.

The morning came, however, without the convicts having attempted any attack. Master Jup and Top, on guard at the foot of Granite House, would have quickly given the alarm. The three following day—the 19th, 20th, and 21st of October—were employed in saving everything of value, or of any use whatever, either from the cargo or rigging of the brig. At low tide they overhauled the hold—at high tide they stowed away the rescued articles. A great part of the copper sheathing had been torn from the hull, which every day sank lower. But before the sand had swallowed the heavy things which had fallen through the bottom, Ayrton and Pencroft, diving to the bed of the channel, recovered the chains and anchors of the brig, the iron of her ballast, and even four guns, which, floated by means of empty casks, were brought to shore.

It may be seen that the arsenal of the colony had gained by the wreck, as well as the storerooms of Granite House. Pencroft, always enthusiastic in his projects, already spoke of constructing a battery to command the channel and the mouth of the river. With four guns, he engaged to prevent any fleet, 'however powerful it might be,' from venturing into the waters of Lincoln Island!

In the meantime, when nothing remained of the brig but a useless hulk, bad weather came on, which soon finished her. Cyrus Harding had intended to blow her up, so as to collect the remains on the shore, but a strong gale from the northeast and a heavy sea compelled him to economize his powder.

In fact, on the night of the 23rd, the hull entirely broke up, and some of the wreck was cast up on the beach.

As to the papers on board, it is useless to say that, although he carefully searched the lockers of the poop, Harding did not discover any trace of them. The pirates had evidently destroyed everything that concerned either the captain or the owners of the 'Speedy,' and, as the name of her port was not painted on her counter, there was nothing which would tell them her nationality. However, by the shape of her boats Ayrton and Pencroft believed that the brig was of English build.

A week after the castrophe—or, rather, after the fortunate, though inexplicable, event to which the colony owed its preservation—nothing more could be seen of the vessel, even at low tide. The wreck had disappeared, and Granite House was enriched by nearly all it had contained.

However, the mystery which enveloped its strange destruction would doubtless never have been cleared away if, on the 30th of November, Neb, strolling on the beach, had not found a piece of a thick iron cylinder, bearing traces of explosion. The edges of this cylinder were twisted and broken, as if they had been subjected to the action of some explosive substance.

Neb brought this piece of metal to his master, who was then occupied with his companions in the workshop of the Chimneys.

Cyrus Harding examined the cylinder attentively, then, turning to Pencroft,—

'You persist, my friend,' said he, 'in maintaining that the 'Speedy' was not lost in consequence of a collision?'

'Yes, captain,' answered the sailor. 'You know as well as I do that there are no rocks in the channel.'

'But suppose she had run against this piece of iron?' said the engineer, showing the broken cylinder.

'What, that bit of pipe!' exclaimed Pencroft in a tone of perfect incredulity.

'My friends,' resumed Harding, 'you remember that before she foundered the brig rose on the summit of a regular waterspout?'

'Yes, captain,' replied Herbert.

'Well, would you like to know what occasioned that waterspout? It was this,' said the engineer, holding up the broken tube.

'That?' returned Pencroft.

'Yes! This cylinder is all that remains of a torpedo!'

'A torpedo!' exclaimed the engineer's companions.

'And who put the torpedo there?' demanded Pencroft, who did not like to yield.

'All that I can tell you is, that it was not I,' answered Cyrus Harding; 'but it was there, and you have been able to judge of its incomparable power!'

Chapter 5

So, then, all was explained by the submarine explosion of this torpedo. Cyrus Harding could not be mistaken, as, during the war of the Union, he had had occasion to try these terrible engines of destruction. It was under the action of this cylinder, charged with some explosive substance, nitroglycerine, picrate, or some other material of the same nature, that the water of the channel had been raised like a dome, the bottom of the brig crushed in, and she had sunk instantly, the damage done to her hull being so considerable that it was impossible to refloat her. The 'Speedy' had not been able to withstand a torpedo that would have destroyed an ironclad as easily as a fishing-boat!

Yes! all was explained, everything—except the presence of the torpedo in the waters of the channel!

My friends, then,' said Cyrus Harding, 'we can no longer be in doubt as to the presence of a mysterious being, a castaway like us, perhaps, abandoned on our island, and I say this in order that Ayrton may be acquainted with all the strange events which have occurred during these two years. Who this beneficent stranger is, whose intervention has, so fortunately for us, been manifested on many occasions, I cannot imagine.

What his object can be in acting thus, in concealing himself after rendering us so many services, I cannot understand: But his services are not the less real, and are of such a nature that only a man possessed of prodigious power, could render them. Ayrton is indebted to him as much as we are, for, if it was the stranger who saved me from the waves after the fall from the balloon, evidently it was he who wrote the document, who placed the bottle in the channel, and who has made known to us the situation of our companion. I will add that it was he who guided that chest, provided with everything we wanted, and stranded it on Flotsam Point; that it was he who lighted that fire on the heights of the island, which permitted you to land; that it was he who fired that bullet found in the body of the peccary; that it was he who plunged that torpedo into the channel, which destroyed the brig; in a word, that all those inexplicable events, for which we could not assign a reason, are due to this mysterious being. Therefore, whoever he may be, whether shipwrecked, or exiled on our island, we shall be ungrateful, if we think ourselves freed from gratitude towards him. We have contracted a debt, and I hope that we shall one day pay it.'

'You are right in speaking thus, my dear Cyrus,' replied Gideon Spilett. 'Yes, there is an almost all-powerful being, hidden in some part of the island, and whose influence has been singularly useful to our colony. I will add that the unknown appears to possess means of action which border on the supernatural, if in the events of practical life the supernatural were recognizable. Is it he who is in secret communication with us by the well in Granite House, and has he thus a knowledge of all our plans? Was it he who threw us that bottle, when the vessel made her first cruise? Was it he who threw Top out of the lake, and killed the dugong? Was it he, who as everything leads us to believe, saved you from the waves, and that under circumstances in which any one else would not have been able to act? If it was he, he possesses a power which renders him master of the elements.'

The reporter's reasoning was just, and every one felt it to be so.

'Yes,' rejoined Cyrus Harding, 'if the intervention of a human being is not more questionable for us, I agree that he has at his disposal means of action beyond those possessed by humanity. There is a mystery still, but if we discover the man, the mystery will be discovered also. The question, then, is, ought we to respect the incognito of this generous being, or ought we to do everything to find him out? What is your opinion on the matter?'

'My opinion,' said Pencroft, 'is that, whoever he may be, he is a brave man, and he has my esteem!'

'Be it so,' answered Harding, 'but that is not an answer, Pencroft.'

'Master,' then said Neb, 'my idea is, that we may search as long as we like for this gentleman whom you are talking about, but that we shall not discover him till he pleases.'

'That's not bad, what you say, Neb,' observed Pencroft.

'I am of Neb's opinion,' said Gideon Spilett, 'but that is no reason for not attempting the adventure. Whether we find this mysterious being or not, we shall at least have fulfilled our duty towards him.'

'And you, my boy, give us your opinion,' said the engineer, turning to Herbert.

'Oh,' cried Herbert, his countenance full of animation, 'how I should like to thank him, he who saved you first, and who has now saved us!'

'Of course, my boy,' replied Pencroft, 'so would I and all of us. I am not inquisitive, but I would give one of my eyes to see this individual face to face! It seems to me that he must be handsome, tall, strong, with a splendid beard, radiant hair, and that he must be seated on clouds, a great ball in his hands!'

'But, Pencroft,' answered Spilett, 'you are describing a picture of the Creator.'

'Possibly, Mr. Spilett,' replied the sailor, 'but that is how I imagine him!'

'And you, Ayrton?' asked the engineer.

'Captain Harding,' replied Ayrton, 'I can give you no better advice in this matter. Whatever you do will be best; when you wish me to join you in your researches, I am ready to follow you.

'I thank you, Ayrton,' answered Cyrus Harding, 'but I should like a more direct answer to the question I put to you. You are our companion; you have already endangered your life several times for us, and you, as well as the rest, ought to be consulted in the matter of any important decision. Speak, therefore.'

'Captain Harding,' replied Ayrton, 'I think that we ought to do everything to discover this unknown benefactor. Perhaps he is alone. Perhaps he is suffering. Perhaps he has a life to be renewed. I, too, as you said, have a debt of gratitude to pay him. It was he, it could be only he who must have come to Tabor Island, who found there the wretch you knew, and who made known to you that there was an unfortunate man there to be saved. Therefore it is, thanks to him, that I have become a man again. No, I will never forget him!'

'That is settled, then,' said Cyrus Harding. 'We will begin our researches as soon as possible. We will not leave a corner of the island unexplored. We will search into its most secret recesses, and will hope that our unknown friend will pardon us in consideration of our intentions!'

For several days the colonists were actively employed in haymaking and the harvest. Before putting their project of exploring the yet unknown parts of the island into execution, they wished to get all possible work finished. It was also the time for collecting the various vegetables from the Tabor Island plants. All was stowed away, and happily there was no want of room in Granite House, in which they might have housed all the treasures of the island. The products of the colony were there, methodically arranged, and in a safe place, as may be believed, sheltered as much from animals as from man.

There was no fear of damp in the middle of that thick mass of granite. Many natural excavations situated in the upper passage were enlarged either by pick-axe or mine, and Granite House thus became a general warehouse, containing all the provisions, arms, tools, and spare utensils—in a word, all the stores of the colony.

As to the guns obtained from the brig, they were pretty pieces of ordnance, which, at Pencroft's entreaty, were hoisted by means of tackle and pulleys, right up into Granite House; embrasures were made between the windows, and the shining muzzles of the guns could soon be seen through the granite cliff. From this height they commanded all Union Bay. It was like a little Gibraltar, and any vessel anchored off the islet would inevitably be exposed to the fire of this aerial battery.

'Captain,' said Pencroft one day, it was the 8th of November, 'now that our fortifications are finished, it would be a good thing if we tried the range of our guns.'

'Do you think that is useful?' asked the engineer.

'It is more than useful, it is necessary! Without that how are we to know to what distance we can send one of those pretty shot with which we are provided?'

'Try them, Pencroft,' replied the engineer. 'However, I think that in making the experiment, we ought to employ, not the ordinary powder, the supply of which, I think, should remain untouched, but the pyroxyle which will never fail us.'

'Can the cannon support the shock of the pyroxyle?' asked the reporter, who was not less anxious than Pencroft to try the artillery of Granite House.

'I believe so. However,' added the engineer, 'we will be prudent.' The engineer was right in thinking that the guns were of excellent make. Made of forged steel, and breech-loaders, they ought consequently to be able to bear a considerable charge, and also have an enormous range. In fact, as regards practical effect, the transit described by the ball ought to be as extended as possible, and this tension could only be obtained under the condition that the projectile should be impelled with a very great initial velocity.

'Now,' said Harding to his companions, 'the initial velocity is in proportion to the quantity of powder used. In the fabrication of these pieces, everything depends on employing a metal with the highest possible power of resistance, and steel is incontestably that metal of all others which resists the best. I have, therefore, reason to believe that our guns will bear without risk the expansion of the pyroxyle gas, and will give excellent results.'

'We shall be a great deal more certain of that when we have tried them!' answered Pencroft.

It is unnecessary to say that the four cannons were in perfect order. Since they had been taken from the water, the sailor had bestowed great care upon them. How many hours he had spent, in rubbing, greasing, and polishing them, and in cleaning the mechanism! And now the pieces were as brilliant as if they had been on board a frigate of the United States Navy.

On this day, therefore, in presence of all the members of the colony, including Master Jup and Top, the four cannon were successively tried. They were charged with pyroxyle, taking into consideration its explosive power, which, as has been said, is four times that of ordinary powder: the projectile to be fired was cylindroconic.

Pencroft, holding the end of the quick-match, stood ready to fire.

At Harding's signal, he fired. The shot, passing over the islet, fell into the sea at a distance which could not be calculated with exactitude.

The second gun was pointed at the rocks at the end of Flotsam Point, and the shot striking a sharp rock nearly three miles from Granite House, made it fly into splinters. It was Herbert who had pointed this gun and fired it, and very proud he was of his first shot. Pencroft only was prouder than he! Such a shot, the honour of which belonged to his dear boy.

The third shot, aimed this time at the downs forming the upper side of Union Bay, struck the sand at a distance of four miles, then having ricocheted: was lost in the sea in a cloud of spray.

For the fourth piece Cyrus Harding slightly increased the charge, so as to try its extreme range. Then, all standing aside for fear of its bursting, the match was lighted by means of a long cord.

A tremendous report was heard, but the piece had held good, and the colonists rushing to the windows, saw the shot graze the rocks of Mandible Cape, nearly five miles from Granite House, and disappear in Shark Gulf.

'Well, captain,' exclaimed Pencroft, whose cheers might have rivalled the reports themselves, 'what do you say of our battery? All the pirates in the Pacific have only to present themselves before Granite House! Not one can land there now without our permission!'

'Believe me, Pencroft,' replied the engineer, 'it would be better not to have to make the experiment.'

'Well,' said the sailor, 'what ought to be done with regard to those six villains who are roaming about the island? Are we to leave them to overrun our forests, our fields, our plantations? These pirates are regular jaguars, and it seems to me we ought not to hesitate to treat them as such! What do you think, Ayrton?' added Pencroft, turning to his companion.

Ayrton hesitated at first to reply, and Cyrus Harding regretted that Pencroft had so thoughtlessly put this question. And he was much moved when Ayrton replied in a humble tone,—

'I have been one of those jaguars, Mr. Pencroft. I have no right to speak.'

And with a slow step he walked away.

Pencroft understood.

'What a brute I am!' he exclaimed. 'Poor Ayrton! He has as much right to speak here as any one!'

'Yes,' said Gideon Spilett, 'but his reserve does him honour, and it is right to respect the feeling which he has about his sad past.'

'Certainly, Mr. Spilett,' answered the sailor, 'and there is no fear of my doing so again. I would rather bite my tongue off than cause Ayrton any pain! But to return to the question. It seems to me that these ruffians have no right to any pity, and that we ought to rid the island of them as soon as possible.'

'Is that your opinion, Pencroft?' asked the engineer.

'Quite my opinion.'

'And before hunting them mercilessly, you would not wait until they had committed some fresh act of hostility against us?'

'Isn't what they have done already enough?' asked Pencroft, who did not understand these scruples.

'They may adopt other sentiments!' said Harding, 'and perhaps repent.'

'They repent!' exclaimed the sailor, shrugging his shoulders.

'Pencroft, think of Ayrton!' said Herbert, taking the sailor's hand. 'He became an honest man again!'

Pencroft looked at his companions one after the other. He had never thought of his proposal being met with any objection. His rough nature could not allow that they ought to come to terms with the rascals who had landed on the island with Bob Harvey's accomplices, the murderers of the crew of the 'Speedy,' and he looked upon them as wild beasts which ought to be destroyed without delay and without remorse.

'Come!' said be. 'Everybody is against me! You wish to be generous to those villains! Very well; I hope we may not repent it!'

'What danger shall we run,' said Herbert, 'if we take care to be always on our guard?'

'Hum!' observed the reporter, who had not given any decided opinion. 'They are six and well armed. If they each lay hid in a corner, and each fired at one of us, they would soon be masters of the colony!'

'Why have they not done so?' said Herbert. 'No doubt because it was not their interest to do it. Besides, we are six also.'

'Well, well!' replied Pencroft, whom no reasoning could have convinced. 'Let us leave these good people to do what they like, and don't think anything more about them!'

'Come, Pencroft,' said Neb, 'don't make yourself out so bad as all that! Suppose one of these unfortunate men were here before you, within good range of your guns, you would not fire.'

'I would fire on him as I would on a mad dog, Neb,' replied Pencroft coldly.

'Pencroft,' said the engineer, 'you have always shown much deference to my advice; will you, in this matter, yield to me?'

'I will do as you please, Captain Harding,' answered the sailor, who was not at all convinced.

'Very well, wait, and we will not attack them unless we are attacked first.'

Thus their behaviour towards the pirates was agreed upon, although Pencroft augured nothing good from it. They were not to attack them, but were to be on their guard. After all, the island was large and fertile. If any sentiment of honesty yet remained in the bottom of their hearts, these wretches might perhaps be reclaimed. Was it not their interest in the situation in which they found themselves to begin a new life? At any rate, for humanity's sake alone, it would be right to wait. The colonists would no longer as before, be able to go and come without fear. Hitherto they had only wild beasts to guard against, and now six convicts of the worst description, perhaps, were roaming over their island. It was serious, certainly, and to less brave men, it would have been security lost! No matter! At present, the colonists had reason on their side against Pencroft. Would they be right in the future? That remained to be seen.

Chapter 6

However, the chief business of the colonists was to make that complete exploration of the island which had been decided upon, and which would have two objects: to discover the mysterious being whose existence was now indisputable, and at the same time to find out what had become of the pirates, what retreat they had chosen, what sort of life they were leading, and what was to be feared from them. Cyrus Harding wished to set out without delay; but as the expedition would be of some days duration, it appeared best to load the cart with different materials and tools in order to facilitate the organization of the encampments. One of the onagers, however, having hurt its leg, could not be harnessed at present, and a few days' rest was necessary. The departure was, therefore, put off for a week, until the 20th of November. The month of November in this latitude corresponds to the month of May in the northern zones. It was, therefore, the fine season. The sun was entering the tropic of Capricorn, and gave the longest days in the year. The time was, therefore, very favourable for the projected expedition, which, if it did not accomplish its principal object, would at any rate be fruitful in discoveries, especially of natural productions, since Harding proposed to explore those dense forests of the Far West, which stretched to the extremity of the Serpentine Peninsula.

During the nine days which preceded their departure, it was agreed that the work on Prospect Heights should be finished off.

Moreover, it was necessary for Ayrton to return to the corral, where the domesticated animals required his care. It was decided that he should spend two days there, and return to Granite House after having liberally supplied the stables.

As he was about to start, Harding asked him if he would not like one of them to accompany him, observing that the island was less safe than formerly. Ayrton replied that this was unnecessary, as he was enough for the work, and that besides he apprehended no danger. If anything occurred at the corral, or in the neighbourhood, he could instantly warn the colonists by sending a telegram to Granite House.

Ayrton departed at dawn on the 9th, taking the cart drawn by one onager, and two hours after, the electric wire announced that he had found all in order at the corral.

During these two days Harding busied himself in executing a project which would completely guard Granite House against any surprise. It was necessary to completely conceal the opening of the old outlet, which was already walled up and partly hidden under grass and plants, at the southern angle of Lake Grant. Nothing was easier, since if the level of the lake was raised two or three feet, the opening would be quite beneath it. Now, to raise this level they had only to establish a dam at the two openings made by the lake, and by which were fed Creek Glycerine and Falls River.

The colonists worked with a will, and the two dams which besides did not exceed eight feet in width by three in height, were rapidly erected by means of well-cemented blocks of stone.

This work finished, it would have been impossible to guess that at that part of the lake, there existed a subterranean passage through which the overflow of the lake formerly escaped.

Of course the little stream which fed the reservoir of Granite House and worked the lift, had been carefully preserved, and the water could not fail. The lift once raised, this sure and comfortable retreat would be safe from any surprise.

This work had been so quickly done, that Pencroft, Gideon Spilett, and Herbert found time to make an expedition to Port Balloon, The sailor was very anxious to know if the little creek in which the 'Bonadventure' was moored, had been visited by the convicts.

'These gentlemen,' he observed, 'landed on the south coast, and if they followed the shore, it is to be feared that they may have discovered the little harbour, and in that case, I wouldn't give half-a-dollar for our 'Bonadventure."

Pencroft's apprehensions were not without foundation, and a visit to Port Balloon appeared to be very desirable. The sailor and his companions set off on the 10th of November, after dinner, well armed. Pencroft, ostentatiously slipping two bullets into each barrel of his rifle, shook his head in a way which betokened nothing good to any one who approached too near him, whether 'man or beast,' as he said. Gideon Spilett and Herbert also took their guns, and about three o'clock all three left Granite House.

Neb accompanied them to the turn of the Mercy, and after they had crossed, he raised the bridge. It was agreed that a gunshot should announce the colonists' return, and that at the signal Neb should return and re-establish the communication between the two banks of the river.

The little band advanced directly along the road which led to the southern coast of the island. This was only a distance of three miles and a half, but Gideon Spilett and his companions took two hours to traverse it. They examined all the border of the road, the thick forest, as well as Tabor Marsh. They found no trace of the fugitives who, no doubt, not having yet discovered the number of the colonists, or the means of defence which they had at their disposal, had gained the less accessible parts of the island.

Arrived at Port Balloon, Pencroft saw with extreme satisfaction that the 'Bonadventure' was tranquilly floating in the narrow creek. However, Port Balloon was so well hidden among high rocks, that it could scarcely be discovered either from the land or the sea.

'Come,' said Pencroft, 'the blackguards have not been there yet. Long grass suits reptiles best, and evidently we shall find them in the Far West.'

'And it's very lucky, for if they had found the 'Bonadventure' added Herbert, 'they would have gone off in her, and we should have been prevented from returning to Tabor Island.'

'Indeed,' remarked the reporter, 'it will be important to take a document there which will make known the situation of Lincoln Island, and Ayrton's new residence, in case the Scotch yacht returns to fetch him.'

'Well, the 'Bonadventure' is always there, Mr. Spilett,' answered the sailor. 'She and her crew are ready to start at a moment's notice!'

'I think, Pencroft, that that is a thing to be done after our exploration of the island is finished. It is possible after all that the stranger, if we manage to find him, may know as much about Tabor Island as about Lincoln Island. Do not forget that he is certainly the author of the document, and he may, perhaps, know how far we may count on the return of the yacht!'

'But!' exclaimed Pencroft, 'who in the world can he be? The fellow knows us and we know nothing about him! If he is a simple castaway, why should he conceal himself! We are honest men, I suppose, and the society of honest men isn't unpleasant to any one. Did he come here voluntarily? Can he leave the island if he likes? Is he here still? Will he remain any longer?'

Chatting thus, Pencroft, Gideon Spilett, and Herbert got on board and looked about the deck of the 'Bonadventure.' All at once, the sailor having examined the bits to which the cable of the anchor was secured,—

'Hallo,' he cried, 'this is queer!'

'What is the matter, Pencroft?' asked the reporter.

'The matter is, that it was not I who made this knot!'

And Pencroft showed a rope which fastened the cable to the bit itself.

'What, it was not you?' asked Gideon Spilett.

'No! I can swear to it. This is a reef knot, and I always make a running bowline.'

'You must be mistaken, Pencroft.'

'I am not mistaken!' declared the sailor. 'My hand does it so naturally, and one's hand is never mistaken!'

'Then can the convicts have been on board?' asked Herbert.

'I know nothing about that,' answered Pencroft, 'but what is certain, is that some one has weighed the 'Bonadventure's' anchor and dropped it again! And look here, here is another proof! The cable of the anchor has been run out, and its service is no longer at the hawse-hole. I repeat that some one has been using our vessel!'

'But if the convicts had used her, they would have pillaged her, or rather gone off with her.'

'Gone off! where to—to Tabor Island?' replied Pencroft. 'Do you think, they would risk themselves in a boat of such small tonnage?'

'We must, besides, be sure that they know of the islet,' rejoined the reporter.

'However that may be,' said the sailor, 'as sure as my name is Bonadventure Pencroft, of the Vineyard, our 'Bonadventure' has sailed without us!'

The sailor was positive that neither Gideon Spilett nor Herbert could dispute his statement. It was evident that the vessel had been moved, more or less, since Pencroft had brought her to Port Balloon. As to the sailor, he had not the slightest doubt that the anchor had been raised and then dropped again. Now, what was the use of these two manoeuvres, unless the vessel had been employed in some expedition?

'But how was it we did not see the 'Bonadventure' pass in the sight of the island?' observed the reporter, who was anxious to bring forward every possible objection.

'Why, Mr. Spilett,' replied the sailor, 'they would only have to start in the night with a good breeze, and they would be out of sight of the island in two hours.'

'Well,' resumed Gideon Spilett, 'I ask again, what object could the convicts have had in using the 'Bonadventure,' and why, after they had made use of her, should they have brought her back to port?'

'Why, Mr. Spilett,' replied the sailor, 'we must put that among the unaccountable things, and not think anything more about it. The chief thing is that the 'Bonadventure' was there, and she is there now. Only, unfortunately, if the convicts take her a second time, we shall very likely not find her again in her place!'

'Then, Pencroft,' said Herbert, 'would it not be wisest to bring the 'Bonadventure' off to Granite House?'

'Yes and no,' answered Pencroft, 'or rather no. The mouth of the

Mercy is a bad place for a vessel, and the sea is heavy there.'

'But by hauling her up on the sand, to the foot of the Chimneys?'

'Perhaps yes,' replied Pencroft. 'At any rate, since we must leave Granite House for a long expedition, I think the 'Bonadventure' will be safer here during our absence, and we shall do best to leave her here until the island is rid of these blackguards.'

'That is exactly my opinion,' said the reporter. 'At any rate in the event of bad weather, she will not be exposed here as she would be at the mouth of the Mercy.'

'But suppose the convicts pay her another visit,' said Herbert.

'Well, my boy,' replied Pencroft, 'not finding her here, they would not be long in finding her on the sands of Granite House, and, during our absence, nothing could hinder them from seizing her! I agree, therefore, with Mr. Spilett, that she must be left in Port Balloon. But, if on our return we have not rid the island of those rascals, it will be prudent to bring our boat to Granite House, until the time when we need not fear any unpleasant visits.'

'That's settled. Let us be off,' said the reporter.

Pencroft, Herbert, and Gideon Spilett, on their return to Granite House, told the engineer all that had passed, and the latter approved of their arrangements both for the present and the future. He also promised the sailor that he would study that part of the channel situated between the islet and the coast, so as to ascertain if it would not be possible to make an artificial harbour there by means of dams. In this way, the 'Bonadventure' would be always within reach, under the eyes of the colonists, and if necessary, under lock and key.

That evening a telegram was sent to Ayrton, requesting him to bring from the corral a couple of goats, which Neb wished to acclimatize to the plateau. Singularly enough, Ayrton did not acknowledge the receipt of the despatch, as he was accustomed to do. This could not but astonish the engineer. But it might be that Ayrton was not at that moment in the corral, or even that he was on his way back to Granite House. In fact, two days had already passed since his departure, and it had been decided that on the evening of the 10th or at the latest the morning of the 11th, he should return. The colonists waited, therefore, for Ayrton to appear on Prospect Heights. Neb and Herbert even watched at the bridge so as to be ready to lower it the moment their companion presented himself.

But up to ten in the evening, there were no signs of Ayrton. It was, therefore, judged best to send a fresh despatch, requiring an immediate reply.

The bell of the telegraph at Granite House remained mute.

The colonists' uneasiness was great. What had happened? Was Ayrton no longer at the corral, or if he was still there, had he no longer control over his movements? Could they go to the corral in this dark night?

They consulted. Some wished to go, the others to remain.

'But,' said Herbert, 'perhaps some accident has happened to the telegraphic apparatus, so that it works no longer?'

'That may be,' said the reporter.

'Wait till tomorrow,' replied Cyrus Harding. 'It is possible, indeed, that Ayrton has not received our despatch, or even that we have not received his.'

They waited, of course not without some anxiety.

At dawn of day, the 11th of November, Harding again sent the electric current along the wire and received no reply.

He tried again: the same result.

'Off to the corral,' said he.

'And well armed!' added Pencroft.

It was immediately decided that Granite House should not be left alone and that Neb should remain there. After having accompanied his friends to Creek Glycerine, he raised the bridge; and waiting behind a tree he watched for the return of either his companions or Ayrton.

In the event of the pirates presenting themselves and attempting to force the passage, he was to endeavour to stop them by firing on them, and as a last resource he was to take refuge in Granite House, where, the lift once raised, he would be in safety.

Cyrus Harding, Gideon Spilett, Herbert, and Pencroft were to repair to the corral, and if they did not find Ayrton, search the neighbouring woods.

At six o'clock in the morning, the engineer and his three companions had passed Creek Glycerine, and Neb posted himself behind a small mound crowned by several dragon trees, on the left bank of the stream.

The colonists, after leaving the plateau of Prospect Heights, immediately took the road to the corral. They shouldered their guns, ready to fire on the slightest hostile demonstration. The two rifles and the two guns had been loaded with ball.

The wood was thick on each side of the road and might easily have concealed the convicts, who owing to their weapons would have been really formidable.

The colonists walked rapidly and in silence. Top preceded them, sometimes running on the road, sometimes taking a ramble into the wood, but always quiet and not appearing to fear anything unusual. And they could be sure that the faithful dog would not allow them to be surprised, but would bark at the least appearance of danger.

Cyrus Harding and his companions followed beside the road the wire which connected the corral with Granite House. After walking for nearly two miles, they had not as yet discovered any explanation of the difficulty. The posts were in good order, the wire regularly extended. However, at that moment the engineer observed that the wire appeared to be slack, and on arriving at post No. 74, Herbert, who was in advance stopped, exclaiming,—

'The wire is broken!'

His companions hurried forward and arrived at the spot where the lad was standing. The post was rooted up and lying across the path. The unexpected explanation of the difficulty was here, and it was evident that the despatches from Granite House had not been received at the corral, nor those from the corral at Granite House.

'It wasn't the wind that blew down this post,' observed Pencroft.

'No,' replied Gideon Spilett. 'The earth has been dug, up round its foot, and it has been torn up by the hand of man.'

'Besides, the wire is broken,' added Herbert, showing that the wire had been snapped.

'Is the fracture recent?' asked Harding.

'Yes,' answered Herbert, 'it has certainly been done quite lately.'

'To the corral! to the corral!' exclaimed the sailor.

The colonists were now half way between Granite House and the corral, having still two miles and a half to go. They pressed forward with redoubled speed.

Indeed, it was to be feared that some serious accident had occurred in the corral. No doubt, Ayrton might have sent a telegram which had not arrived, but this was not the reason why his companions were so uneasy, for, a more unaccountable circumstance, Ayrton, who had promised to return the evening before, had not reappeared. In short, it was not without a motive that all communication had been stopped between the corral and Granite House, and who but the convicts could have any interest in interrupting this communication?

The settlers hastened on, their hearts oppressed with anxiety. They were sincerely attached to their new companion. Were they to find him struck down by the hands of those of whom he was formerly the leader?

Soon they arrived at the place where the road led along the side of the little stream which flowed from the Red Creek and watered the meadows of the corral. They then moderated their pace so that they should not be out of breath at the moment when a struggle might be necessary. Their guns were in their hands ready cocked. The forest was watched on every side. Top uttered sullen groans which were rather ominous.

At last the palisade appeared through the trees. No trace of any damage could be seen. The gate was shut as usual. Deep silence reigned in the corral. Neither the accustomed bleating of the sheep nor Ayrton's voice could be heard.

'Let us enter,' said Cyrus Harding.

And the engineer advanced, while his companions, keeping watch about twenty paces behind him, were ready to fire at a moment's notice.

Harding raised the inner latch of the gate and was about to push it back, when Top barked loudly. A report sounded and was responded to by a cry of pain.

Herbert, struck by a bullet, lay stretched on the ground.

Chapter 7

At Herbert's cry, Pencroft, letting his gun fall, rushed towards him.

'They have killed him!' he cried. 'My boy! They have killed him!'

Cyrus Harding and Gideon Spilett ran to Herbert.

The reporter listened to ascertain if the poor lad's heart was still beating.

'He lives,' said he, 'but he must be carried—'

'To Granite House? that is impossible!' replied the engineer.

'Into the corral, then!' said Pencroft.

'In a moment,' said Harding.

And he ran round the left corner of the palisade. There he found a convict, who aiming at him, sent a ball through his hat. In a few seconds, before he had even time to fire his second barrel, he fell, struck to the heart by Harding's dagger, more sure even than his gun.

During this time, Gideon Spilett and the sailor hoisted themselves over the palisade, leaped into the enclosure, threw down the props which supported the inner door, ran into the empty house, and soon, poor Herbert was lying on Ayrton's bed. In a few moments, Harding was by his side.

On seeing Herbert senseless, the sailor's grief was terrible.

He sobbed, he cried, he tried to beat his head against the wall.

Neither the engineer nor the reporter could calm him. They themselves were choked with emotion. They could not speak.

However, they knew that it depended on them to rescue from death the poor boy who was suffering beneath their eyes. Gideon Spilett had not passed through the many incidents by which his life had been checkered without acquiring some slight knowledge of medicine. He knew a little of everything, and several times he had been obliged to attend to wounds produced either by a sword-bayonet or shot. Assisted by Cyrus Harding, he proceeded to render the aid Herbert required.

The reporter was immediately struck by the complete stupor in which Herbert lay, a stupor owing either to the haemorrhage, or to the shock, the ball having struck a bone with sufficient force to produce a violent concussion.

Herbert was deadly pale, and his pulse so feeble that Spilett only felt it beat at long intervals, as if it was on the point of stopping.

These symptoms were very serious.

Herbert's chest was laid bare, and the blood having been stanched with handkerchiefs, it was bathed with cold water.

The contusion, or rather the contused wound appeared,—an oval below the chest between the third and fourth ribs. It was there that Herbert had been hit by the bullet.

Cyrus Harding and Gideon Spilett then turned the poor boy over; as they did so, he uttered a moan so feeble that they almost thought it was his last sigh.

Herberts back was covered with blood from another contused wound, by which the ball had immediately escaped.

'God be praised!' said the reporter, 'the ball is not in the body, and we shall not have to extract it.'

'But the heart?' asked Harding.

'The heart has not been touched; if it had been, Herbert would be dead!'

'Dead!' exclaimed Pencroft, with a groan.

The sailor had only heard the last words uttered by the reporter.

'No, Pencroft,' replied Cyrus Harding, 'no! He is not dead. His pulse still beats. He has even uttered a moan. But for your boy's sake, calm yourself. We have need of all our self-possession.'

'Do not make us lose it, my friend.'

Pencroft was silent, but a reaction set in, and great tears rolled down his cheeks.

In the meanwhile, Gideon Spilett endeavoured to collect his ideas, and proceed methodically. After his examination he had no doubt that the ball, entering in front, between the seventh and eighth ribs, had issued behind between the third and fourth. But what mischief had the ball committed in its passage? What important organs had been reached? A professional surgeon would have had difficulty in determining this at once, and still more so the reporter.

However, he knew one thing, this was that he would have to prevent the inflammatory strangulation of the injured parts, then to contend with the local inflammation and fever which would result from the wound, perhaps mortal! Now, what styptics, what antiphiogistics ought to be employed? By what means could inflammation be prevented?

At any rate, the most important thing was that the two wounds should be dressed without delay. It did not appear necessary to Gideon Spilett that a fresh flow of blood should be caused by bathing them in tepid water, and compressing their lips. The hemorrhage had been very abundant, and Herbert was already too much enfeebled by the loss of blood.

The reporter, therefore, thought it best to simply bathe the two wounds with cold water.

Herbert was placed on his left side, and was maintained in that position.

'He must not be moved.' said Gideon Spilett. 'He is in the most favourable position for the wounds in his back and chest to suppurate easily, and absolute rest is necessary.'

'What! can't we carry him to Granite House?' asked Pencroft.

'No, Pencroft,' replied the reporter.

'I'll pay the villains off!' cried the sailor, shaking his fist in a menacing manner.

'Pencroft!' said Cyrus Harding.

Gideon Spilett had resumed his examination of the wounded boy. Herbert was still so frightfully pale, that the reporter felt anxious.

'Cyrus,' said he, 'I am not a surgeon. I am in terrible perplexity. You must aid me with your advice, your experience!'

'Take courage, my friend,' answered the engineer, pressing the reporter's hand. 'Judge coolly. Think only of this: Herbert must be saved!'

These words restored to Gideon Spilett that self-possession which he had lost in a moment of discouragement on feeling his great responsibility. He seated himself close to the bed. Cyrus Harding stood near. Pencroft had torn up his shirt, and was mechanically making lint.

Spilett then explained to Cyrus Harding that he thought he ought first of all to stop the hemorrhage, but not close the two wounds, or cause their immediate cicatrization, for there had been internal perforation, and the suppuration must not be allowed to accumulate in the chest.

Harding approved entirely, and it was decided that the two wounds should be dressed without attempting to close them by immediate coaptation.

And now did the colonists possess an efficacious agent to act against the inflammation which might occur?

Yes. They had one, for nature had generously lavished it. They had cold water, that is to say, the most powerful sedative that can be employed against inflammation of wounds, the most efficacious therapeutic agent in grave cases, and the one which is now adopted by all physicians. Cold water has, moreover, the advantage of leaving the wound in absolute rest, and preserving it from all premature dressing, a considerable advantage, since it has been found by experience that contact with the air is dangerous during the first days.

Gideon Spilett and Cyrus Harding reasoned thus with their simple good sense, and they acted as the best surgeon would have done. Compresses of linen were applied to poor Herbert's two wounds, and were kept constantly wet with cold water.

The sailor had at first lighted a fire in the hut, which was not wanting in things necessary for life. Maple sugar, medicinal plants, the same which the lad had gathered on the banks of Lake Grant, enabled them to make some refreshing drinks, which they gave him without his taking any notice of it. His fever was extremely high, and all that day and night passed without his becoming conscious.

Herbert's life hung on a thread, and this thread might break at any moment. The next day, the 12th of November, the hopes of Harding and his companions slightly revived. Herbert had come out of his long stupor. He opened his eyes, he recognized Cyrus Harding, the reporter, and Pencroft. He uttered two or three words. He did not know what had happened. They told him, and Spilett begged him to remain perfectly still, telling him that his life was not in danger, and that his wounds would heal in a few days. However, Herbert scarcely suffered at all, and the cold water with which they were constantly bathed, prevented any inflammation of the wounds. The suppuration was established in a regular way, the fever did not increase, and it might now be hoped that this terrible wound would not involve any catastrophe. Pencroft felt the swelling of his heart gradually subside. He was like a sister of mercy. like a mother by the bed of her child.

Herbert dozed again, but his sleep appeared more natural.

'Tell me again that you hope, Mr. Spilett,' said Pencroft. 'Tell me again that you will save Herbert!'

'Yes, we will save him!' replied the reporter. 'The wound is serious, and, perhaps, even the ball has traversed the lungs, but the perforation of this organ is not fatal.'

'God bless you!' answered Pencroft.

As may be believed, during the four-and-twenty hours they had been in the corral, the colonists had no other thought than that of nursing Herbert. They did not think either of the danger which threatened them should the convicts return, or of the precautions to be taken for the future.

But on this day, while Pencroft watched by the sick-bed, Cyrus Harding and the reporter consulted as to what it would be best to do.

First of all they examined the corral. There was not a trace of Ayrton. Had the unhappy man been dragged away by his former accomplices? Had he resisted, and been overcome in the struggle? This last supposition was only too probable. Gideon Spilett, at the moment he scaled the palisade, had clearly seen some one of the convicts running along the southern spur of Mount Franklin, towards whom Top had sprung. It was one of those whose object had been so completely defeated by the rocks at the mouth of the Mercy. Besides, the one killed by Harding, and whose body was found outside the enclosure, of course belonged to Bob Harvey's crew.

As to the corral, it had not suffered any damage. The gates were closed, and the animals had not been able to disperse in the forest. Nor could they see traces of any struggle, any devastation, either in the hut, or in the palisade. The ammunition only, with which Ayrton had been supplied, had disappeared with him.

'The unhappy man has been surprised,' said Harding, 'and as he was a man to defend himself, he must have been overpowered.'

'Yes, that is to be feared!' said the reporter. 'Then, doubtless, the convicts installed themselves in the corral where they found plenty of everything, and only fled when they saw us coming. It is very evident, too, that at this moment Ayrton, whether living or dead, is not here!'

'We shall have to beat the forest,' said the engineer, 'and rid the island of these wretches. Pencroft's presentiments were not mistaken, when he wished to hunt them as wild beasts. That would have spared us all these misfortunes!'

'Yes,' answered the reporter, 'but now we have the right to be merciless!'

'At any rate,' said the engineer, 'we are obliged to wait some time, and to remain at the corral until we can carry Herbert without danger to Granite House.'

'But Neb?' asked the reporter.

'Neb is in safety.'

'But if, uneasy at our absence, he would venture to come?'

'He must not come!' returned Cyrus Harding quickly. 'He would be murdered on the road!'

'It is very probable, however, that he will attempt to rejoin us!'

'Ah, if the telegraph still acted, he might be warned! But that is impossible now! As to leaving Pencroft and Herbert here alone, we could not do it! Well, I will go alone to Granite House.'

'No, no! Cyrus,' answered the reporter, 'you must not expose yourself! Your courage would be of no avail. The villains are evidently watching the corral, they are hidden in the thick woods which surround it, and if you go we shall soon have to regret two misfortunes instead of one!'

'But Neb?' repeated the engineer. 'It is now four-and-twenty hours since he has had any news of us! He will be sure to come!'

'And as he will be less on his guard than we should be ourselves,' added Spilett, 'he will be killed!'

'Is there really no way of warning him?'

While the engineer thought, his eyes fell on Top, who, going backwards and forwards seemed to say,—

'Am not I here?'

'Top!' exclaimed Cyrus Harding.

The animal sprang at his master's call.

'Yes, Top will go,' said the reporter, who had understood the engineer.

'Top can go where we cannot! He will carry to Granite House the news of the corral, and he will bring back to us that from Granite House!'

'Quick!' said Harding. 'Quick!'

Spilett rapidly tore a leaf from his notebook, and wrote these words:—

'Herbert wounded. We are at the corral. Be on your guard. Do not leave Granite House. Have the convicts appeared in the neighbourhood? Reply by Top.'

This laconic note contained all that Neb ought to know, and at the same time asked all that the colonists wished to know. It was folded and fastened to Top's collar in a conspicuous position.

'Top, my dog,' said the engineer, caressing the animal, 'Neb, Top! Neb! Go, go!'

Top bounded at these words. He understood, he knew what was expected of him. The road to the corral was familiar to him. In less than an hour he could clear it, and it might be hoped that where neither Cyrus Harding nor the reporter could have ventured without danger, Top, running among the grass or in the wood, would pass unperceived.

The engineer went to the gate of the corral and opened it.

'Neb, Top! Neb!' repeated the engineer, again pointing in the direction of Granite House.

Top sprang forwards, then almost immediately disappeared.

'He will get there!' said the reporter.

'Yes, and he will come back, the faithful animal!'

'What o'clock is it?' asked Gideon Spilett.

'Ten.'

'In an hour he may be here. We will watch for his return.'

The gate of the corral was closed. The engineer and the reporter re-entered the house. Herbert was still in a sleep. Pencroft kept the compressor always wet. Spilett, seeing there was nothing he could do at that moment, busied himself in preparing some nourishment, while attentively watching that part of the enclosure against the hill, at which an attack might be expected.

The settlers awaited Top's return with much anxiety. A little before eleven o'clock, Cyrus Harding and the reporter, rifle in hand, were behind the gate, ready to open it at the first bark of their dog.

They did not doubt that if Top had arrived safely at Granite House, Neb would have sent him back immediately.

They had both been there for about ten minutes, when a report was heard, followed by repeated barks.

The engineer opened the gate, and seeing smoke a hundred feet off in the wood, he fired in that direction.

Almost immediately Top bounded into the corral, and the gate was quickly shut.

'Top, Top!' exclaimed the engineer, taking the dog's great honest head between his hands.

A note was fastened to his neck, and Cyrus Harding read these words, traced in Neb's large writing:—'No pirates in the neighbourhood of Granite House. I will not stir. Poor Mr. Herbert!'

Chapter 8

So the convicts were still there, watching the corral, and determined to kill the settlers one after the other. There was nothing to be done but to treat them as wild beasts. But great precautions must be taken, for just now the wretches had the advantage on their side, seeing, and not being seen, being able to surprise by the suddenness of their attack, yet not to be surprised themselves. Harding made arrangements, therefore, for living in the corral, of which the provisions would last for a tolerable length of time. Ayrton's house had been provided with all that was necessary for existence, and the convicts, scared by the arrival of the settlers, had not had time to pillage it. It was probable, as Gideon Spilett observed, that things had occurred as follows:

The six convicts, disembarking on the island, had followed the southern shore, and after having traversed the double shore of the Serpentine Peninsula, not being inclined to venture into the Far West woods, they had reached the mouth of Falls River. From this point, by following the right bank of the watercourse, they would arrive at the spurs of Mount Franklin, among which they would naturally seek a retreat, and they could not have been long in discovering the corral, then uninhabited. There they had regularly installed themselves, awaiting the moment to put their abominable schemes into execution. Ayrton's arrival had surprised them, but they had managed to overpower the unfortunate man, and—the rest may be easily imagined!

Now, the convicts,—reduced to five, it is true, but well armed,—were roaming the woods, and to venture there was to expose themselves to their attacks, which could be neither guarded against nor prevented.

'Wait! There is nothing else to be done!' repeated Cyrus Harding. 'When Herbert is cured, we can organize a general battle of the island, and have satisfaction of these convicts. That will be the object of our grand expedition at the same time—'

'As the search for our mysterious protector,' added Gideon Spilett, finishing the engineer's sentence. 'An, it must be acknowledged, my dear Cyrus, that this time his protection was wanting at the very moment when it was most necessary to us!'

'Who knows?' replied the engineer.

'What do you mean?' asked the reporter.

'That we are not at the end of our trouble yet, my dear Spilett, and that his powerful intervention may have another opportunity of exercising itself. But that is not the question now. Herbert's life before everything.'

This was the colonists' saddest thought. Several days passed, and the poor boy's state was happily no worse. Cold water, always kept at a suitable temperature, had completely prevented the inflammation of the wounds. It even seemed to the reporter that this water, being slightly sulphurous,—which was explained by the neighbourhood of the volcano, had a more direct action on the healing. The suppuration was much less abundant, and thanks to the incessant care by which he was surrounded!—Herbert returned to life, and his fever abated. He was besides subjected to a severe diet, and consequently his wealmess was and would be extreme; but there was no want of refreshing drinks, and absolute rest was of the greatest benefit to him. Cyrus Harding, Gideon Spilett, and Pencroft had become very skilful in dressing the lad's wounds. All the linen in the house had been sacrificed. Herbert's wounds, covered with compresses and lint, were pressed neither too much nor too little, so as to cause their cicatrization without effecting any inflammatory reaction. The reporter used extreme care in the dressing, knowing well the importance of it, and repeating to his companions that which most surgeons willingly admit, that it is perhaps rarer to see a dressing well done than an operation well performed.

In ten days, on the 22nd of November, Herbert was considerably better. He had begun to take some nourishment.

The colour was returning to his cheeks, and his bright eyes smiled at his nurses. He talked a little, notwithstanding Pencroft's efforts, who talked incessantly to prevent him from beginning to speak, and told him the most improbable stories. Herbert had questioned him on the subject of Ayrton, whom he was astonished not to see near him, thinking that he was at the corral. But the sailor, not wishing to distress Herbert, contented himself by replying that Ayrton had rejoined Neb, so as to defend Granite House.

'Humph!' said Pencroft, 'these pirates! they are gentlemen who have no right to any consideration! And the captain wanted to win them by kindness! I'll send them some kindness, but in the shape of a good bullet!'

'And have they not been seen again?' asked Herbert.

'No, my boy,' answered the sailor, 'but we shall find them, and when you are cured we shall see if the cowards who strike us from behind will dare to meet us face to face!'

'I am still very weak, my poor Pencroft!'

'Well! your strength will return gradually! What's a ball through the chest? Nothing but a joke! I've seen many, and I don't think much of them!'

At last things appeared to be going on well, and if no complication occurred, Herbert's recovery might be regarded as certain. But what would have been the condition of the colonists if his state had been aggravated, —if, for example, the ball had remained in his body, if his arm or his leg had had to be amputated?

'No,' said Spilett more than once, 'I have never thought of such a contingency without shuddering!'

'And yet, if it had been necessary to operate,' said Harding one day to him, 'you would not have hesitated?'

'No, Cyrus!' said Gideon Spilett, 'but thank God that we have been spared this complication!'

As in so many other conjectures, the colonists had appealed to the logic of that simple good sense of which they had made use so often, and once more, thanks to their general knowledge, it had succeeded! But might not a time come when all their science would be at fault? They were alone on the island. Now, men in all states of society are necessary to each other. Cyrus Harding knew this well, and sometimes he asked if some circumstance might not occur which they would be powerless to surmount. It appeared to him besides, that he and his companions, till then so fortunate, had entered into an unlucky period. During the two years and a half which had elapsed since their escape from Richmond, it might be said that they had had everything their own way. The island had abundantly supplied them with minerals, vegetables, animals, and as Nature had constantly loaded them, their science had known how to take advantage of what she offered them.

The wellbeing of the colony was therefore complete. Moreover, in certain occurrences an inexplicable influence had come to their aid!... But all that could only be for a time.

In short, Cyrus Harding believed that fortune had turned against them.

In fact, the convicts' ship had appeared in the waters of the island, and if the pirates had been, so to speak, miraculously destroyed, six of them, at least, had escaped the catastrophe. They had disembarked on the island, and it was almost impossible to get at the five who survived. Ayrton had no doubt been murdered by these wretches, who possessed firearms, and at the first use that they had made of them, Herbert had fallen, wounded almost mortally. Were these the first blows aimed by adverse fortune at the colonists? This was often asked by Harding. This was often repeated by the reporter; and it appeared to him also that the intervention, so strange, yet so efficacious, which till then had served them so well, had now failed them. Had this mysterious being, whatever he was, whose existence could not be denied, abandoned the island? Had he in his turn succumbed?

No reply was possible to these questions. But it must not be imagined that because Harding and his companions spoke of these things, they were men to despair. Far from that. They looked their situation in the face, they analysed the chances, they prepared themselves for any event, they stood firm and straight before the future, and if adversity was at last to strike them, it would find in them men prepared to struggle against it.

Chapter 9

The convalescence of the young invalid was regularly progressing. One thing only was now to be desired, that his state would allow him to be brought to Granite House. However well built and supplied the corral house was, it could not be so comfortable as the healthy granite dwelling. Besides, it did not offer the same security, and its tenants, notwithstanding their watchfulness, were here always in fear of some shot from the convicts. There, on the contrary, in the middle of that impregnable and inaccessible cliff, they would have nothing to fear, and any attack on their persons would certainly fail. They therefore waited impatiently for the moment when Herbert might be moved without danger from his wound, and they were determined to make this move, although the communication through Jacamar Wood was very difficult.

They had no news from Neb, but were not uneasy on that account. The courageous Negro, well entrenched in the depths of Granite House, would not allow himself to be surprised. Top had not been sent again to him, as it appeared useless to expose the faithful dog to some shot which might deprive the settlers of their most useful auxiliary.

They waited, therefore, although they were anxious to be reunited at Granite House. It pained the engineer to see his forces divided, for it gave great advantage to the pirates. Since Ayrton's disappearance they were only four against five, for Herbert could not yet be counted, and this was not the least care of the brave boy, who well understood the trouble of which he was the cause.

The question of knowing how, in their condition, they were to act against the pirates, was thoroughly discussed on the 29th of November by Cyrus Harding, Gideon Spilett, and Pencroft, at a moment when Herbert was asleep and could not hear them.

'My friends,' said the reporter, after they had talked of Neb and of the impossibility of communicating with him, 'I think, —like you, that to venture on the road to the corral would be to risk receiving a gunshot without being able to return it. But do you not think that the best thing to be done now is to openly give chase to these wretches?'

'That is just what I was thinking,' answered Pencroft. 'I believe we're not fellows to be afraid of a bullet, and as for me, if Captain Harding approves, I'm ready to dash into the forest! Why, hang it, one man is equal to another!'

'But is he equal to five?' asked the engineer.

'I will join Pencroft,' said the reporter, 'and both of us, well-armed and accompanied by Top—'

'My dear Spilett, and you, Pencroft,' answered Harding, 'let us reason coolly. If the convicts were hid in one spot of the island, if we knew that spot, and had only to dislodge them, I would undertake a direct attack; but is there not occasion to fear, on the contrary, that they are sure to fire the first shot?'

'Well, captain,' cried Pencroft, 'a bullet does not always reach its mark.'

'That which struck Herbert did not miss, Pencroft,' replied the engineer. 'Besides, observe that if both of you left the corral I should remain here alone to defend it. Do you imagine that the convicts will not see you leave it, that they will not allow you to enter the forest, and that they will not attack it during your absence, knowing that there is no one here but a wounded boy and a man?'

'You are right, captain,' replied Pencroft, his chest swelling with sullen anger. 'You are right; they will do all they can to retake the corral, which they know to be well stored; and alone you could not hold it against them.'

'Oh, if we were only at Granite House!'

'If we were at Granite House,' answered the engineer, 'the case would be very different. There I should not be afraid to leave Herbert with one, while the other three went to search the forests of the island. But we are at the corral, and it is best to stay here until we can leave it together.'

Cyrus Harding's reasoning was unanswerable, and his companions understood it well.

'If only Ayrton was still one of us!' said Gideon Spilett. 'Poor fellow! his return to social life will have been but of short duration.'

'If he is dead,' added Pencroft, in a peculiar tone.

'Do you hope, then, Pencroft, that the villains have spared him?' asked Gideon Spilett.

'Yes, if they had any interest in doing so.'

'What! you suppose that Ayrton finding his old companions, forgetting all that he owes us—'

'Who knows?' answered the sailor, who did not hazard this shameful supposition without hesitating.

'Pencroft,' said Harding, taking the sailor's arm, 'that is a wicked idea of yours, and you will distress me much if you persist in speaking thus. I will answer for Ayrton's fidelity.'

'And I also,' added the reporter quickly.

'Yes, yes, captain, I was wrong,' replied Pencroft; 'it was a wicked idea indeed that I had, and nothing justifies it. But what can I do? I'm not in my senses. This imprisonment in the corral wearies me horribly, and I have never felt so excited as I do now.

'Be patient, Pencroft,' replied the engineer. 'How long will it be, my dear Spilett, before you think Herbert may be carried to Granite House?'

'That is difficult to say, Cyrus,' answered the reporter, 'for any imprudence might involve terrible consequences. But his convalescence is progressing, and if he continues to gain strength, in eight days from now— well, we shall see.'

Eight days! That would put off the return to Granite House until the first days of December. At this time two months of spring had already passed. The weather was fine, and the heat began to be great. The forests of the island were in full leaf, and the time was approaching when the usual crops ought to be gathered. The return to the plateau of Prospect Heights would, therefore, be followed by extensive agricultural labours, interrupted only by the projected expedition through the island.

It can, therefore, be well understood how injurious this seclusion in the corral must have been to the colonists.

But if they were compelled to bow before necessity, they did not do so without impatience.

Once or twice the reporter ventured out into the road and made the tour of the palisade. Top accompanied him, and Gideon Spilett, his gun cocked, was ready for any emergency.

He met with no misadventure and found no suspicious traces. His dog would have warned him of any danger, and, as Top did not bark, it might be concluded that there was nothing to fear at the moment at least, and that the convicts were occupied in another part of the island.

However, on his second sortie, on the 27th of November, Gideon Spilett, who had ventured a quarter of a mile into the woods, towards the south of the mountain, remarked that Top scented something. The dog had no longer his unconcerned manner; he went backwards and forwards, ferreting among the grass and bushes as if his smell had revealed some suspicious object to him.

Gideon Spilett followed Top, encouraged him, excited him by his voice, while keeping a sharp lookout, his gun ready to fire, and sheltering himself behind the trees. It was not probable that Top scented the presence of man, for in that case, he would have announced it by half-uttered, sullen, angry barks. Now, as he did not growl, it was because danger was neither near nor approaching.

Nearly five minutes passed thus, Top rummaging, the reporter following him prudently when, all at once, the dog rushed towards a thick bush, and drew out a rag.

It was a piece of cloth, stained and torn, which Spilett immediately brought back to the corral. There it was examined by the colonists, who found that it was a fragment of Ayrton's waistcoat, a piece of that felt, manufactured solely by the Granite House factory.

'You see, Pencroft,' observed Harding, 'there has been resistance on the part of the unfortunate Ayrton. The convicts have dragged him away in spite of himself! Do you still doubt his honesty?'

'No, captain,' answered the sailor, 'and I repented of my suspicion a long time ago! But it seems to me that something may be learned from the incident.'

'What is that?' asked the reporter.

'It is that Ayrton was not killed at the corral! That they dragged him away living, since he has resisted. Therefore, perhaps, he is still living!'

'Perhaps, indeed,' replied the engineer, who remained thoughtful.

This was a hope, to which Ayrton's companions could still hold. Indeed, they had before believed that, surprised in the corral, Ayrton had fallen by a bullet, as Herbert had fallen. But if the convicts had not killed him at first, if they had brought him living to another part of the island, might it not be admitted that he was still their prisoner? Perhaps, even, one of them had found in Ayrton his old Australian companion Ben Joyce, the chief of the escaped convicts. And who knows but that they had conceived the impossible hope of bringing back Ayrton to themselves? He would have been very useful to them, if they had been able to make him turn traitor!

This incident was, therefore, favourably interpreted at the corral, and it no longer appeared impossible that they should find Ayrton again. On his side, if he was only a prisoner, Ayrton would no doubt do all he could to escape from the hands of the villains, and this would be a powerful aid to the settlers!

'At any rate,' observed Gideon Spilett, 'if happily Ayrton did manage to escape, he would go directly to Granite House, for he could not know of the attempted assassination of which Herbert has been a victim, and consequently would never think of our being imprisoned in the corral.'

'Oh! I wish that he was there, at Granite House!' cried Pencroft, 'and that we were there, too! For, although the rascals can do nothing to our house, they may plunder the plateau, our plantations, our poultry-yard!'

Pencroft had become a thorough farmer, heartily attached to his crops. But it must be said that Herbert was more anxious than any to return to Granite House, for he knew how much the presence of the settlers was needed there. And it was he who was keeping them at the corral!

Therefore, one idea occupied his mind—to leave the corral, and when! He believed he could bear removal to Granite House. He was sure his strength would return more quickly in his room, with the air and sight of the sea!

Several times he pressed Gideon Spilett, but the latter, fearing, with good reason, that Herbert's wounds, half healed, might reopen on the way, did not give the order to start.

However, something occurred which compelled Cyrus Harding and his two friends to yield to the lad's wish, and God alone knew that this determination might cause them grief and remorse.

It was the 29th of November, seven o'clock in the evening. The three settlers were talking in Herbert's room, when they heard Top utter quick barks.

Harding, Pencroft, and Spilett seized their guns and ran out of the house. Top, at the foot of the palisade, was jumping, barking, but it was with pleasure, not anger.

'Some one is coming.'

'Yes.'

'It is not an enemy!'

'Neb, perhaps?'

'Or Ayrton?'

These words had hardly been exchanged between the engineer and his two companions when a body leaped over the palisade and fell on the ground inside the corral.

It was Jup, Master Jup in person, to whom Top immediately gave a most cordial reception.

'Jup!' exclaimed Pencroft.

'Neb has sent him to us,' said the reporter.

'Then,' replied the engineer, 'he must have some note on him.'

Pencroft rushed up to the orang. Certainly if Neb had any important matter to communicate to his master he could not employ a more sure or more rapid messenger, who could pass where neither the colonists could, nor even Top himself.

Cyrus Harding was not mistaken. At Jup's neck hung a small bag, and in this bag was found a little note traced by Neb's hand.

The despair of Harding and his companions may be imagined when they read these words:—

'Friday, six o'clock in the morning.

'Plateau invaded by convicts.

'Neb.'

They gazed at each other without uttering a word, then they re-entered the house. What were they to do? The convicts on Prospect Heights! that was disaster, devastation, ruin.

Herbert, on seeing the engineer, the reporter, and Pencroft re-enter, guessed that their situation was aggravated, and when he saw Jup, he no longer doubted that some misfortune menaced Granite House.

'Captain Harding,' said he, 'I must go; I can bear the journey. I must go.'

Gideon Spilett approached Herbert; then, having looked at him,—

'Let us go, then!' said he.

The question was quickly decided whether Herbert should be carried on a litter or in the cart which had brought Ayrton to the corral. The motion of the litter would have been more easy for the wounded lad, but it would have necessitated two bearers, that is to say, there would have been two guns less for defence if an attack was made on the road. Would they not, on the contrary, by employing the cart leave every arm free? Was it impossible to place the mattress on which Herbert was lying in it, and to advance with so much care that any jolt should be avoided? It could be done.

The cart was brought. Pencroft harnessed the onager. Cyrus Harding and the reporter raised Herbert's mattress and placed it on the bottom of the cart. The weather was fine. The sun's bright rays glanced through the trees.

'Are the guns ready?' asked Cyrus Harding.

They were. The engineer and Pencroft, each armed with a double-barrelled gun, and Gideon Spilett carrying his rifle, had nothing to do but start.

'Are you comfortable, Herbert?' asked the engineer.

'Ah, captain,' replied the lad, 'don't be uneasy, I shall not die on the road!'

While speaking thus, it could be seen that the poor boy had called up all his energy, and by the energy of a powerful will had collected his failing strength.

The engineer felt his heart sink painfully. He still hesitated to give the signal for departure; but that would have driven Herbert to despair—killed him perhaps.

'Forward!' said Harding.

The gate of the corral was opened. Jup and Top, who knew when to be silent, ran in advance. The cart came out, the gate was reclosed, and the onager, led by Pencroft, advanced at a slow pace.

Certainly, it would have been safer to have taken a different road than that which led straight from the corral to Granite House, but the cart would have met with great difficulties in moving under the trees. It was necessary, therefore, to follow this way, although it was well known to the convicts.

Cyrus Harding and Gideon Spilett walked one on each side of the cart, ready to answer to any attack. However, it was not probable that the convicts would have yet left the plateau of Prospect Heights.

Neb's note had evidently been written and sent as soon as the convicts had shown themselves there. Now, this note was dated six o'clock in the morning, and the active orang, accustomed to come frequently to the corral, had taken scarcely three quarters of an hour to cross the five miles which separated it from Granite House. They would, therefore, be safe at that time, and if there was any occasion for firing, it would probably not be until they were in the neighbourhood of Granite House. However, the colonists kept a strict watch. Top and Jup, the latter armed with his club, sometimes in front, sometimes beating the wood at the sides of the road, signalized no danger.

The cart advanced slowly under Pencroft's guidance. It had left the corral at half-past seven. An hour after, four out of the five miles had been cleared, without any incident having occurred. The road was as deserted as all that part of the Jacamar Wood which lay between the Mercy and the lake. There was no occasion for any warning. The wood appeared as deserted as on the day when the colonists first landed on the island.

They approached the plateau. Another mile and they would see the bridge over Creek Glycerine. Cyrus Harding expected to find it in its place; supposing that the convicts would have crossed it, and that, after having passed one of the streams which enclosed the plateau, they would have taken the precaution to lower it again, so as to keep open a retreat.

At length an opening in the trees allowed the sea-horizon to be seen. But the cart continued its progress, for not one of its defenders thought of abandoning it.

At that moment Pencroft stopped the onager, and in a hoarse voice,—

'Oh! the villains!' he exclaimed.

And he pointed to a thick smoke rising from the mill, the sheds, and the buildings at the poultry-yard.

A man was moving about in the midst of the smoke. It was Neb.

His companions uttered a shout. He heard, and ran to meet them.

The convicts had left the plateau nearly half-an-hour before, having devastated it!

'And Mr. Herbert?' asked Neb.

Gideon Spilett returned to the cart.

Herbert had lost consciousness!

Chapter 10

Of the convicts, the dangers which menaced Granite House, the ruins with which the plateau was covered, the colonists thought no longer. Herbert's critical state outweighed all other considerations. Would the removal prove fatal to him by causing some internal injury? The reporter could not affirm it, but he and his companions almost despaired of the result. The cart was brought to the bend of the river. There some branches, disposed as a liner, received the mattress on which lay the unconscious Herbert. Ten minutes after, Cyrus Harding, Spilett, and Pencroft were at the foot of the cliff, leaving Neb to take the cart on to the plateau of Prospect Heights. The lift was put in motion, and Herbert was soon stretched on his bed in Granite House.

What cares were lavished on him to bring him back to life! He smiled for a moment on finding himself in his room, but could scarcely even murmur a few words, so great was his weakness. Gideon Spilett examined his wounds. He feared to find them reopened, having been imperfectly healed. There was nothing of the sort. From whence, then, came this prostration? why was Herbert so much worse? The lad then fell into a kind of feverish sleep, and the reporter and Pencroft remained near the bed. During this time, Harding told Neb all that had happened at the corral, and Neb recounted to his master the events of which the plateau had just been the theatre.

It was only during the preceding night that the convicts had appeared on the edge of the forest, at the approaches to Creek Glycerine. Neb, who was watching near the poultry-yard, had not hesitated to fire at one of the pirates, who was about to cross the stream; but in the darkness he could not tell whether the man had been hit or not. At any rate, it was not enough to frighten away the band, and Neb had only just time to get up to Granite House, where at least he was in safety.

But what was he to do there? How prevent the devastations with which the convicts threatened the plateau? Had Neb any means by which to warn his master? And, besides, in what situation were the inhabitants of the corral themselves? Cyrus Harding and his companions had left on the 11th of November, and it was now the 29th. It was, therefore, nineteen days since Neb had had other news than that brought by Top—disastrous news: Ayrton disappeared, Herbert severely wounded, the engineer, reporter, and sailor, as it were, imprisoned in the corral!

What was he to do? asked poor Neb. Personally he had nothing to fear, for the convicts could not reach him in Granite House. But the buildings, the plantations, all their arrangements at the mercy of the pirates! Would it not be best to let Cyrus Harding judge of what he ought to do, and to warn him, at least, of the danger which threatened him?

Neb then thought of employing Jup, and confiding a note to him. He knew the orang's great intelligence, which had been often put to the proof. Jup understood the word corral, which had been frequently pronounced before him, and it may be remembered, too, that he had often driven the cart thither in company with Pencroft. Day had not yet dawned. The active orang would know how to pass unperceived through the woods, of which the convicts, besides, would think he was a native.

Neb did not hesitate. He wrote the note, he tied it to Jup's neck, he brought the ape to the door of Granite House, from which he let down a long cord to the ground; then, several times he repeated these words,—

'Jup Jup! corral, corral!'

The creature understood, seized the cord, glided rapidly down the beach, and disappeared in the darkness without the convicts' attention having been in the least excited.

'You did well, Neb,' said Harding, 'but perhaps in not warning us you would have done still better!'

And, in speaking thus, Cyrus Harding thought of Herbert, whose recovery the removal had so seriously checked.

Neb ended his account. The convicts had not appeared at all on the beach. Not knowing the number of the island's inhabitants, they might suppose that Granite House was defended by a large party. They must have remembered that during the attack by the brig numerous shot had been fired both from the lower and upper rocks, and no doubt they did not wish to expose themselves. But the plateau of Prospect Heights was open to them, and not covered by the fire of Granite House. They gave themselves up, therefore, to their instinct of destruction,—plundering, burning, devastating everything,—and only retiring half an hour before the arrival of the colonists, whom they believed still confined in the corral.

On their retreat, Neb hurried out. He climbed the plateau at the risk of being perceived and fired at, tried to extinguish the fire which was consuming the buildings of the poultry-yard, and had struggled, though in vain, against it until the cart appeared at the edge of the wood.

Such had been these serious events. The presence of the convicts constituted a permanent source of danger to the settlers in Lincoln Island, until then so happy, and who might now expect still greater misfortunes.

Spilett remained in Granite House with Herbert and Pencroft, while

Cyrus Harding, accompanied by Neb, proceeded to judge for himself of the extent of the disaster.

It was fortunate that the convicts had not advanced to the foot of Granite House. The workshop at the Chimneys would in that case not have escaped destruction. But after all, this evil would have been more easily reparable than the ruins accumulated on the plateau of Prospect Heights. Harding and Neb proceeded towards the Mercy, and ascended its left bank without meeting with any trace of the convicts; nor on the other side of the river, in the depths of the wood, could they perceive any suspicious indications.

Besides, it might be supposed that in all probability either the convicts knew of the return of the settlers to Granite House, by having seen them pass on the road from the corral, or, after the devastation of the plateau, they had penetrated into Jacamar Wood, following the course of the Mercy, and were thus ignorant of their return.

In the former case, they must have returned towards the corral, now without defenders, and which contained valuable stores.

In the latter, they must have regained their encampment, and would wait on opportunity to recommence the attack.

It was, therefore, possible to prevent them, but any enterprise to clear the island was now rendered difficult by reason of Herbert's condition. Indeed, their whole force would have been barely sufficient to cope with the convicts, and just now no one could leave Granite House.

The engineer and Neb arrived on the plateau. Desolation reigned everywhere. The fields had been trampled over; the ears of wheat, which were nearly full-grown, lay on the ground. The other plantations had not suffered less.

The kitchen-garden was destroyed. Happily, Granite House possessed a store of seed which would enable them to repair these misfortunes.

As to the wall and buildings of the poultry-yard and the onagers stable, the fire had destroyed all. A few terrified creatures roamed over the plateau. The birds, which during the fire had taken refuge on the waters of the lake, had already returned to their accustomed spot, and were dabbling on the banks. Everything would have to be reconstructed.

Cyrus Harding's face, which was paler than usual, expressed an internal anger which he commanded with difficulty, but he did not utter a word. Once more he looked at his devastated fields, and at the smoke which still rose from the ruins, then he returned to Granite House.

The following days were the saddest of any that the colonists had passed on the island! Herbert's weakness visibly increased. It appeared that a more serious malady, the consequence of the profound physiological disturbance he had gone through, threatened to declare itself, and Gideon Spilett feared such an aggravation of his condition that he would be powerless to fight against it!

In fact, Herbert remained in an almost continuous state of drowsiness, and symptoms of delirium began to manifest themselves. Refreshing drinks were the only remedies at the colonists' disposal. The fever was not as yet very high, but it soon appeared that it would probably recur at regular intervals. Gideon Spilett first recognized this on the 6th of December.

The poor boy, whose fingers, nose, and ears had become extremely pale, was at first seized with slight shiverings, horripilations, and tremblings. His pulse was weak and irregular, his skin dry, his thirst intense. To this soon succeeded a hot fit; his face became flushed; his skin reddened; his pulse quick; then a profuse perspiration broke out after which the fever seemed to diminish. The attack had lasted nearly five hours.

Gideon Spilett had not left Herbert, who, it was only too certain, was now seized by an intermittent fever, and this fever must be cured at any cost before it should assume a more serious aspect.

'And in order to cure it,' said Spilett to Cyrus Harding, 'we need a febrifuge.'

'A febrifuge—' answered the engineer. 'We have neither Peruvian bark, nor sulphate of quinine.'

'No,' said Gideon Spilett, 'but there are willows on the border of the lake, and the bark of the willow might, perhaps, prove to be a substitute for quinine.'

'Let us try it without losing a moment,' replied Cyrus Harding.

The bark of the willow has, indeed, been justly considered as a succedaneum for Peruvian bark, as has also that of the horse-chestnut tree, the leaf of the holly, the snake-root, etc. It was evidently necessary to make trial of this substance, although not so valuable as Peruvian bark, and to employ it in its natural state, since they had no means for extracting its essence.

Cyrus Harding went himself to cut from the trunk of a species of black willow, a few pieces of bark; he brought them back to Granite House, and reduced them to a powder, which was administered that same evening to Herbert.

The night passed without any important change. Herbert was somewhat delirious, but the fever did not reappear in the night, and did not return either during the following day.

Pencroft again began to hope. Gideon Spilett said nothing. It might be that the fever was not quotidian, but tertian, and that it would return next day. Therefore, he awaited the next day with the greatest anxiety.

It might have been remarked besides that during this period Herbert remained utterly prostrate, his head weak and giddy. Another symptom alarmed the reporter to the highest degree. Herbert's liver became congested, and soon a more intense delirium showed that his brain was also affected.

Gideon Spilett was overwhelmed by this new complication. He took the engineer aside.

'It is a malignant fever,' said he.

'A malignant fever!' cried Harding. 'You are mistaken, Spilett. A malignant fever does not declare itself spontaneously; its germ must previously have existed.'

'I am not mistaken,' replied the reporter. 'Herbert no doubt contracted the germ of this fever in the marshes of the island. He has already had one attack; should a second come on and should we not be able to prevent a third, he is lost.'

'But the willow bark?'

'That is insufficient,' answered the reporter, 'and the third attack of a malignant fever, which is not arrested by means of quinine, is always fatal.'

Fortunately, Pencroft heard nothing of this conversation or he would have gone mad.

It may be imagined what anxiety the engineer and the reporter suffered during the day of the 7th of December and the following night.

Towards the middle of the day the second attack came on. The crisis was terrible. Herbert felt himself sinking. He stretched his arms towards Cyrus Harding, towards Spilett, towards Pencroft. He was so young to die! The scene was heart-rending. They were obliged to send Pencroft away.

The fit lasted five hours. It was evident that Herbert could not survive a third.

The night was frightful. In his delirium Herbert uttered words which went to the hearts of his companions. He struggled with the convicts, he called to Ayrton, he poured forth entreaties to that mysterious being,—that powerful unknown protector,—whose image was stamped upon his mind; then he again fell into a deep exhaustion which completely prostrated him. Several times Gideon Spilett thought that the poor boy was dead.

The next day, the 8th of December, was but a succession of the fainting fits. Herbert's thin hands clutched the sheets. They had administered further doses of pounded bark, but the reporter expected no result from it.

'If before tomorrow morning we have not given him a more energetic febrifuge,' said the reporter, 'Herbert will be dead.'

Night arrived—the last night, it was too much to be feared, of the good, brave, intelligent boy, so far in advance of his years, and who was loved by all as their own child. The only remedy which existed against this terrible malignant fever, the only specific which could overcome it, was not to be found in Lincoln Island.

During the night of the 8th of December, Herbert was seized by a more violent delirium. His liver was fearfully congested, his brain affected, and already it was impossible for him to recognize any one.

Would he live until the next day, until that third attack which must infallibly carry him off? It was not probable. His strength was exhausted, and in the intervals of fever he lay as one dead.

Towards three o'clock in the morning Herbert uttered a piercing cry. He seemed to be torn by a supreme convulsion. Neb, who was near him, terrified, ran into the next room where his companions were watching.

Top, at that moment, barked in a strange manner.

All rushed in immediately and managed to restrain the dying boy, who was endeavouring to throw himself out of his bed, while Spilett, taking his arm, felt his pulse gradually quicken.

It was five in the morning. The rays of the rising sun began to shine in at the windows of Granite House. It promised to be a fine day, and this day was to be poor Herbert's last!

A ray glanced on the table placed near the bed.

Suddenly Pencroft, uttering a cry, pointed to the table.

On it lay a little oblong box, of which the cover bore these words:—
'SULPHATE OF QUININE.'

Chapter 11

Gideon Spilett took the box and opened it. It contained nearly two hundred grains of a white powder, a few particles of which he carried to his lips. The extreme bitterness of the substance precluded all doubt; it was certainly the precious extract of quinine, that preeminent antifebrile.

This powder must be administered to Herbert without delay. How it came there might be discussed later.

'Some coffee!' said Spilett.

In a few moments Neb brought a cup of the warm infusion. Gideon Spilett threw into it about eighteen grains of quinine, and they succeeded in making Herbert drink the mixture.

There was still time, for the third attack of the malignant fever had not yet shown itself. How they longed to be able to add that it would not return!

Besides, it must be remarked, the hopes of all had now revived. The mysterious influence had been again exerted, and in a critical moment, when they had despaired of it.

In a few hours Herbert was much calmer. The colonists could now discuss this incident. The intervention of the stranger was more evident than ever. But how had he been able to penetrate during the night into Granite House? It was inexplicable, and, in truth, the proceedings of the genius of the island were not less mysterious than was that genius himself. During this day the sulphate of quinine was administered to Herbert every three hours.

The next day some improvement in Herbert's condition was apparent. Certainly, he was not out of danger, intermittent fevers being subject to frequent and dangerous relapses, but the most assiduous care was bestowed on him. And besides, the specific was at hand; nor, doubtless, was he who had brought it far distant! And the hearts of all were animated by returning hope.

This hope was not disappointed. Ten days after, on the 20th of December, Herbert's convalescence commenced.

He was still weak, and strict diet had been imposed upon him, but no access of fever supervened. And then, the poor boy submitted with such docility to all the prescriptions ordered him! He longed so to get well!

Pencroft was as a man who has been drawn up from the bottom of an abyss. Fits of joy approaching delirium seized him. When the time for the third attack had passed by, he nearly suffocated the reporter in his embrace. Since then, he always called him Dr. Spilett.

The real doctor, however, remained undiscovered.

'We will find him!' repeated the sailor.

Certainly, this man, whoever he was, might expect a somewhat too energetic embrace from the worthy Pencroft!

The month of December ended, and with it the year 1867, during which the colonists of Lincoln Island had of late been so severely tried. They commenced the year 1868 with magnificent weather, great heat, and a tropical temperature, delightfully cooled by the sea-breeze. Herbert's recovery progressed, and from his bed, placed near one of the windows of Granite House, he could inhale the fresh air, charged with ozone, which could not fail to restore his health. His appetite returned, and what numberless delicate, savoury little dishes Neb prepared for him!

'It is enough to make one wish to have a fever oneself!' said Pencroft.

During all this time, the convicts did not once appear in the vicinity of Granite House. There was no news of Ayrton, and though the engineer and Herbert still had some hopes of finding him again, their companions did not doubt but that the unfortunate man had perished. However, this uncertainty could not last, and when once the lad should have recovered, the expedition, the result of which must be so important, would be undertaken. But they would have to wait a month, perhaps, for all the strength of the colony must be put into requisition to obtain satisfaction from the convicts.

However, Herbert's convalescence progressed rapidly. The congestion of the liver had disappeared, and his wounds might be considered completely healed.

During the month of January, important work was done on the plateau of Prospect Heights; but it consisted solely in saving as much as was possible from the devastated crops, either of corn or vegetables. The grain and the plants were gathered, so as to provide a new harvest for the approaching half-season. With regard to rebuilding the poultry-yard, wall, or stables, Cyrus Harding preferred to wait. While he and his companions were in pursuit of the convicts, the latter might very probably pay another visit to the plateau, and it would be useless to give them an opportunity of recommencing their work of destruction. When the island should be cleared of these miscreants, they would set about rebuilding. The young convalescent began to get up in the second week of January, at first for one hour a day, then two, then three. His strength visibly returned, so vigorous was his constitution. He was now eighteen years of age. He was tall, and promised to become a man of noble and commanding presence. From this time his recovery, while still requiring care,—and Dr. Spilett was very strict,—made rapid progress. Towards the end of the month, Herbert was already walking about on Prospect Heights, and the beach.

He derived, from several sea-baths, which he took in company with Pencroft and Neb, the greatest possible benefit. Cyrus Harding thought he might now settle the day for their departure, for which the 15th of February was fixed. The nights, very clear at this time of year, would be favourable to the researches they intended to make all over the island.

The necessary preparations for this exploration were now commenced, and were important, for the colonists had sworn not to return to Granite House until their twofold object had been achieved; on the one hand, to exterminate the convicts, and rescue Ayrton, if he was still living; on the other, to discover who it was that presided so effectually over the fortunes of the colony.

Of Lincoln Island, the settlers knew thoroughly all the eastern coast from Claw Cape to the Mandible Capes, the extensive Tadorn Marsh, the neighbourhood of Lake Grant, Jacamar Wood, between the road to the corral and the Mercy, the courses of the Mercy and Red Creek, and lastly, the spurs of Mount Franklin, among which the corral had been established.

They had explored, though only in an imperfect manner, the vast shore of Washington Bay from Claw Cape to Reptile End, the woody and marshy border of the west coast, and the interminable downs, ending at the open mouth of Shark Gulf. But they had in no way surveyed the woods which covered the Serpentine Peninsula, all to the right of the Mercy, the left bank of Falls River, and the wilderness of spurs and valleys which supported three quarters of the base of Mount Franklin, to the east, the north, and the west, and where doubtless many secret retreats existed. Consequently, many millions of acres of the island had still escaped their investigations.

It was, therefore, decided that the expedition should be carried through the Far West, so as to include all that region situated on the right of the Mercy.

It might, perhaps, be better worth while to go direct to the corral, where it might be supposed that the convicts had again taken refuge, either to pillage or to establish themselves there. But either the devastation of the corral would have been an accomplished fact by this time, and it would be too late to prevent it, or it had been the convicts' interest to entrench themselves there, and there would be still time to go and turn them out on their return.

Therefore, after some discussion, the first plan was adhered to, and the settlers resolved to proceed through the wood to Reptile End. They would make their way with their hatchets, and thus lay the first draft of a road which would place Granite House in communication with the end of the peninsula for a length of from sixteen to seventeen miles.

The cart was in good condition. The onagers, well rested, could go a long journey. Provisions, camp effects, a portable stove, and various utensils were packed in the cart, as also weapons and ammunition, carefully chosen from the now complete arsenal of Granite House. But it was necessary to remember that the convicts were, perhaps, roaming about the woods, and that in the midst of these thick forests a shot might quickly be fired and received. It was therefore resolved that the little band of settlers should remain together and not separate under any pretext whatever.

It was also decided that no one should remain at Granite House. Top and Jup themselves were to accompany the expedition; the inaccessible dwelling needed no guard. The 14th of February, eve of the departure, was consecrated entirely to repose, and—thanksgiving addressed by the colonists to the Creator. A place in the cart was reserved for Herbert, who, though thoroughly convalescent, was still a little weak. The next morning, at daybreak, Cyrus Harding took the necessary measures to protect Granite House from any invasion. The ladders, which were formerly used for the ascent, were brought to the Chimneys and buried deep in the sand, so that they might be available on the return of the colonists, for the machinery of the lift had been taken to pieces, and nothing of the apparatus remained. Pencroft stayed the last in Granite House in order to finish this work, and he then lowered himself down by means of a double rope held below, and which, when once hauled down, left no communication between the upper landing and the beach.

The weather was magnificent.

'We shall have a warm day of it,' said the reporter, laughing.

'Pooh! Dr. Spilett,' answered Pencroft, 'we shall walk under the shade of the trees and shan't even see the sun!'

'Forward!' said the engineer.

The cart was waiting on the beach before the Chimneys. The reporter made Herbert take his place in it during the first hours at least of the journey, and the lad was obliged to submit to his doctor's orders.

Neb placed himself at the onagers' heads. Cyrus Harding, the reporter, and the sailor, walked in front. Top bounded joyfully along. Herbert offered a seat in his vehicle to Jup, who accepted it without ceremony. The moment for departure had arrived, and the little band set out.

The cart first turned the angle of the mouth of the Mercy, then, having ascended the left bank for a mile, crossed the bridge, at the other side of which commenced the road to Port Balloon, and there the explorers, leaving this road on their left, entered the cover of the immense woods which formed the region of the Far West.

For the first two miles the widely scattered trees allowed the cart to pass with ease; from time to time it became necessary to cut away a few creepers and bushes, but no serious obstacle impeded the progress of the colonists.

The thick foliage of the trees threw a grateful shade on the ground. Deodars, Douglas firs, casuarinas, banksias, gum-trees, dragon-trees, and other well-known species, succeeded each other far as the eye could reach. The feathered tribes of the island were all represented—grouse, jacamars, pheasants, lories, as well as the chattering cockatoos, parrots, and paroquets. Agouties, kangaroos, and capybaras fled swiftly at their approach; and all this reminded the settlers of the first excursions they had made on their arrival at the island.

'Nevertheless,' observed Cyrus Harding, 'I notice that these creatures, both birds and quadrupeds, are more timid than formerly. These woods have, therefore, been recently traversed by the convicts, and we shall certainly find some traces of them.'

And, in fact, in several places they could distinguish traces, more or less recent, of the passage of a band of men—here branches broken off the trees, perhaps to mark out the way; there the ashes of a fire, and footprints in clayey spots; but nothing which appeared to belong to a settled encampment.

The engineer had recommended his companions to refrain from hunting. The reports of the firearms might give the alarm to the convicts, who were, perhaps, roaming through the forest. Moreover, the hunters would necessarily ramble some distance from the cart, which it was dangerous to leave unguarded.

In the afterpart of the day, when about six miles from Granite House, their progress became much more difficult. In order to make their way through some thickets, they were obliged to cut down trees. Before entering such places Harding was careful to send in Top and Jup, who faithfully accomplished their commission, and when the dog and orang returned without giving any warning, there was evidently nothing to fear, either from convicts or wild beasts, two varieties of the animal kingdom, whose ferocious instincts placed them on the same level. On the evening of the first day the colonists encamped about nine miles from Granite House, on the border of a little stream falling into the Mercy, and of the existence of which they had till then been ignorant; it evidently, however, belonged to the hydiographical system to which the soil owed its astonishing fertility. The settlers made a hearty meal, for their appetites were sharpened, and measures were then taken that the night might be passed in safety. If the engineer had had only to deal with wild beasts, jaguars or others, he would have simply lighted fires all around his camp, which would have sufficed for its defence; but the convicts would be rather attracted than terrified by the flames, and it was, therefore, better to be surrounded by the profound darkness of night.

The watch was, however, carefully organized. Two of the settlers were to watch together, and every two hours it was agreed that they should be relieved by their comrades. And so, notwithstanding his wish to the contrary, Herbert was exempted from guard. Pencroft and Gideon Spilett in one party, the engineer and Neb in another, mounted guard in turns over the camp.

The night, however, was but of few hours. The darkness was due rather to the thickness of the foliage than to the disappearance of the sun. The silence was scarcely disturbed by the howling of jaguars and the chattering of the monkeys, the latter appearing to particularly irritate Master Jup. The night passed without incident, and on the next day, the 15th of February, the journey through the forest, tedious rather than difficult, was continued. This day they could not accomplish more than six miles, for every moment they were obliged to cut a road with their hatchets.

Like true settlers, the colonists spared the largest and most beautiful trees, which would besides have cost immense labour to fell, and the small ones only were sacrificed, but the result was that the road took a very winding direction, and lengthened itself by numerous detours.

During the day Herbert discovered several new specimens not before met with in the island, such as the tree-fern, with its leaves spread out like the waters of a fountain, locust-trees, on the long pods of which the onagers browsed greedily, and which supplied a sweet pulp of excellent flavour. There, too, the colonists again found groups of magnificent kauries, their cylindrical trunks, crowded with a cone of verdure, rising to a height of two hundred feet. These were the tree-kings of New Zealand, as celebrated as the cedars of Lebanon.

As to the fauna, there was no addition to those species already known to the hunters. Nevertheless, they saw, though unable to get near them, a couple of those large birds peculiar to Australia, a sort of cassowary, called emu, five feet in height, and with brown plumage, which belong to the tribe of waders. Top darted after them as fast as his four legs could carry him, but the emus distanced him with ease, so prodigious was their speed.

As to the traces left by the convicts, a few more were discovered. Some footprints found near an apparently recently extinguished fire were attentively examined by the settlers. By measuring them one after the other, according to their length and breadth, the marks of five men's feet were easily distinguished. The five convicts had evidently camped on this spot; but,—and this was the object of so minute an examination,—a sixth footprint could not be discovered, which in that case would have been that of Ayrton.

'Ayrton was not with them!' said Herbert.

'No,' answered Pencroft, 'and if he was not with them, it was because the wretches had already murdered him! but then these rascals have not a den to which they may be tracked like tigers!'

'No,' replied the reporter, 'it is more probable that they wander at random, and it is their interest to rove about until the time when they will be masters of the island!'

'The masters of the island!' exclaimed the sailor; 'the masters of the island!...' he repeated, and his voice was choked, as if his throat was seized in an iron grasp. Then in a calmer tone, 'Do you know, Captain Harding,' said he, 'what the ball is which I have rammed into my gun?'

'No, Pencroft!'

'It is the ball that went through Herbert's chest, and I promise you it won't miss its mark!'

But this just retaliation would not bring Ayrton back to life, and from the examination of the footprints left in the ground, they must, alas! conclude that all hopes of ever seeing him again must be abandoned.

That evening they encamped fourteen miles from Granite House, and Cyrus Harding calculated that they could not be more than five miles from Reptile Point.

And indeed, the next day the extremity of the peninsula was reached, and the whole length of the forest had been traversed; but there was nothing to indicate the retreat in which the convicts had taken refuge, nor that, no less secret, which sheltered the mysterious unknown.

Chapter 12

The next day, the 18th of February, was devoted to the exploration of all that wooded region forming the shore from Reptile End to Falls River. The colonists were able to search this forest thoroughly, for, as it was comprised between the two shores of the Serpentine Peninsula, it was only from three to four miles in breadth. The trees, both by their height and their thick foliage, bore witness to the vegetative power of the soil, more astonishing here than in any other part of the island. One might have said that a corner from the virgin forests of America or Africa had been transported into this temperate zone. This led them to conclude that the superb vegetation found a heat in this soil, damp in its upper layer, but warmed in the interior by volcanic fires, which could not belong to a temperate climate. The most frequently occurring trees were knaries and eucalypti of gigantic dimensions.

But the colonists' object was not simply to admire the magnificent vegetation. They knew already that in this respect Lincoln Island would have been worthy to take the first rank in the Canary group, to which the first name given was that of the Happy Isles. Now, alas! their island no longer belonged to them entirely; others had taken possession of it, miscreants polluted its shores, and they must be destroyed to the last man.

No traces were found on the western coast, although they were carefully sought for. No more footprints, no more broken branches, no more deserted camps.

'This does not surprise me,' said Cyrus Harding to his companions. 'The convicts first landed on the island in the neighbourhood of Flotsam Point, and they immediately plunged into the Far West forests, after crossing Tadorn Marsh. They then followed almost the same route that we took on leaving Granite House. This explains the traces we found in the wood. But, arriving on the shore, the convicts saw at once that they would discover no suitable retreat there, and it was then that, going northwards again, they came upon the corral.'

'Where they have perhaps returned,' said Pencroft.

'I do not think so,' answered the engineer, 'for they would naturally suppose that our researches would be in that direction. The corral is only a storehouse to them, and not a definitive encampment.'

'I am of Cyrus' opinion,' said the reporter, 'and I think that it is among the spurs of Mount Franklin that the convicts will have made their lair.'

'Then, captain, straight to the corral!' cried Pencroft. 'We must finish them off, and till now we have only lost time!'

'No, my friend,' replied the engineer; 'you forget that we have a reason for wishing to know if the forests of the Far West do not contain some habitation. Our exploration has a double object, Pencroft. If, on the one hand, we have to chastise crime, we have, on the other, an act of gratitude to perform.'

'That was well said, captain,' replied the sailor, 'but, all the same, it is my opinion that we shall not find the gentleman until he pleases.'

And truly Pencroft only expressed the opinion of all. It was probable that the stranger's retreat was not less mysterious than was he himself.

That evening the cart halted at the mouth of Falls River. The camp was organized as usual, and the customary precautions were taken for the night. Herbert, become again the healthy and vigorous lad he was before his illness, derived great benefit from this life in the open air, between the sea breezes and the vivifying air from the forests. His place was no longer in the cart, but at the head of the troop.

The next day, the 19th of February, the colonists, leaving the shore, where, beyond the mouth, basalts of every shape were so picturesquely piled up, ascended the river by its left bank. The road had been already partly cleared in their former excursions made from the corral to the west coast. The settlers were now about six miles from Mount Franklin.

The engineer's plan was this:—To minutely survey the valley forming the bed of the river, and to cautiously approach the neighbourhood of the corral; if the corral was occupied, to seize it by force; if it was not, to entrench themselves there and make it the centre of the operations which had for their object the exploration of Mount Franklin.

This plan was unanimously approved by the colonists, for they were impatient to regain entire possession of their island.

They made their way then along the narrow valley separating two of the largest spurs of Mount Franklin. The trees, crowded on the river's bank, became rare on the upper slopes of the mountain. The ground was hilly and rough, very suitable for ambushes, and over which they did not venture without extreme precaution. Top and Jup skirmished on the flanks, springing right and left through the thick brushwood, and emulating each other in intelligence and activity. But nothing showed that the banks of the stream had been recently frequented—nothing announced either the presence or the proximity of the convicts. Towards five in the evening the cart stopped nearly 600 feet from the palisade. A semicircular screen of trees still hid it.

It was necessary to reconnoitre the corral, in order to ascertain if it was occupied. To go there openly, in broad daylight, when the convicts were probably in ambush, would be to expose themselves, as poor Herbert had done, to the firearms of the ruffians. It was better, then, to wait until night came on.

However, Gideon Spilett wished without further delay to reconnoitre the approaches to the corral, and Pencroft, who was quite out of patience, volunteered to accompany him.

'No, my friends,' said the engineer, 'wait till night. I will not allow one of you to expose himself in open day.'

'But, captain—' answered the sailor, little disposed to obey.

'I beg of you, Pencroft,' said the engineer.

'Very well!' replied the sailor, who vented his anger in another way, by bestowing on the convicts the worst names in his maritime vocabulary.

The colonists remained, therefore, near the cart, and carefully watched the neighbouring parts of the forest.

Three hours passed thus. The wind had fallen, and absolute silence reigned under the great trees. The snapping of the smallest twig, a footstep on the dry leaves, the gliding of a body among the grass, would have been heard without difficulty. All was quiet. Besides, Top, lying on the grass, his head stretched out on his paws, gave no sign of uneasiness. At eight o'clock the day appeared far enough advanced for the reconnaissance to be made under favourable conditions. Gideon Spilett declared himself ready to set out accompanied by Pencroft. Cyrus Harding consented. Top and Jup were to remain with the engineer, Herbert, and Neb, for a bark or a cry at a wrong moment would give the alarm.

'Do not be imprudent,' said Harding to the reporter and Pencroft, 'you have not to gain possession of the corral, but only to find out whether it is occupied or not.'

'All right,' answered Pencroft.

And the two departed.

Under the trees, thanks to the thickness of their foliage, the obscurity rendered any object invisible beyond a radius of from thirty to forty feet. The reporter and Pencroft, halting at any suspicious sound, advanced with great caution.

They walked a little distance apart from each other so as to offer a less mark for a shot. And, to tell the truth, they expected every moment to hear a report. Five minutes after leaving the cart, Gideon Spilett and Pencroft arrived at the edge of the wood before the clearing beyond which rose the palisade.

They stopped. A few straggling beams still fell on the field clear of trees. Thirty feet distant was the gate of the corral, which appeared to be closed. This thirty feet, which it was necessary to cross from the wood to the palisade, constituted the dangerous zone, to borrow a ballistic term: in fact, one or more bullets fired from behind the palisade might knock over any one who ventured on to this zone. Gideon Spilett and the sailor were not men to draw back, but they knew that any imprudence on their part, of which they would be the first victims, would fall afterwards on their companions. If they themselves were killed, what would become of Harding, Neb, and Herbert?

But Pencroft, excited at feeling himself so near the corral where he supposed the convicts had taken refuge, was about to press forward, when the reporter held him back with a grasp of iron.

'In a few minutes it will be quite dark,' whispered Spilett in the sailor's ear, 'then will be the time to act.'

Pencroft, convulsively clasping the butt-end of his gun, restrained his energies, and waited, swearing to himself.

Soon the last of the twilight faded away. Darkness, which seemed as if it issued from the dense forest, covered the clearing. Mount Franklin rose like an enormous screen before the western horizon, and night spread rapidly over all, as it does in regions of low latitudes. Now was the time.

The reporter and Pencroft, since posting themselves on the edge of the wood, had not once lost sight of the palisade. The corral appeared to be absolutely deserted. The top of the palisade formed a line, a little darker than the surrounding shadow, and nothing disturbed its distinctness. Nevertheless, if the convicts were there, they must have posted one of their number to guard against any surprise.

Spilett grasped his companion's hand, and both crept towards the corral, their guns ready to fire.

They reached the gate without the darkness being illuminated by a single ray of light.

Pencroft tried to push open the gate, which, as the reporter and he had supposed, was closed. However, the sailor was able to ascertain that the outer bars had not been put up. It might, then, be concluded that the convicts were there in the corral, and that very probably they had fastened the gate in such a way that it could not be forced open.

Gideon Spilett and Pencroft listened.

Not a sound could be heard inside the palisade. The musmons and the goats, sleeping no doubt in their huts, in no way disturbed the calm of night.

The reporter and the sailor hearing nothing, asked themselves whether they had not better scale the palisades and penetrate into the corral. This would have been contrary to Cyrus Harding's instructions.

It is true that the enterprise might succeed, but it might also fail. Now, if the convicts were suspecting nothing, if they knew nothing of the expedition against them, if, lastly, there now existed a chance of surprising them, ought this chance to be lost by inconsiderately attempting to cross the palisades?

This was not the reporter's opinion. He thought it better to wait until all the settlers were collected together before attempting to penetrate into the corral. One thing was certain, that it was possible to reach the palisade without being seen, and also that it did not appear to be guarded. This point settled, there was nothing to be done but to return to the cart, where they would consult.

Pencroft probably agreed with this decision, for he followed the reporter without making any objection when the latter turned back to the wood.

In a few minutes the engineer was made acquainted with the state of affairs.

'Well,' said he, after a little thought, 'I now have reason to believe that the convicts are not in the corral.'

'We shall soon know,' said Pencroft, 'when we have scaled the palisade.'

'To the corral, my friends!' said Cyrus Harding.

'Shall we leave the cart in the wood?' asked Neb.

'No,' replied the engineer, 'it is our wagon of ammunition and provisions, and, if necessary, it would serve as an entrenchment.'

'Forward, then!' said Gideon Spilett.

The cart emerged from the wood and began to roll noiselessly towards the palisade. The darkness was now profound, the Silence as complete as when Pencroft and the reporter crept over the ground. The thick grass completely muffled their footsteps. The colonists held themselves ready to fire. Jup, at Pencroft's orders, kept behind. Neb led Top in a leash, to prevent him from bounding forward.

The clearing soon came in sight. It was deserted. Without hesitating, the little band moved towards the palisade. In a short space of time the dangerous zone was passed. Neb remained at the onagers' heads to hold them. The engineer, the reporter, Herbert, and Pencroft, proceeded to the door, in order to ascertain if it was barricaded inside. It was open!

'What do you say now?' asked the engineer, turning to the sailor and Spilett.

Both were stupefied.

'I can swear,' said Pencroft, 'that this gate was shut just now!'

The colonists now hesitated. Were the convicts in the corral when Pencroft and the reporter made their reconnaissance? It could not be doubted, as the gate then closed could only have been opened by them. Were they still there, or had one of their number just gone out?

All these questions presented themselves simultaneously to the minds of the colonists, but how could they be answered?

At that moment, Herbert, who had advanced a few steps into the enclosure, drew back hurriedly, and seized Harding's hand.

'What's the matter?' asked the engineer.

'A light!'

'In the house?'

'Yes!'

All five advanced and indeed, through the window fronting them, they saw glimmering a feeble light. Cyrus Harding made up his mind rapidly. 'It is our only chance,' said he to his companions, 'of finding the convicts collected in this house, suspecting nothing! They are in our power! Forward!' The colonists crossed through the enclosure, holding their guns ready in their hands. The cart had been left outside under the charge of Jup and Top, who had been prudently tied to it.

Cyrus Harding, Pencroft, and Gideon Spilett on one side, Herbert and Neb on the other, going along by the palisade, surveyed the absolutely dark and deserted corral.

In a few moments they were near the closed door of the house.

Harding signed to his companions not to stir, and approached the window, then feebly lighted by the inner light.

He gazed into the apartment.

On the table burned a lantern. Near the table was the bed formerly used by Ayrton.

On the bed lay the body of a man.

Suddenly Cyrus Harding drew back, and in a hoarse voice,—'Ayrton!' he exclaimed.

Immediately the door was forced rather than opened, and the colonists rushed into the room.

Ayrton appeared to be asleep. His countenance showed that he had long and cruelly suffered. On his wrists and ankles could be seen great bruises.

Harding bent over him.

'Ayrton!' cried the engineer, seizing the arm of the man whom he had just found again under such unexpected circumstances.

At this exclamation Ayrton opened his eyes, and, gazing at Harding, then at the others,—

'You!' he cried, 'you?'

'Ayrton! Ayrton!' repeated Harding.

'where am I?'

'In the house in the corral!'

'Alone?'

'Yes!'

'But they will come back!' cried Ayrton. 'Defend yourselves! defend yourselves!'

And he fell back exhausted.

'Spilett,' exclaimed the engineer, 'we may be attacked at any moment. Bring the cart into the corral. Then, barricade the door, and all come back here.'

Pencroft, Neb, and the reporter hastened to execute the engineer's orders. There was not a moment to be lost. Perhaps even now the cart was in the hands of the convicts!

In a moment the reporter and his two companions had crossed the corral and reached the gate of the palisade behind which Top was heard growling sullenly.

The engineer, leaving Ayrton for an instant, came out ready to fire. Herbert was at his side. Both surveyed the crest of the spur overlooking the corral. If the convicts were lying in ambush there, they might knock the settlers over one after the other.

At that moment the moon appeared in the east, above the black curtain of the forest, and a white sheet of light spread over the interior of the enclosure. The corral, with its clumps of trees, the little stream which watered it, its wide carpet of grass, was suddenly illuminated. From the side of the mountain, the house and a part of the palisade stood out white in the moonlight. On the opposite side towards the door, the enclosure remained dark. A black mass soon appeared. This was the cart entering the circle of light, and Cyrus Harding could hear the noise made by the door, as his companions shut it and fastened the interior bars.

But, at that moment, Top, breaking loose, began to bark furiously and rush to the back of the corral, to the right of the house.

'Be ready to fire, my friends!' cried Harding.

The colonists raised their pieces and waited the moment to fire.

Top still barked, and Jup, running towards the dog, uttered shrill cries.

The colonists followed him, and reached the borders of the little stream, shaded by large trees. And there, in the bright moonlight, what did they see? Five corpses, stretched on the bank!

They were those of the convicts who, four months previously, had landed on Lincoln Island!

Chapter 13

How had it happened? who had killed the convicts? Was it Ayrton? No, for a moment before he was dreading their return.

But Ayrton was now in a profound stupor, from which it was no longer possible to rouse him. After uttering those few words he had again become unconscious, and had fallen back motionless on the bed.

The colonists, a prey to a thousand confused thoughts, under the influence of violent excitement, waited all night, without leaving Ayrton's house, or returning to the spot where lay the bodies of the convicts. It was very probable that Ayrton would not be able to throw any light on the circumstances under which the bodies had been found, since he himself was not aware that he was in the corral. But at any rate he would be in a position to give an account of what had taken place before this terrible execution. The next day Ayrton awoke from his torpor, and his companions cordially manifested all the joy they felt, on seeing him again, almost safe and sound, after a hundred and four days separation.

Ayrton then in a few words recounted what had happened, or, at least, as much as he knew.

The day after his arrival at the corral, on the 10th of last November, at nightfall, he was surprised by the convicts, who had scaled the palisade. They bound and gagged him; then he was led to a dark cavern, at the foot of Mount Franklin, where the convicts had taken refuge.

His death had been decided upon, and the next day the convicts were about to kill him, when one of them recognized him and called him by the name which he bore in Australia. The wretches had no scruples as to murdering Ayrton! They spared Ben Joyce!

But from that moment Ayrton was exposed to the importunities of his former accomplices. They wished him to join them again, and relied upon his aid to enable them to gain possession of Granite House, to penetrate into that hitherto inaccessible dwelling, and to become masters of the island, after murdering the colonists!

Ayrton remained firm. The once convict, now repentant and pardoned, would rather die than betray his companions. Ayrton—bound, gagged, and closely watched—lived in this cave for four months.

Nevertheless the convicts had discovered the corral a short time after their arrival in the island, and since then they had subsisted on Ayrton's stores, but did not live at the corral.

On the 11th of November, two of the villains, surprised by the colonists' arrival, fired at Herbert, and one of them returned, boasting of having killed one of the inhabitants of the island; but he returned alone. His companion, as is known, fell by Cyrus Harding's dagger.

Ayrton's anxiety and despair may be imagined when he learned the news of Herbert's death. The settlers were now only four, and, as it seemed, at the mercy of the convicts. After this event, and during all the time that the colonists, detained by Herbert's illness, remained in the corral, the pirates did not leave their cavern, and even after they had pillaged the plateau of Prospect Heights, they did not think it prudent to abandon it.

The ill-treatment inflicted on Ayrton was now redoubled. His hands and feet still bore the bloody marks of the cords which bound him day and night. Every moment he expected to be put to death, nor did it appear possible that he could escape.

Matters remained thus until the third week of February. The convicts, still watching for a favourable opportunity, rarely quitted their retreat, and only made a few hunting excursions, either to the interior of the island, or the south coast.

Ayrton had no further news of his friends, and relinquished all hope of ever seeing them again. At last, the unfortunate man, weakened by ill-treatment, fell into a prostration so profound that sight and hearing failed him. From that moment, that is to say, since the last two days, he could give no information whatever of what had occurred

'But, Captain Harding,' he added, 'since I was imprisoned in that cavern, how is it that I find myself in the corral?'

'How is it that the convicts are lying yonder dead, in the middle of the enclosure?' answered the engineer.

'Dead!' cried Ayrton, half rising from his bed, notwithstanding his weakness.

His companions supported him. He wished to get up, and with their assistance he did so. They then proceeded together towards the little stream.

It was now broad daylight.

There, on the bank, in the position in which they had been stricken by death in its most instantaneous form, lay the corpses of the five convicts!

Ayrton was astounded. Harding and his companions looked at him without uttering a word. On a sign from the engineer, Neb and Pencroft examined the bodies, already stiffened by the cold.

They bore no apparent trace of any wound.

Only, after carefully examining them, Pencroft found on the forehead of one, on the chest of another, on the back of this one, on the shoulder of that, a little red spot, a sort of scarcely visible bruise, the cause of which it was impossible to conjecture.

'It is there that they have been struck!' said Cyrus Harding.

'But with what weapon?' cried the reporter.

'A weapon, lightning-like in its effects, and of which we have not the secret!'

'And who has struck the blow?' asked Pencroft.

'The avenging power of the island,' replied Harding, 'he who brought you here, Ayrton, whose influence has once more manifested itself, who does for us all that which we cannot do for ourselves, and who, his will accomplished, conceals himself from us.'

'Let us make search for him, then!' exclaimed Pencroft.

'Yes, we will search for him,' answered Harding, 'but we shall not discover this powerful being who performs such wonders, until he pleases to call us to him!'

This invisible protection, which rendered their own action unavailing, both irritated and piqued the engineer. The relative inferiority which it proved was of a nature to wound a haughty spirit. A generosity evinced in such a manner as to elude all tokens of gratitude, implied a sort of disdain for those on whom the obligation was conferred, which in Cyrus Harding's eyes marred, in some degree, the worth of the benefit.

'Let us search,' he resumed, 'and God grant that we may some day be permitted to prove to this haughty protector that he has not to deal with ungrateful people! What would I not give could we repay him, by rendering him in our turn, although at the price of our lives, some signal service!'

From this day, the thoughts of the inhabitants of Lincoln Island were solely occupied with the intended search. Everything incited them to discover the answer to this enigma, an answer which would only be the name of a man endowed with a truly inexplicable, and in some degree superhuman power.

In a few minutes, the settlers re-entered the house, where their influence soon restored to Ayrton his moral and physical energy. Neb and Pencroft carried the corpses of the convicts into the forest, some distance from the corral, and buried them deep in the ground.

Ayrton was then made acquainted with the facts which had occurred during his seclusion. He learned Herbert's adventures, and through what various trials the colonists had passed. As to the settlers, they had despaired of ever seeing Ayrton again, and had been convinced that the convicts had ruthlessly murdered him.

'And now,' said Cyrus Harding, as he ended his recital, 'a duty remains for us to perform. Half of our task is accomplished, but although the convicts are no longer to be feared, it is not owing to ourselves that we are once more masters of the island.'

'Well!' answered Gideon Spilett, 'let us search all this labyrinth of the spurs of Mount Franklin. We will not leave a hollow, not a hole unexplored! Ah! if ever a reporter found himself face to face with a mystery, it is I who now speak to you, my friends!'

'And we will not return to Granite House until we have found our benefactor,' said Herbert.

'Yes,' said the engineer, 'we will do all that it is humanly possible to do, but I repeat we shall not find him until he himself permits us.'

'Shall we stay at the corral?' asked Pencroft.

'We shall stay here,' answered Harding. 'Provisions are abundant, and we are here in the very centre of the circle we have to explore. Besides, if necessary, the cart will take us rapidly to Granite House.'

'Good!' answered the sailor. 'Only I have a remark to make.'

'What is it?'

'Here is the fine season getting on, and we must not forget that we have a voyage to make.'

'A voyage?' said Gideon Spilett.

'Yes, to Tabor Island,' answered Pencroft. 'It is necessary to carry a notice there to point out the position of our island and say that Ayrton is here in case the Scotch yacht should come to take him off. Who knows if it is not already too late?'

'But, Pencroft,' asked Ayrton, 'how do you intend to make this voyage?'

'In the 'Bonadventure."'

'The 'Bonadventure!"' exclaimed Ayrton. 'She no longer exists.'

'My 'Bonadventure' exists no longer!' shouted Pencroft, bounding from his seat.

'No,' answered Ayrton. 'The convicts discovered her in her little harbour only eight days ago, they put to sea in her,

'And?' said Pencroft, his heart beating.

'And not having Bob Harvey to steer her, they ran on the rocks, and the vessel went to pieces.'

'Oh, the villains, the cutthroats, the infamous scoundrels!' exclaimed Pencroft.

'Pencroft,' said Herbert, taking the sailor's hand, 'we will build another 'Bonadventure'—a larger one. We have all the ironwork—all the rigging of the brig at our disposal.'

'But do you know,' returned Pencroft, 'that it will take at least five or six months to build a vessel of from thirty to forty tons?'

'We can take our time,' said the reporter, 'and we must give up the voyage to Tabor Island for this year.'

'Oh, my 'Bonadventure!' my poor 'Bonadventure!"' cried Pencroft, almost broken-hearted at the destruction of the vessel of which he was so proud.

The loss of the 'Bonadventure' was certainly a thing to be lamented by the colonists, and it was agreed that this loss should be repaired as soon as possible. This settled, they now occupied themselves with bringing their researches to bear on the most secret parts of the island.

The exploration was commenced at daybreak on the 19th of February, and lasted an entire week. The base of the mountain, with its spurs and their numberless ramifications, formed a labyrinth of valleys and elevations. It was evident that there, in the depths of these narrow gorges, perhaps even in the interior of Mount Franklin itself, was the proper place to pursue their researches. No part of the island could have been more suitable to conceal a dwelling whose occupant wished to remain unknown. But so irregular was the formation of the valleys that Cyrus Harding was obliged to conduct the exploration in a strictly methodical manner.

The colonists first visited the valley opening to the south of the volcano, and which first received the waters of Falls River. There Ayrton showed them the cavern where the convicts had taken refuge, and in which he had been imprisoned until his removal to the corral. This cavern was just as Ayrton had left it. They found there a considerable quantity of ammunition and provisions, conveyed thither by the convicts in order to form a reserve.

The whole of the valley bordering on the cave, shaded by fir and other trees, was thoroughly explored, and on turning the point of the southwestern spur, the colonists entered a narrower gorge similar to the picturesque columns of basalt on the coast. Here the trees were fewer. Stones took the place of grass. Goats and musmons gambolled among the rocks. Here began the barren part of the island. It could already be seen that, of the numerous valleys branching off at the base of Mount Franklin, three only were wooded and rich in pasturage like that of the corral, which bordered on the west on the Falls River valley, and on the east on the Red Creek valley. These two streams, which lower down became rivers by the absorption of several tributaries, were formed by all the springs of the mountain and thus caused the fertility of its southern part. As to the Mercy, it was more directly fed from ample springs concealed under the cover of Jacamar Wood, and it was by springs of this nature, spreading in a thousand streamlets, that the soil of the Serpentine Peninsula was watered.

Now, of these three well-watered valleys, either might have served as a retreat to some solitary who would have found there everything necessary for life. But the settlers had already explored them, and in no part had they discovered the presence of man.

Was it then in the depths of those barren gorges, in the midst of the piles of rock, in the rugged northern ravines, among the streams of lava, that this dwelling and its occupant would be found?

The northern part of Mount Franklin was at its base composed solely of two valleys, wide, not very deep, without any appearance of vegetation, strewn with masses of rock, paved with lava, and varied with great blocks of mineral. This region required a long and careful exploration. It contained a thousand cavities, comfortless no doubt, but perfectly concealed and difficult of access.

The colonists even visited dark tunnels, dating from the volcanic period, still black from the passage of the fire, and penetrated into the depths of the mountain. They traversed these sombre galleries, waving lighted torches; they examined the smallest excavations; they sounded the shallowest depths, but all was dark and silent. It did not appear that the foot of man had ever before trodden these ancient passages, or that his arm had ever displaced one of these blocks, which remained as the volcano had cast them up above the waters, at the time of the submersion of the island.

However, although these passages appeared to be absolutely deserted, and the obscurity was complete, Cyrus Harding was obliged to confess that absolute silence did not reign there.

On arriving at the end of one of these gloomy caverns, extending several hundred feet into the interior of the mountain, he was surprised to hear a deep rumbling noise, increased in intensity by the sonorousness of the rocks.

Gideon Spilett, who accompanied him, also heard these distant mutterings, which indicated a revivification of the subterranean fires. Several times both listened, and they agreed that some chemical process was taking place in the bowels of the earth.

'Then the volcano is not totally extinct?' said the reporter.

'It is possible that since our exploration of the crater,' replied Cyrus Harding, 'some change has occurred. Any volcano, although considered extinct, may evidently again burst forth.'

'But if an eruption of Mount Franklin occurred,' asked Spilett, 'would there not be some danger to Lincoln Island?'

'I do not think so,' answered the reporter. 'The crater, that is to say, the safety-valve, exists, and the overflow of smoke and lava, would escape, as it did formerly, by this customary outlet.'

'Unless the lava opened a new way for itself towards the fertile parts of the island!'

'And why, my dear Spilett,' answered Cyrus Harding, 'should it not follow the road naturally traced out for it?'

'Well, volcanoes are capricious,' returned the reporter.

'Notice,' answered the engineer, 'that the inclination of Mount Franklin favours the flow of water towards the valleys which we are exploring just now. To turn aside this flow, an earthquake would be necessary to change the mountain's centre of gravity.'

'But an earthquake is always to be feared at these times,' observed Gideon Spilett.

'Always,' replied the engineer, 'especially when the subterranean forces begin to awake, as they risk meeting with some obstruction, after a long rest. Thus, my dear Spilett, an eruption would be a serious thing for us, and it would be better that the volcano should not have the slightest desire to wake up. But we could not prevent it, could we? At any rate, even if it should occur, I do not think Prospect Heights would he seriously threatened. Between them and the mountain, the ground is considerably depressed, and if the lava should ever take a course towards the lake, it would be cast on the downs and the neighbouring parts of Shark Gulf.'

'We have not yet seen any smoke at the top of the mountain, to indicate an approaching eruption,' said Gideon Spilett.

'No,' answered Harding, 'not a vapour escapes from the crater, for it was only yesterday that I attentively surveyed the summit. But it is probable that at the lower part of the chimney, time may have accumulated rocks, cinders, hardened lava, and that this valve of which I spoke, may at any time become overcharged. But at the first serious effort, every obstacle will disappear, and you may be certain, my dear Spilett, that neither the island, which is the boiler, nor the volcano, which is the chimney, will burst under the pressure of gas. Nevertheless, I repeat, it would be better that there should not be an eruption.'

'And yet we are not mistaken,' remarked the reporter. 'Mutterings can be distinctly heard in the very bowels of the volcano!'

'You are right,' said the engineer, again listening attentively. 'There can be no doubt of it. A commotion is going on there, of which we can neither estimate the importance nor the ultimate result.'

Cyrus Harding and Spilett, on coming out, rejoined their companions, to whom they made known the state of affairs.

'Very well!' cried Pencroft, 'The volcano wants to play his pranks! Let him try, if he likes! He will find his master!'

'Who?' asked Neb.

'Our good genius, Neb, our good genius, who will shut his mouth for him, if he so much as pretends to open it!'

As may be seen, the sailor's confidence in the tutelary deity of his island was absolute, and, certainly, the occult power, manifested until now in so many inexplicable ways, appeared to be unlimited; but also it knew how to escape the colonists' most minute researches, for, in spite of all their efforts, in spite of the more than zeal,—the obstinacy,—with which they carried on their exploration, the retreat of the mysterious being could not be discovered.

From the 19th to the 20th of February the circle of investigation was extended to all the northern region of Lincoln Island, whose most secret nooks were explored. The colonists even went the length of tapping every rock. The search was extended to the extreme verge of the mountain. It was explored thus to the very summit of the truncated cone terminating the first row of rocks, then to the upper ridge of the enormous hat, at the bottom of which opened the crater.

They did more; they visited the gulf, now extinct, but in whose depths the rumbling could be distinctly heard. However, no sign of smoke or vapour, no heating of the rock, indicated an approaching eruption. But neither there, nor in any other part of Mount Franklin, did the colonists find any traces of him of whom they were in search.

Their investigations were then directed to the downs. They carefully examined the high lava-cliffs of Shark Gulf from the base to the crest, although it was extremely difficult to reach even the level of the gulf. No one!—nothing!

Indeed, in these three words was summed up so much fatigue uselessly expended, so much energy producing no results, that somewhat of anger mingled with the discomfiture of Cyrus Harding and his companions.

It was now time to think of returning, for these researches could not be prolonged indefinitely. The colonists were certainly right in believing that the mysterious being did not reside on the surface of the island, and the wildest fancies haunted their excited imaginations. Pencroft and Neb, particularly, were not contented with the mystery, but allowed their imaginations to wander into the domain of the supernatural.

On the 25th of February the colonists re-entered Granite House, and by means of the double cord, carried by an arrow to the threshold of the door, they re-established communication between their habitation and the ground.

A month later they commemorated, on the 25th of March, the third anniversary of their arrival on Lincoln Island.

Chapter 14

Three years had passed away since the escape of the prisoners from Richmond, and how often during those three years had they spoken of their country, always present in their thoughts!

They had no doubt that the civil war was at an end, and to them it appeared impossible that the just cause of the North had not triumphed. But what had been the incidents of this terrible war? How much blood had it not cost? How many of their friends must have fallen in the struggle? They often spoke of these things, without as yet being able to foresee the day when they would be permitted once more to see their country. To return thither, were it but for a few days, to renew the social link with the inhabited world, to establish a communication between their native land and their island, then to pass the longest, perhaps the best, portion of their existence in this colony, founded by them, and which would then be dependent on their country, was this a dream impossible to realize?

There were only two ways of accomplishing it—either a ship must appear off Lincoln Island, or the colonists must themselves build a vessel strong enough to sail to the nearest land.

'Unless,' said Pencroft, 'our good genius, himself provides us with the means of returning to our country.'

And, really, had any one told Pencroft and Neb that a ship of 300 tons was waiting for them in Shark Gulf or at Port Balloon, they would not even have made a gesture of surprise. In their state of mind nothing appeared improbable.

But Cyrus Harding, less confident, advised them to confine themselves to fact, and more especially so with regard to the building of a vessel—a really urgent work, since it was for the purpose of depositing, as soon as possible, at Tabor Island a document indicating Ayrton's new residence.

As the 'Bonadventure' no longer existed, six months at least would be required for the construction of a new vessel. Now winter was approaching, and the voyage would not be made before the following spring.

'We have time to get everything ready for the fine season,' remarked the engineer, who was consulting with Pencroft about these matters. 'I think, therefore, my friend, that since we have to rebuild our vessel it will be best to give her larger dimensions. The arrival of the Scotch yacht at Tabor Island is very uncertain. It may even be that, having arrived several months ago, she has again sailed after having vainly searched for some trace of Ayrton. Will it not then he best to build a ship which, if necessary, could take us either to the Polynesian Archipelago or to New Zealand? What do you think?'

'I think, captain,' answered the sailor; 'I think that you are as capable of building a large vessel as a small one. Neither the wood nor the tools are wanting. It is only a question of time.'

'And how many months would be required to build a vessel of from 250 to 300 tons?' asked Harding.

'Seven or eight months at least,' replied Pencroft. 'But it must not be forgotten that winter is drawing near, and that in severe frost wood is difficult to work. We must calculate on several weeks delay, and if our vessel is ready by next November we may think ourselves very lucky.'

'Well,' replied Cyrus Harding, 'that will be exactly the most favourable time for undertaking a voyage of any importance, either to Tabor Island or to a more distant land.'

'So it will, captain,' answered the sailor. 'Make out your plans then; the workmen are ready, and I imagine that Ayrton can lend us a good helping hand.'

The colonists, having been consulted, approved the engineer's plan, and it was, indeed, the best thing to be done. It is true that the construction of a ship of from two to three hundred tons would be great labour, but the colonists had confidence in themselves, justified by their previous success.

Cyrus Harding then busied himself in drawing the plan of the vessel and making the model. During this time his companions employed themselves in felling and carting trees to furnish the ribs, timbers, and planks. The forest of the Far West supplied the best oaks and elms. They took advantage of the opening already made on their last excursion to form a practicable road, which they named the Far West Road, and the trees were carried to the Chimneys, where the dockyard was established. As to the road in question, the choice of trees had rendered its direction somewhat capricious, but at the same time it facilitated the access to a large part of the Serpentine Peninsula.

It was important that the trees should be quickly felled and cut up, for they could not be used while yet green, and some time was necessary to allow them to get seasoned. The carpenters, therefore, worked vigorously during the month of April, which was troubled only by a few equinoctial gales of some violence. Master Jup aided them dexterously, either by climbing to the top of a tree to fasten the ropes or by lending his stout shoulders to carry the lopped trunks.

All this timber was piled up under a large shed, built near the Chimneys, and there awaited the time for use.

The month of April was tolerably fine, as October often is in the northern zone. At the same time other work was actively continued, and soon all trace of devastation disappeared from the plateau of Prospect Heights. The mill was rebuilt, and new buildings rose in the poultry-yard. It had appeared necessary to enlarge their dimensions, for the feathered population had increased considerably. The stable now contained five onagers, four of which were well broken, and allowed themselves to be either driven or ridden, and a little colt. The colony now possessed a plow, to which the onagers were yoked like regular Yorkshire or Kentucky oxen. The colonists divided their work, and their arms never tired. Then who could have enjoyed better health than these workers, and what good humour enlivened the evenings in Granite House as they formed a thousand plans for the future!

As a matter of course Ayrton shared the common lot in every respect, and there was no longer any talk of his going to live at the corral. Nevertheless he was still sad and reserved, and joined more in the work than in the pleasures of his companions. But he was a valuable workman at need—strong, skilful, ingenious, intelligent. He was esteemed and loved by all, and he could not be ignorant of it.

In the meanwhile the corral was not abandoned. Every other day one of the settlers, driving the cart or mounted on an onager, went to look after the flock of musmons and goats and bring back the supply of milk required by Neb. These excursions at the same time afforded opportunities for hunting. Therefore Herbert and Gideon Spilett, with Top in front, traversed more often than their companions the road to the corral, and with the capital guns which they carried, capybaras, agouties, kangaroos, and wild pigs for large game, ducks, grouse, jacamars, and snipe for small game, were never wanting in the house. The produce of the warren, of the oyster-bed, several turtles which were taken, excellent salmon which came up the Mercy, vegetables from the plateau, wild fruit from the forest, were riches upon riches, and Neb, the head cook, could scarcely by himself store them away.

The telegraphic wire between the corral and Granite House had of course been repaired, and it was worked whenever one or other of the settlers was at the corral and found it necessary to spend the night there. Besides, the island was safe now and no attacks were to be feared, at any rate from men.

However, that which had happened might happen again. A descent of pirates, or even of escaped convicts, was always to be feared. It was possible that companions or accomplices of Bob Harvey had been in the secret of his plans, and might be tempted to imitate him. The colonists, therefore, were careful to observe the sea around the island, and every day their telescope covered the horizon enclosed by Union and Washington Bays. when they went to the corral they examined the sea to the west with no less attention, and by climbing the spur their gaze extended over a large section of the western horizon.

Nothing suspicious was discerned, but still it was necessary for them to be on their guard.

The engineer one evening imparted to his friends a plan which he had conceived for fortifying the corral. It appeared prudent to him to heighten the palisade and to flank it with a sort of blockhouse, which, if necessary, the settlers could hold against the enemy. Granite House might, by its very position, be considered impregnable; therefore the corral with its buildings, its stores, and the animals it contained, would always be the object of pirates, whoever they were, who might land on the island, and should the colonists be obliged to shut themselves up there they ought also to be able to defend themselves without any disadvantage. This was a project which might be left for consideration, and they were, besides, obliged to put off its execution until the next spring.

About the 15th of May the keel of the new vessel lay along the dockyard, and soon the stem and stern-post, mortised at each of its extremities, rose almost perpendicularly. The keel, of good oak, measured 110 feet in length, this allowing a width of five-and-twenty feet to the midship beam. But this was all the carpenters could do before the arrival of the frosts and bad weather. During the following week they fixed the first of the stern timbers, but were then obliged to suspend work.

During the last days of the month the weather was extremely bad. The wind blew from the east, sometimes with the violence of a tempest. The engineer was somewhat uneasy on account of the dockyard shed—which besides, he could not have established in any other place near to Granite House—for the islet only imperfectly sheltered the shore from the fury of the open sea, and in great storms the waves beat against the very foot of the granite cliff.

But, very fortunately, these fears were not realized. The wind shifted to the southeast, and there the beach of Granite House was completely covered by Flotsam Point.

Pencroft and Ayrton, the most zealous workmen at the new vessel, pursued their labour as long as they could. They were not men to mind the wind tearing at their hair, nor the rain wetting them to the skin, and a blow from a hammer is worth just as much in bad as in fine weather. But when a severe frost succeeded this wet period, the wood, its fibres acquiring the hardness of iron, became extremely difficult to work, and about the 10th of June shipbuilding was obliged to be entirely discontinued.

Cyrus Harding and his companions had not omitted to observe how severe was the temperature during the winters of Lincoln Island. The cold was comparable to that experienced in the States of New England, situated at almost the same distance from the equator. In the northern hemisphere, or at any rate in the part occupied by British America and the north of the United States, this phenomenon is explained by the flat conformation of the territories bordering on the pole, and on which there is no intumescence of the soil to oppose any obstacle to the north winds; here, in Lincoln Island, this explanation would not suffice.

'It has even been observed,' remarked Harding one day to his companions, 'that in equal latitudes the islands and coast regions are less tried by the cold than inland countries. I have often heard it asserted that the winters of Lombardy, for example, are not less rigorous than those of Scotland, which results from the sea restoring during the winter the heat which it received during the summer. Islands are, therefore, in a better situation for benefiting by this restitution.'

'But then, Captain Harding,' asked Herbert, 'why does Lincoln Island appear to escape the common law?'

'That is difficult to explain,' answered the engineer. 'However, I should be disposed to conjecture that this peculiarity results from the situation of the island in the Southern Hemisphere, which, as you know, my boy, is colder than the Northern Hemisphere.'

'Yes,' said Herbert, 'and icebergs are met with in lower latitudes in the south than in the north of the Pacific.'

'That is true,' remarked Pencroft, 'and when I have been serving on board whalers I have seen icebergs off Cape Horn.'

'The severe cold experienced in Lincoln Island,' said Gideon Spilett, 'may then perhaps be explained by the presence of floes or icebergs comparatively near to Lincoln Island.'

'Your opinion is very admissible indeed, my dear Spilett,' answered Cyrus Harding, 'and it is evidently to the proximity of icebergs that we owe our rigorous winters. I would draw your attention also to an entirely physical cause, which renders the Southern colder than the Northern Hemisphere. In fact, since the sun is nearer to this hemisphere during the summer, it is necessarily more distant during the winter. This explains then the excess of temperature in the two seasons, for, if we find the winters very cold in Lincoln Island, we must not forget that the summers here, on the contrary, are very hot.'

'But why, if you please, captain,' asked Pencroft, knitting his brows, 'why should our hemisphere, as you say, be so badly divided? It isn't just, that!'

'Friend Pencroft,' answered the engineer, laughing, 'whether just or not, we must submit to it, and here lies the reason for this peculiarity. The earth does not describe a circle around the sun, but an ellipse, as it must by the laws of rational mechanics. Now, the earth occupies one of the foci of the ellipse, and so at one point in its course is at its apogee, that is, at its farthest from the sun, and at another point it is at its perigee, or nearest to the sun. Now it happens that it is during the winter of the southern countries that it is at its most distant point from the sun, and consequently, in a situation for those regions to feel the greatest cold. Nothing can be done to prevent that, and men, Pencroft, however learned they may be, can never change anything of the cosmographical order established by God Himself.'

'And yet,' added Pencroft, 'the world is very learned. What a big book, captain, might be made with all that is known!'

'And what a much bigger book still with all that is not known!' answered Harding.

At last, for one reason or another, the month of June brought the cold with its accustomed intensity, and the settlers were often confined to

Granite House. Ah! how wearisome this imprisonment was to them, and more particularly to Gideon Spilett.

'Look here,' said he to Neb one day, 'I would give you by notarial deed all the estates which will come to me some day, if you were a good enough fellow to go, no matter where, and subscribe to some newspaper for me! Decidedly the thing that is most essential to my happiness is the knowing every morning what has happened the day before in other places than this!'

Neb began to laugh.

"Pon my word,' he replied, 'the only thing I think about is my daily work!'

The truth was that indoors as well as out there was no want of work.

The colony of Lincoln Island was now at its highest point of prosperity, achieved by three years of continued hard work. The destruction of the brig had been a new source of riches. Without speaking of the complete rig which would serve for the vessel now on the stocks, utensils and tools of all sorts, weapons and ammunition, clothes and instruments, were now piled in the storerooms of Granite House. It had not even been necessary to resort again to the manufacture of the coarse felt materials. Though the colonists had suffered from cold during their first winter, the bad season might now come without their having any reason to dread its severity. Linen was plentiful also, and besides, they kept it with extreme care. From chloride of sodium, which is nothing else than sea salt, Cyrus Harding easily extracted the soda and chlorine. The soda, which it was easy to change into carbonate of soda, and the chlorine, of which he made chloride of lime, were employed for various domestic purposes, and especially in bleaching linen. Besides, they did not wash more than four times a year, as was done by families in the olden times, and it may be added, that Pencroft and Gideon Spilett, while waiting for the postman to bring him his newspaper, distinguished themselves as washermen.

So passed the winter months, June, July, and August. They were severe, and the average observations of the thermometer did not give more than eight degrees of Fahrenheit. It was therefore lower in temperature than the preceding winter. But then, what splendid fires blazed continually on the hearths of Granite House, the smoke marking the granite wall with long, zebra-like streaks! Fuel was not spared, as it grew naturally a few steps from them. Besides, the chips of the wood destined for the construction of the ship enabled them to economize the coal, which required more trouble to transport.

Men and animals were all well. Master Jup was a little chilly, it must be confessed. This was perhaps his only weakness, and it was necessary to make him a well-padded dressing-gown. But what a servant he was, clever, zealous, indefatigable, not indiscreet, not talkative, and he might have been with reason proposed as a model for all his biped brothers in the Old and New Worlds!

'As for that,' said Pencroft, 'when one has four hands at one's service, of course one's work ought to be done so much the better!'

And indeed the intelligent creature did it well.

During the seven months which had passed since the last researches made round the mountain, and during the month of September, which brought back fine weather, nothing was heard of the genius of the island. His power was not manifested in any way. It is true that it would have been superfluous, for no incident occurred to put the colonists to any painful trial.

Cyrus Harding even observed that if by chance the communication between the unknown and the tenants of Granite House had ever been established through the granite, and if Top's instinct had as it were felt it, there was no further sign of it during this period. The dog's growling had entirely ceased, as well as the uneasiness of the orang. The two friends—for they were such—no longer prowled round the opening of the inner well, nor did they bark or whine in that singular way which from the first the engineer had noticed. But could he be sure that this was all that was to be said about this enigma, and that he should never arrive at a solution? Could he be certain that some conjuncture would not occur which would bring the mysterious personage on the scene? who could tell what the future might have in reserve?

At last the winter was ended, but an event, the consequences of which might be serious occurred in the first days of the returning spring.

On the 7th of September, Cyrus Harding, having observed the crater, saw smoke curling round the summit of the mountain, its first vapours rising in the air.

Chapter 15

The colonists, warned by the engineer, left their work and gazed in silence at the summit of Mount Franklin.

The volcano had awoke, and the vapour had penetrated the mineral layer heaped at the bottom of the crater. But would the subterranean fires provoke any violent eruption? This was an event which could not be foreseen. However, even while admitting the possibility of an eruption, it was not probable that the whole of Lincoln Island would suffer from it. The flow of volcanic matter is not always disastrous, and the island had already undergone this trial, as was shown by the streams of lava hardened on the northern slopes of the mountain. Besides, from the shape of the crater—the opening broken in the upper edge—the matter would be thrown to the side opposite the fertile regions of the island.

However, the past did not necessarily answer for the future. Often, at the summit of volcanoes, the old craters close and new ones open. This had occurred in the two hemispheres—at Etna, Popocatepetl, at Orizabaand on the eve of an eruption there is everything to be feared. In fact, an earthquake—a phenomenon which often accompanies volcanic eruption—is enough to change the interior arrangement of a mountain, and to open new outlets for the burning lava.

Cyrus Harding explained these things to his companions, and, without exaggerating the state of things, he told them all the pros and cons. After all, they could not prevent it. It did not appear likely that Granite House would be threatened unless the ground was shaken by an earthquake. But the corral would be in great danger should a new crater open in the southern side of Mount Franklin.

From that day the smoke never disappeared from the top of the mountain, and it could even be perceived that it increased in height and thickness, without any flame mingling in its heavy volumes. The phenomenon was still concentrated in the lower part of the central crater.

However, with the fine days work had been continued. The building of the vessel was hastened as much as possible, and, by means of the waterfall on the shore, Cyrus Harding managed to establish an hydraulic sawmill, which rapidly cut up the trunks of trees into planks and joists. The mechanism of this apparatus was as simple as those used in the rustic sawmills of Norway. A first horizontal movement to move the piece of wood, a second vertical movement to move the saw—this was all that was wanted; and the engineer succeeded by means of a wheel, two cylinders, and pulleys properly arranged. Towards the end of the month of September the skeleton of the vessel, which was to be rigged as a schooner, lay in the dockyard. The ribs were almost entirely completed, and, all the timbers having been sustained by a provisional band, the shape of the vessel could already be seen. The schooner, sharp in the bows, very slender in the after-part, would evidently be suitable for a long voyage, if wanted; but laying the planking would still take a considerable time. Very fortunately, the iron work of the pirate brig had been saved after the explosion. From the planks and injured ribs Pencroft and Ayrton had extracted the bolts and a large quantity of copper nails. It was so much work saved for the smiths, but the carpenters had much to do.

Shipbuilding was interrupted for a week for the harvest, the haymaking, and the gathering in of the different crops on the plateau. This work finished, every moment was devoted to finishing the schooner. When night came the workmen were really quite exhausted. So as not to lose any time they had changed the hours for their meals; they dined at twelve o'clock, and only had their supper when daylight failed them. They then ascended to Granite House, when they were always ready to go to bed.

Sometimes, however, when the conversation bore on some interesting subject the hour for sleep was delayed for a time. The colonists then spoke of the future, and talked willingly of the changes which a voyage in the schooner to inhabited lands would make in their situation. But always, in the midst of these plans, prevailed the thought of a subsequent return to Lincoln Island. Never would they abandon this colony, founded with so much labour and with such success, and to which a communication with America would afford a fresh impetus. Pencroft and Neb especially hoped to end their days there.

'Herbert,' said the sailor, 'you will never abandon Lincoln Island?'

'Never, Pencroft, and especially if you make up your mind to stay there.'

'That was made up long ago, my boy,' answered Pencroft. 'I shall expect you. You will bring me your wife and children, and I shall make jolly chaps of your youngsters!'

'That's agreed,' replied Herbert, laughing and blushing at the same time.

'And you, Captain Harding,' resumed Pencroft enthusiastically, 'you will be still the governor of the island! Ah, how many inhabitants could it support? Ten thousand at least!'

They talked in this way, allowing Pencroft to run on, and at last the reporter actually started a newspaper—the New Lincoln Herald!

So is man's heart. The desire to perform a work which will endure, which will survive him, is the origin of his superiority over all other living creatures here below. It is this which has established his dominion, and this it is which justifies it, over all the world.

After that, who knows if Jup and Top had not themselves their little dream of the future.

Ayrton silently said to himself that he would like to see Lord Glenarvan again and show himself to all restored.

One evening, on the 15th of October, the conversation was prolonged later than usual. It was nine o'clock. Already, long badly concealed yawns gave warning of the hour of rest, and Pencroft was proceeding towards his bed, when the electric bell, placed in the dining room, suddenly rang.

All were there, Cyrus Harding, Gideon Spilett, Herbert, Ayrton, Pencroft, Neb. Therefore none of the colonists were at the corral.

Cyrus Harding rose. His companions stared at each other, scarcely believing their ears.

'What does that mean?' cried Neb. 'Was it the devil who rang it?'

No one answered.

'The weather is stormy,' observed Herbert. 'Might not its influence of electricity—'

Herbert did not finish his phrase. The engineer, towards whom all eyes were turned, shook his head negatively.

'We must wait,' said Gideon Spilett. 'If it is a signal, whoever it may be who has made it, he will renew it.'

'But who do you think it is?' cried Neb.

'Who?' answered Pencroft, 'but he—'

The sailor's sentence was cut short by a new tinkle of the bell.

Harding went to the apparatus, and sent this question to the corral:—

'What do you want?'

A few moments later the needle, moving on the alphabetic dial, gave this reply to the tenants of Granite House:—

'Come to the corral immediately.'

'At last!' exclaimed Harding.

Yes! At last! The mystery was about to be unveiled. The colonists' fatigue had disappeared before the tremendous interest which was about to urge them to the corral, and all wish for rest had ceased. Without having uttered a word, in a few moments they had left Granite House, and were standing on the beach. Jup and Top alone were left behind. They could do without them.

The night was black. The new moon had disappeared at the same time as the sun. As Herbert had observed, great stormy clouds formed a lowering and heavy vault, preventing any star rays. A few lightning flashes, reflections from a distant storm, illuminated the horizon.

It was possible that a few hours later the thunder would roll over the island itself. The night was very threatening.

But however deep the darkness was, it would not prevent them from finding the familiar road to the corral.

They ascended the left bank of the Mercy, reached the plateau, passed the bridge over Creek Glycerine, and advanced through the forest.

They walked at a good pace, a prey to the liveliest emotions. There was no doubt but that they were now going to learn the long-searched-for answer to the enigma, the name of that mysterious being, so deeply concerned in their life, so generous in his influence, so powerful in his action! Must not this stranger have indeed mingled with their existence, have known the smallest details, have heard all that was said in Granite House, to have been able always to act in the very nick of time?

Every one, wrapped up in his own reflections, pressed forward. Under the arch of trees the darkness was such that even the edge of the road could not be seen. Not a sound in the forest. Both animals and birds, influenced by the heaviness of the atmosphere, remained motionless and silent. Not a breath disturbed the leaves. The footsteps of the colonists alone resounded on the hardened ground.

During the first quarter of an hour the silence was only interrupted by this remark from Pencroft:—

'We ought to have brought a torch.'

And by this reply from the engineer:—

'We shall find one at the corral.'

Harding and his companions had left Granite House at twelve minutes past nine. At forty-seven minutes past nine they had traversed three out of the five miles which separated the mouth of the Mercy from the corral.

At that moment sheets of lightning spread over the island and illuminated the dark trees. The flashes dazzled and almost blinded them. Evidently the storm would not be long in bursting forth.

The flashes gradually became brighter and more rapid. Distant thunder growled in the sky. The atmosphere was stifling.

The colonists proceeded as if they were urged onwards by some irresistible force.

At ten o'clock a vivid flash showed them the palisade, and as they reached the gate the storm burst forth with tremendous fury.

In a minute the corral was crossed, and Harding stood before the hut.

Probably the house was occupied by the stranger, since it was from thence that the telegram had been sent. However, no light shone through the window.

The engineer knocked at the door.

No answer.

Cyrus Harding opened the door, and the settlers entered the room, which was perfectly dark. A light was struck by Neb, and in a few moments the lantern was lighted and the light thrown into every corner of the room.

There was no one there. Everything was in the state in which it had been left.

'Have we been deceived by an illusion?' murmured Cyrus Harding.

No! that was not possible! The telegram had clearly said,—

'Come to the corral immediately.'

They approached the table specially devoted to the use of the wire. Everything was in order—the pile on the box containing it, as well as all the apparatus.

'Who came here the last time?' asked the engineer.

'I did, captain,' answered Ayrton.

'And that was-'

'Four days ago.'

'Ah! a note!' cried Herbert, pointing to a paper lying on the table.

On this paper were written these words in English:—

'Follow the new wire.'

'Forward!' cried Harding, who understood that the despatch had not been sent from the corral, but from the mysterious retreat, communicating directly with Granite House by means of a supplementary wire joined to the old one.

Neb took the lighted lantern, and all left the corral. The storm then burst forth with tremendous violence. The interval between each lightning- flash and each thunderclap diminished rapidly. The summit of the volcano, with its plume of vapour, could be seen by occasional flashes.

There was no telegraphic communication in any part of the corral between the house and the palisade; but the engineer, running straight to the first post, saw by the light of a flash a new wire hanging from the isolator to the ground.

'There it is!' said he.

This wire lay along the ground, and was surrounded with an isolating substance like a submarine cable, so as to assure the free transmission of the current. It appeared to pass through the wood and the southern spurs of the mountain, and consequently it ran towards the west.

'Follow it!' said Cyrus Harding.

And the settlers immediately pressed forward, guided by the wire.

The thunder continued to roar with such violence that not a word could be heard. However, there was no occasion for speaking, but to get forward as fast as possible.

Cyrus Harding and his companions then climbed the spur rising between the corral valley and that of Falls River, which they crossed at its narrowest part. The wire, sometimes stretched over the lower branches of the trees, sometimes lying on the ground, guided them surely. The engineer had supposed that the wire would perhaps stop at the bottom of the valley, and that the stranger's retreat would be there.

Nothing of the sort. They were obliged to ascend the south-western spur, and re-descend on that arid plateau terminated by the strangely-wild basalt cliff. From time to time one of the colonists stooped down and felt for the wire with his hands; but there was now no doubt that the wire was running directly towards the sea. There, to a certainty, in the depths of those rocks, was the dwelling so long sought for in vain.

The sky was literally on fire. Flash succeeded flash. Several struck the summit of the volcano in the midst of the thick smoke. It appeared there as if the mountain was vomiting flame. At a few minutes to eleven the colonists arrived on the high cliff overlooking the ocean to the west. The wind had risen. The surf roared 500 feet below.

Harding calculated that they had gone a mile and a half from the corral.

At this point the wire entered among the rocks, following the steep side of a narrow ravine. The settlers followed it at the risk of occasioning a fall of the slightly-balanced rocks, and being dashed into the sea. The descent was extremely perilous, but they did not think of the danger; they were no longer masters of themselves, and an irresistible attraction drew them towards this mysterious place as the magnet draws iron.

Thus they almost unconsciously descended this ravine, which even in broad daylight would have been considered impracticable.

The stones rolled and sparkled like fiery balls when they crossed through the gleams of light. Harding was first—Ayrton last. On they went, step by step. Now they slid over the slippery rock; then they struggled to their feet and scrambled on.

At last the wire touched the rocks on the beach. The colonists had reached the bottom of the basalt cliff.

There appeared a narrow ridge, running horizontally and parallel with the sea. The settlers followed the wire along it. They had not gone a hundred paces when the ridge by a moderate incline sloped down to the level of the sea.

The engineer seized the wire and found that it disappeared beneath the waves.

His companions were stupefied.

A cry of disappointment, almost a cry of despair, escaped them! Must they then plunge beneath the water and seek there for some submarine cavern? In their excited state they would not have hesitated to do it.

The engineer stopped them.

He led his companions to a hollow in the rocks, and there—

'We must wait,' said he. 'The tide is high. At low water the way will be open.'

'But what can make you think-' asked Pencroft.

'He would not have called us if the means had been wanting to enable us to reach him!'

Cyrus Harding spoke in a tone of such thorough conviction that no objection was raised. His remark, besides, was logical. It was quite possible that an opening, practicable at low water, though hidden now by the high tide, opened at the foot of the cliff.

There was some time to wait. The colonists remained silently crouching in a deep hollow. Rain now began to fall in torrents. The thunder was re-echoed among the rocks with a grand sonorousness.

The colonists' emotion was great. A thousand strange and extraordinary ideas crossed their brains, and they expected some grand and superhuman apparition, which alone could come up to the notion they had formed of the mysterious genius of the island.

At midnight, Harding carrying the lantern, descended to the beach to reconnoitre.

The engineer was not mistaken. The beginning of an immense excavation could be seen under the water. There the wire, bending at a right angle, entered the yawning gulf.

Cyrus Harding returned to his companions, and said simply,—

'In an hour the opening will be practicable.'

'It is there, then?' said Pencroft.

'Did you doubt it?' returned Harding.

'But this cavern must be filled with water to a certain height,' observed Herbert.

'Either the cavern will be completely dry,' replied Harding, 'and in that case we can traverse it on foot, or it will not be dry, and some means of transport will be put at our disposal.'

An hour passed. All climbed down through the rain to the level of the sea. There was now eight feet of the opening above the water. It was like the arch of a bridge, under which rushed the foaming water.

Leaning forward, the engineer saw a black object floating on the water. He drew it towards him. It was a boat, moored to some interior projection of the cave. This boat was iron-plated. Two oars lay at the bottom.

'Jump in!' said Harding.

In a moment the settlers were in the boat. Neb and Ayrton took the oars, Pencroft the rudder. Cyrus Harding in the bows, with the lantern, lighted the way.

The elliptical roof, under which the boat at first passed, suddenly rose; but the darkness was too deep, and the light of the lantern too slight, for either the extent, length, height, or depth of the cave to be ascertained. Solemn silence reigned in this basaltic cavern. Not a sound could penetrate into it, even the thunder peals could not pierce its thick sides.

Such immense caves exist in various parts of the world, natural crypts dating from the geological epoch of the globe. Some are filled by the sea; others contain entire lakes in their sides. Such is Fingal's Cave, in the island of Staffa, one of the Hebrides; such are the caves of Morgat, in the bay of Douarnenez, in Brittany, the caves of Bonifacio, in Corsica, those of Lyse-Fjord, in Norway; such are the immense Mammoth caverns in Kentucky, 500 feet in height, and more than twenty miles in length! In many parts of the globe, nature has excavated these caverns, and preserved them for the admiration of man.

Did the cavern which the settlers were now exploring extend to the centre of the island? For a quarter of an hour the boat had been advancing, making detours, indicated to Pencroft by the engineer in short sentences, when all at once,—

'More to the right!' he commanded.

The boat, altering its course, came up alongside the right wall. The engineer wished to see if the wire still ran along the side.

The wire was there fastened to the rock.

'Forward!' said Harding.

And the two oars, plunging into the dark waters, urged the boat onwards.

On they went for another quarter of an hour, and a distance of half-a-mile must have been cleared from the mouth of the cave, when Harding's voice was again heard.

'Stop!' said he.

The boat stopped, and the colonists perceived a bright light illuminating the vast cavern, so deeply excavated in the bowels of the island, of which nothing had ever led them to suspect the existence.

At a height of a hundred feet rose the vaulted roof, supported on basalt shafts. Irregular arches, strange mouldings, appeared on the columns erected by nature in thousands from the first epochs of the formation of the globe. The basalt pillars, fitted one into the other, measured from forty to fifty feet in height, and the water, calm in spite of the tumult outside, washed their base. The brilliant focus of light, pointed out by the engineer, touched every point of rocks, and flooded the walls with light.

By reflection the water reproduced the brilliant sparkles, so that the boat appeared to be floating between two glittering zones. They could not be mistaken in the nature of the irradiation thrown from the glowing nucleus, whose clear rays were shattered by all the angles, all the projections of the cavern. This light proceeded from an electric source, and its white colour betrayed its origin. It was the sun of this cave, and it filled it entirely.

At a sign from Cyrus Harding the oars again plunged into the water, causing a regular shower of gems, and the boat was urged forward towards the light, which was now not more than half a cable's length distant.

At this place the breadth of the sheet of water measured nearly 350 feet, and beyond the dazzling centre could be seen an enormous basaltic wall, blocking up any issue on that side. The cavern widened here considerably, the sea forming a little lake. But the roof, the side walls, the end cliff, all the prisms, all the peaks, were flooded with the electric fluid, so that the brilliancy belonged to them, and as if the light issued from them.

In the centre of the lake a long cigar-shaped object floated on the surface of the water, silent, motionless. The brilliancy which issued from it escaped from its sides as from two kilns heated to a white heat. This apparatus, similar in shape to an enormous whale, was about 250 feet long, and rose about ten or twelve above the water.

The boat slowly approached it, Cyrus Harding stood up in the bows. He gazed, a prey to violent excitement. Then, all at once, seizing the reporter's arm,—

'It is he! It can only be he!' he cried, 'he!—'

Then, falling back on the seat, he murmured a name which Gideon Spilett alone could hear.

The reporter evidently knew this name, for it had a wonderful effect upon him, and he answered in a hoarse voice,—

'He! an outlawed man!'

'He!' said Harding.

At the engineer's command the boat approached this singular floating apparatus. The boat touched the left side, from which escaped a ray of light through a thick glass.

Harding and his companions mounted on the platform. An open hatchway was there. All darted down the opening.

At the bottom of the ladder was a deck, lighted by electricity. At the end of this deck was a door, which Harding opened.

A richly-ornamented room, quickly traversed by the colonists, was joined to a library, over which a luminous ceiling shed a flood of light.

At the end of the library a large door, also shut, was opened by the engineer.

An immense saloon—a sort of museum, in which were heaped up, with all the treasures of the mineral world, works of art, marvels of industry— appeared before the eyes of the colonists, who almost thought themselves suddenly transported into a land of enchantment.

Stretched on a rich sofa they saw a man, who did not appear to notice their presence.

Then Harding raised his voice, and to the extreme surprise of his companions, he uttered these words,—

'Captain Nemo, you asked for us! We are here.—'

Chapter 16

At these words the reclining figure rose, and the electric light fell upon his countenance; a magnificent head, the forehead high, the glance commanding, beard white, hair abundant and falling over the shoulders.

His hand rested upon the cushion of the divan from which he had just risen. He appeared perfectly calm. It was evident that his strength had been gradually undermined by illness, but his voice seemed yet powerful, as he said in English, and in a tone which evinced extreme surprise,—

'Sir, I have no name.'

'Nevertheless, I know you!' replied Cyrus Harding.

Captain Nemo fixed his penetrating gaze upon the engineer, as though he were about to annihilate him.

Then, falling back amid the pillows of the divan,—

'After all, what matters now?' he murmured; 'I am dying!'

Cyrus Harding drew near the captain, and Gideon Spilett took his hand—it was of a feverish heat. Ayrton, Pencroft, Herbert, and Neb stood respectfully apart in an angle of the magnificent saloon, whose atmosphere was saturated with the electric fluid.

Meanwhile Captain Nemo withdrew his hand, and motioned the engineer and the reporter to be seated.

All regarded him with profound emotion. Before them they beheld that being whom they had styled the 'genius of the island,' the powerful protector whose intervention, in so many circumstances, had been so efficacious, the benefactor to whom they owed such a debt of gratitude! Their eyes beheld a man only, and a man at the point of death, where Pencroft and Neb had expected to find an almost supernatural being!

But how happened it that Cyrus Harding had recognized Captain Nemo? why had the latter so suddenly risen on hearing this name uttered, a name which he had believed known to none?—

The captain had resumed his position on the divan, and leaning on his arm, he regarded the engineer, seated near him.

'You know the name I formerly bore, sir?' he asked.

'I do,' answered Cyrus Harding, 'and also that of this wonderful submarine vessel—'

'The 'Nautilus'?' said the captain, with a faint smile.

'The 'Nautilus.''

'But do you—do you know who I am?'

'I do.'

'It is nevertheless many years since I have held any communication with the inhabited world; three long years have I passed in the depth of the sea, the only place where I have found liberty! Who then can have betrayed my secret?'

'A man who was bound to you by no tie, Captain Nemo, and who, consequently, cannot be accused of treachery.'

'The Frenchman who was cast on board my vessel by chance sixteen years since?'

'The same.'

'He and his two companions did not then perish in the maelstrom, in the midst of which the 'Nautilus' was struggling?'

'They escaped, and a book has appeared under the title of 'Twenty Thousand Leagues Under the Sea,' which contains your history.'

'The history of a few months only of my life!' interrupted the captain impetuously.

'It is true,' answered Cyrus Harding, 'but a few months of that strange life have sufficed to make you known.'

'As a great criminal, doubtless!' said Captain Nemo, a haughty smile curling his lips. 'Yes, a rebel, perhaps an outlaw against humanity!'

The engineer was silent.

'Well, sir?'

'It is not for me to judge you, Captain Nemo,' answered Cyrus Harding, 'at any rate as regards your past life. I am, with the rest of the world, ignorant of the motives which induced you to adopt this strange mode of existence, and I cannot judge of effects without knowing their causes; but what I do know is, that a beneficent hand has constantly protected us since our arrival on Lincoln Island, that we all owe our lives to a good, generous, and powerful being, and that this being so powerful, good and generous, Captain Nemo, is yourself!'

'It is I,' answered the captain simply.

The engineer and the reporter rose. Their companions had drawn near, and the gratitude with which their hearts were charged was about to express itself in their gestures and words.

Captain Nemo stopped them by a sign, and in a voice which betrayed more emotion than he doubtless intended to show.

'Wait till you have heard all,' he said.

And the captain, in a few concise sentences, ran over the events of his life.

His narrative was short, yet he was obliged to summon up his whole remaining energy to arrive at the end. He was evidently contending against extreme weakness. Several times Cyrus Harding entreated him to repose for a while, but he shook his head as a man to whom the morrow may never come, and when the reporter offered his assistance,—

'It is useless,' he said; 'my hours are numbered.'

Captain Nemo was an Indian, the Prince Dakkar, son of a rajah of the then independent territory of Bundelkund. His father sent him, when ten years of age, to Europe, in order that he might receive an education in all respects complete, and in the hopes that by his talents and knowledge he might one day take a leading part in raising his long degraded and heathen country to a level with the nations of Europe.

From the age of ten years to that of thirty Prince Dakkar, endowed by Nature with her richest gifts of intellect, accumulated knowledge of every kind, and in science, literature, and art his researches were extensive and profound.

He travelled over the whole of Europe. His rank and fortune caused him to be everywhere sought after; but the pleasures of the world had for him no attractions. Though young and possessed of every personal advantage, he was ever grave—sombre even—devoured by an unquenchable thirst for knowledge, and cherishing in the recesses of his heart the hope that he might become a great and powerful ruler of a free and enlightened people.

Still, for long the love of science triumphed over all other feelings. He became an artist deeply impressed by the marvels of art, a philosopher to whom no one of the higher sciences was unknown, a statesman versed in the policy of European courts. To the eyes of those who observed him superficially he might have passed for one of those cosmopolitans, curious of knowledge, but disdaining action; one of those opulent travellers, haughty and cynical, who move incessantly from place to place, and are of no country.

The history of Captain Nemo has, in fact, been published under the title of 'Twenty Thousand Leagues Under the Sea.' Here, therefore, will apply the observation already made as to the adventures of Ayrton with regard to the discrepancy of dates. Readers should therefore refer to the note already published on this point.

This artist, this philosopher, this man was, however, still cherishing the hope instilled into him from his earliest days.

Prince Dakkar returned to Bundelkund in the year 1849. He married a noble Indian lady, who was imbued with an ambition not less ardent than that by which he was inspired. Two children were born to them, whom they tenderly loved. But domestic happiness did not prevent him from seeking to carry out the object at which he aimed. He waited an opportunity. At length, as he vainly fancied, it presented itself.

Instigated by princes equally ambitious and less sagacious and more unscrupulous than he was, the people of India were persuaded that they might successfully rise against their English rulers, who had brought them out of a state of anarchy and constant warfare and misery, and had established peace and prosperity in their country. Their ignorance and gross superstition made them the facile tools of their designing chiefs.

In 1857 the great sepoy revolt broke out. Prince Dakkar, under the belief that he should thereby have the opportunity of attaining the object of his long-cherished ambition, was easily drawn into it. He forthwith devoted his talents and wealth to the service of this cause. He aided it in person; he fought in the front ranks; he risked his life equally with the humblest of the wretched and misguided fanatics; he was ten times wounded in twenty engagements, seeking death but finding it not, but at length the sanguinary rebels were utterly defeated, and the atrocious mutiny was brought to an end.

Never before had the British power in India been exposed to such danger, and if, as they had hoped, the sepoys had received assistance from without, the influence and supremacy in Asia of the United Kingdom would have been a thing of the past.

The name of Prince Dakkar was at that time well known. He had fought openly and without concealment. A price was set upon his head, but he managed to escape from his pursuers.

Civilization never recedes; the law of necessity ever forces it onwards. The sepoys were vanquished, and the land of the rajahs of old fell again under the rule of England.

Prince Dakkar, unable to find that death he courted, returned to the mountain fastnesses of Bundelkund. There, alone in the world, overcome by disappointment at the destruction of all his vain hopes, a prey to profound disgust for all human beings, filled with hatred of the civilized world, he realized the wreck of his fortune, assembled some score of his most faithful companions, and one day disappeared, leaving no trace behind.

Where, then, did he seek that liberty denied him upon the inhabited earth? Under the waves, in the depths of the ocean, where none could follow.

The warrior became the man of science. Upon a deserted island of the Pacific he established his dockyard, and there a submarine vessel was constructed from his designs. By methods which will at some future day be revealed he had rendered subservient the illimitable forces of electricity, which, extracted from inexhaustible sources, was employed for all the requirements of his floating equipage, as a moving, lighting, and heating agent. The sea, with its countless treasures, its myriads of fish, its numberless wrecks, its enormous mammalia, and not only all that nature supplied, but also all that man had lost in its depths, sufficed for every want of the prince and his crew—and thus was his most ardent desire accomplished, never again to hold communication with the earth. He named his submarine vessel the 'Nautilus,' called himself simply Captain Nemo, and disappeared beneath the seas.

During many years this strange being visited every ocean, from pole to pole. Outcast of the inhabited earth in these unknown worlds he gathered incalculable treasures. The millions lost in the Bay of Vigo, in 1702, by the galleons of Spain, furnished him with a mine of inexhaustible riches which he devoted always, anonymously, in favour of those nations who fought for the independence of their country.

(This refers to the resurrection of the Candiotes, who were, in fact, largely assisted by Captain Nemo.)

For long, however, he had held no communication with his fellow-creatures, when, during the night of the 6th of November, 1866, three men were cast on board his vessel. They were a French professor, his servant, and a Canadian fisherman. These three men had been hurled overboard by a collision which had taken place between the 'Nautilus' and the United States frigate 'Abraham Lincoln,' which had chased her.

Captain Nemo learned from this professor that the 'Nautilus,' taken now for a gigantic mammal of the whale species, now for a submarine vessel carrying a crew of pirates, was sought for in every sea.

He might have returned these three men to the ocean, from whence chance had brought them in contact with his mysterious existence. Instead of doing this he kept them prisoners, and during seven months they were enabled to behold all the wonders of a voyage of twenty thousand leagues under the sea.

One day, the 22nd of June, 1867, these three men, who knew nothing of the past history of Captain Nemo, succeeded in escaping in one of the

'Nautilus's' boats. But as at this time the 'Nautilus' was drawn into the vortex of the maelstrom, off the coast of Norway, the captain naturally believed that the fugitives, engulfed in that frightful whirlpool, found their death at the bottom of the abyss. He was unaware that the Frenchman and his two companions had been miraculously cast on shore, that the fishermen of the Lofoten Islands had rendered them assistance, and that the professor, on his return to France, had published that work in which seven months of the strange and eventful navigation of the 'Nautilus' were narrated and exposed to the curiosity of the public.

For a long time alter this, Captain Nemo continued to live thus, traversing every sea. But one by one his companions died, and found their last resting-place in their cemetery of coral, in the bed of the Pacific. At last Captain Nemo remained the solitary survivor of all those who had taken refuge with him in the depths of the ocean.

He was now sixty years of age. Although alone, he succeeded in navigating the 'Nautilus' towards one of those submarine caverns which had sometimes served him as a harbour.

One of these ports was hollowed beneath Lincoln Island, and at this moment furnished an asylum to the 'Nautilus.'

The captain had now remained there six years, navigating the ocean no longer, but awaiting death, and that moment when he should rejoin his former companions, when by chance he observed the descent of the balloon which carried the prisoners of the Confederates. Clad in his diving dress he was walking beneath the water at a few cables' length from the shore of the island, when the engineer had been thrown into the sea. Moved by a feeling of compassion the captain saved Cyrus Harding.

His first impulse was to fly from the vicinity of the five castaways; but his harbour refuge was closed, for in consequence of an elevation of the basalt, produced by the influence of volcanic action, he could no longer pass through the entrance of the vault. Though there was sufficient depth of water to allow a light craft to pass the bar, there was not enough for the 'Nautilus,' whose draught of water was considerable.

Captain Nemo was compelled, therefore, to remain. He observed these men thrown without resources upon a desert island, but had no wish to be himself discovered by them. By degrees he became interested in their efforts when he saw them honest, energetic, and bound to each other by the ties of friendship. As if despite his wishes, he penetrated all the secrets of their existence. By means of the diving dress he could easily reach the well in the interior of Granite House, and climbing by the projections of rock to its upper orifice he heard the colonists as they recounted the past, and studied the present and future. He learned from them the tremendous conflict of America with America itself, for the abolition of slavery. Yes, these men were worthy to reconcile Captain Nemo with that humanity which they represented so nobly in the island.

Captain Nemo had saved Cyrus Harding. It was he also who had brought back the dog to the Chimneys, who rescued Top from the waters of the lake, who caused to fall at Flotsam Point the case containing so many things useful to the colonists, who conveyed the canoe back into the stream of the Mercy, who cast the cord from the top of Granite House at the time of the attack by the baboons, who made known the presence of Ayrton upon Tabor Island, by means of the document enclosed in the bottle, who caused the explosion of the brig by the shock of a torpedo placed at the bottom of the canal, who saved Herbert from certain death by bringing the sulphate of quinine; and finally, it was he who had killed the convicts with the electric bails, of which he possessed the secret, and which he employed in the chase of submarine creatures. Thus were explained so many apparently supernatural occurrences, and which all proved the generosity and power of the captain.

Nevertheless, this noble misanthrope longed to benefit his proteges still further. There yet remained much useful advice to give them, and, his heart being softened by the approach of death, he invited, as we are aware, the colonists of Granite House to visit the 'Nautilus,' by means of a wire which connected it with the corral. Possibly he would not have done this had he been aware that Cyrus Harding was sufficiently acquainted with his history to address him by the name of Nemo.

The captain concluded the narrative of his life. Cyrus Harding then spoke; he recalled all the incidents which had exercised so beneficent an influence upon the colony, and in the names of his companions and himself thanked the generous being to whom they owed so much.

But Captain Nemo paid little attention; his mind appeared to be absorbed by one idea, and without taking the proffered hand of the engineer,—

'Now, sir,' said he, 'now that you know my history, your judgment!'

In saying this, the captain evidently alluded to an important incident witnessed by the three strangers thrown on board his vessel, and which the French professor had related in his work, causing a profound and terrible sensation. Some days previous to the flight of the professor and his two companions, the 'Nautilus,' being chased by a frigate in the north of the Atlantic had hurled herself as a ram upon this frigate, and sunk her without mercy.

Cyrus Harding understood the captain's allusion, and was silent.

'It was an enemy's frigate,' exclaimed Captain Nemo, transformed for an instant into the Prince Dakkar, 'an enemy's frigate! It was she who attacked me—I was in a narrow and shallow bay—the frigate barred my way— and I sank her!'

A few moments of silence ensued; then the captain demanded,—

'What think you of my life, gentlemen?'

Cyrus Harding extended his hand to the ci-devant prince and replied gravely, 'Sir, your error was in supposing that the past can be resuscitated, and in contending against inevitable progress. It is one of those errors which some admire, others blame; which God alone can judge. He who is mistaken in an action which he sincerely believes to be right may be an enemy, but retains our esteem. Your error is one that we may admire, and your name has nothing to fear from the judgment of history, which does not condemn heroic folly, but its results.'

The old man's breast swelled with emotion, and raising his hand to heaven,—

'Was I wrong, or in the right?' he murmured.

Cyrus Harding replied, 'All great actions return to God, from whom they are derived. Captain Nemo, we, whom you have succoured, shall ever mourn your loss.'

Herbert, who had drawn near the captain, fell on his knees and kissed his hand.

A tear glistened in the eyes of the dying man. 'My child,' he said, 'may God bless you!'

Chapter 17

Day had returned. No ray of light penetrated into the profundity of the cavern. It being high-water, the entrance was closed by the sea. But the artificial light, which escaped in long streams from the skylights of the 'Nautilus' was as vivid as before, and the sheet of water shone around the floating vessel.

An extreme exhaustion now overcame Captain Nemo, who had fallen back upon the divan. It was useless to contemplate removing him to Granite House, for he had expressed his wish to remain in the midst of those marvels of the 'Nautilus' which millions could not have purchased, and to wait there for that death which was swiftly approaching.

During a long interval of prostration, which rendered him almost unconscious, Cyrus Harding and Gideon Spilett attentively observed the condition of the dying man. It was apparent that his strength was gradually diminishing. That frame, once so robust, was now but the fragile tenement of a departing soul. All of life was concentrated in the heart and head.

The engineer and reporter consulted in whispers. Was it possible to render any aid to the dying man? Might his life, if not saved, be prolonged for some days? He himself had said that no remedy could avail, and he awaited with tranquillity that death which had for him no terrors.

'We can do nothing,' said Gideon Spilett.

'But of what is he dying?' asked Pencroft.

'Life is simply fading out,' replied the reporter.

'Nevertheless,' said the sailor, 'if we move him into the open air, and the light of the sun, he might perhaps recover.'

'No, Pencroft,' answered the engineer, 'it is useless to attempt it. Besides, Captain Nemo would never consent to leave his vessel. He has lived for a dozen years on board the 'Nautilus,' and on board the 'Nautilus' he desires to die.'

Without doubt Captain Nemo heard Cyrus Harding's reply, for he raised himself slightly, and in a voice more feeble, but always intelligible,—

'You are right, sir,' he said. 'I shall die here—it is my wish; and therefore I have a request to make of you.'

Cyrus Harding and his companions had drawn near the divan, and now arranged the cushions in such a manner as to better support the dying man.

They saw his eyes wander over all the marvels of this saloon, lighted by the electric rays which fell from the arabesques of the luminous ceiling. He surveyed, one after the other, the pictures hanging from the splendid tapestries of the partitions, the chef-d'oeuvres of the Italian, Flemish, French, and Spanish masters; the statues of marble and bronze on their pedestals; the magnificent organ, leaning against the after-partition; the aquarium, in which bloomed the most wonderful productions of the sea— marine plants, zoophytes, chaplets of pearls of inestimable value; and, finally, his eyes rested on this device, inscribed over the pediment of the museum—the motto of the 'Nautilus'—

'Mobilis in mobile.'

His glance seemed to rest fondly for the last time on these masterpieces of art and of nature, to which he had limited his horizon during a sojourn of so many years in the abysses of the seas.

Cyrus Harding respected the captain's silence, and waited till he should speak.

After some minutes, during which, doubtless, he passed in review his whole life, Captain Nemo turned to the colonists and said,

'You consider yourselves, gentlemen, under some obligations to me?'

'Captain, believe us that we would give our lives to prolong yours.'

'Promise, then,' continued Captain Nemo, 'to carry out my last wishes, and I shall be repaid for all I have done for you.'

'We promise,' said Cyrus Harding.

And by this promise he bound both himself and his companions.

'Gentlemen,' resumed the captain, 'tomorrow I shall be dead.'

Herbert was about to utter an exclamation, but a sign from the captain arrested him.

'Tomorrow I shall die, and I desire no other tomb than the 'Nautilus.' It is my grave! All my friends repose in the depths of the ocean; their resting-place shall be mine.'

These words were received with profound silence.

'Pay attention to my wishes,' he continued. 'The 'Nautilus' is imprisoned in this grotto, the entrance of which is blocked up; but, although egress is impossible, the vessel may at least sink in the abyss, and there bury my remains.'

The colonists listened reverently to the words of the dying man.

'Tomorrow, after my death, Mr. Harding,' continued the captain, 'yourself and companions will leave the 'Nautilus,' for all the treasures it contains must perish with me. One token alone will remain with you of Prince Dakkar, with whose history you are now acquainted. That coffer yonder contains diamonds of the value of many millions, most of them mementoes of the time when, husband and father, I thought happiness possible for me, and a collection of pearls gathered by my friends and myself in the depths of the ocean. Of this treasure at a future day, you may make good use. In the hands of such men as yourself and your comrades, Captain Harding, money will never be a source of danger. From on high I shall still participate in your enterprises, and I fear not but that they will prosper.'

After a few moments' repose, necessitated by his extreme weakness, Captain Nemo continued,—

'Tomorrow you will take the coffer, you will leave the saloon, of which you will close the door; then you will ascend on to the deck of the 'Nautilus,' and you will lower the main hatch so as entirely to close the vessel.'

'It shall be done, captain,' answered Cyrus Harding.

'Good. You will then embark in the canoe which brought you hither; but, before leaving the 'Nautilus,' go to the stern and there open two large stopcocks which you will find upon the water-line. The water will penetrate into the reservoirs, and the 'Nautilus' will gradually sink beneath the water to repose at the bottom of the abyss.'

And comprehending a gesture of Cyrus Harding, the captain added,—

'Fear nothing! You will but bury a corpse!'

Neither Cyrus Harding nor his companions ventured to offer any observation to Captain Nemo. He had expressed his last wishes, and they had nothing to do but to conform to them.

'I have your promise, gentlemen?' added Captain Nemo.

'You have, captain,' replied the engineer.

The captain thanked the colonists by a sign, and requested them to leave him for some hours. Gideon Spilett wished to remain near him, in the event of a crisis coming on, but the dying man refused, saying, 'I shall live until tomorrow, sir.'

All left the saloon, passed through the library and the dining room, and arrived forward, in the machine-room where the electrical apparatus was established, which supplied not only heat and light, but the mechanical power of the 'Nautilus.'

The 'Nautilus' was a masterpiece containing masterpieces with itself, and the engineer was struck with astonishment.

The colonists mounted the platform, which rose seven or eight feet above the water. There they beheld a thick glass lenticular covering, which protected a kind of large eye, from which flashed forth light. Behind this eye was apparently a cabin containing the wheels of the rudder, and in which was stationed the helmsman, when he navigated the 'Nautilus' over the bed of the ocean, which the electric rays would evidently light up to a considerable distance.

Cyrus Harding and his companions remained for a time silent, for they were vividly impressed by what they had just seen and heard, and their hearts were deeply touched by the thought that he whose arm had so often aided them, the protector whom they had known but a few hours, was at the point of death.

Whatever might be the judgment pronounced by posterity upon the events of this, so to speak, extra-human existence, the character of Prince Dakkar would ever remain as one of those whose memory time can never efface.

'What a man!' said Pencroft. 'Is it possible that he can have lived at the bottom of the sea? And it seems to me that perhaps he has not found peace there any more than elsewhere!'

'The 'Nautilus," observed Ayrton, 'might have enabled us to leave Lincoln Island and reach some inhabited country.'

'Good Heavens!' exclaimed Pencroft, 'I for one would never risk myself in such a craft. To sail on the seas, good, but under the seas, never!'

'I believe, Pencroft,' answered the reporter, 'that the navigation of a submarine vessel such as the 'Nautilus' ought to be very easy, and that we should soon become accustomed to it. There would be no storms, no lee-shore to fear. At some feet beneath the surface the waters of the ocean are as calm as those of a lake.'

'That may be,' replied the sailor, 'but I prefer a gale of wind on board a well-found craft. A vessel is built to sail on the sea, and not beneath it.'

'My friends,' said the engineer, 'it is useless, at any rate as regards the 'Nautilus,' to discuss the question of submarine vessels. The 'Nautilus' is not ours, and we have not the right to dispose of it. Moreover, we could in no case avail ourselves of it. Independently of the fact that it would be impossible to get it out of this cavern, whose entrance is now closed by the uprising of the basaltic rocks, Captain Nemo's wish is that it shall be buried with him. His wish is our law, and we will fulfil it.'

After a somewhat prolonged conversation, Cyrus Harding and his companions again descended to the interior of the 'Nautilus.' There they took some refreshment and returned to the saloon.

Captain Nemo had somewhat rallied from the prostration which had overcome him, and his eyes shone with their wonted fire. A faint smile even curled his lips.

The colonists drew around him.

'Gentlemen,' said the captain, 'you are brave and honest men. You have devoted yourselves to the common weal. Often have I observed your conduct. I have esteemed you—I esteem you still! Your hand, Mr. Harding.'

Cyrus Harding gave his hand to the captain, who clasped it affectionately.

'It is well!' he murmured.

He resumed,—

'But enough of myself. I have to speak concerning yourselves, and this Lincoln Island, upon which you have taken refuge. You now desire to leave it?'

'To return, captain!' answered Pencroft quickly.

'To return, Pencroft?' said the captain, with a smile. 'I know, it is true, your love for this island. You have helped to make it what it now is, and it seems to you a paradise!'

'Our project, captain,' interposed Cyrus Harding, 'is to annex it to the United States, and to establish for our shipping a port so fortunately situated in this part of the Pacific.'

'Your thoughts are with your country, gentlemen,' continued the captain; 'your toils are for her prosperity and glory. You are right. One's native land!—there should one live! there die! And I die far from all I loved!'

'You have some last wish to transmit,' said the engineer with emotion, 'some souvenir to send to those friends you have left in the mountains of India?'

'No, Captain Harding; no friends remain to me! I am the last of my race, and to all whom I have known I have long been as are the dead.—But to return to yourselves. Solitude, isolation, are painful things, and beyond human endurance. I die of having thought it possible to live alone! You should, therefore, dare all in the attempt to leave Lincoln Island, and see once more the land of your birth. I am aware that those wretches have destroyed the vessel you have built.'

'We propose to construct a vessel,' said Gideon Spilett, 'sufficiently large to convey us to the nearest land; but if we should succeed, sooner or later we shall return to Lincoln Island. We are attached to it by too many recollections ever to forget it.'

'It is here that we have known Captain Nemo,' said Cyrus Harding.

'It is here only that we can make our home!' added Herbert.

'And here shall I sleep the sleep of eternity, if—' replied the captain.

He paused for a moment, and, instead of completing the sentence, said simply,—

'Mr. Harding, I wish to speak with you—alone!'

The engineer's companions, respecting the wish, retired.

Cyrus Harding remained but a few minutes alone with Captain Nemo, and soon recalled his companions; but he said nothing to them of the private matters which the dying man had confided to him.

Gideon Spilett now watched the captain with extreme care. It was evident that he was no longer sustained by his moral energy, which had lost the power of reaction against his physical weakness.

The day closed without change. The colonists did not quit the 'Nautilus' for a moment. Night arrived, although it was impossible to distinguish it from day in the cavern.

Captain Nemo suffered no pain, but he was visibly sinking. His noble features, paled by the approach of death, were perfectly calm. Inaudible words escaped at intervals from his lips, bearing upon various incidents of his checkered career. Life was evidently ebbing slowly and his extremities were already cold.

Once or twice more he spoke to the colonists who stood around him, and smiled on them with that last smile which continues after death.

At length, shortly after midnight, Captain Nemo by a supreme effort succeeded in folding his arms across his breast, as if wishing in that attitude to compose himself for death.

By one o'clock his glance alone showed signs of life. A dying light gleamed in those eyes once so brilliant. Then, murmuring the words, 'God and my country!' he quietly expired.

Cyrus Harding, bending low closed the eyes of him who had once been the Prince Dakkar, and was now not even Captain Nemo.

Herbert and Pencroft sobbed aloud. Tears fell from Ayrton's eyes. Neb was on his knees by the reporter's side, motionless as a statue.

Then Cyrus Harding, extending his hand over the forehead of the dead, said solemnly, 'May his soul be with God!' Turning to his friends, he added, 'Let us pray for him whom we have lost!'

Some hours later the colonists fulfilled the promise made to the captain by carrying out his dying wishes.

Cyrus Harding and his companions quitted the 'Nautilus,' taking with them the only memento left them by their benefactor, the coffer which contained wealth amounting to millions.

The marvellous saloon, still flooded with light, had been carefully closed. The iron door leading on deck was then securely fastened in such a manner as to prevent even a drop of water from penetrating to the interior of the 'Nautilus.'

The colonists then descended into the canoe, which was moored to the side of the submarine vessel.

The canoe was now brought around to the stern. There, at the water-line, were two large stopcocks communicating with the reservoirs employed in the submersion of the vessel.

The stopcocks were opened, the reservoirs filled, and the 'Nautilus,' slowly sinking, disappeared beneath the surface of the lake.

But the colonists were yet able to follow its descent through the waves. The powerful light it gave forth lighted up the translucent water, while the cavern became gradually obscure. At length this vast effusion of electric light faded away, and soon after the 'Nautilus,' now the tomb of Captain Nemo, reposed in its ocean bed.

Chapter 18

At break of day the colonists regained in silence the entrance of the cavern, to which they gave the name of 'Dakkar Grotto,' in memory of Captain Nemo. It was now low-water, and they passed without difficulty under the arcade, washed on the right by the sea.

The canoe was left here, carefully protected from the waves. As additional precaution, Pencroft, Neb, and Ayrton drew it up on a little beach which bordered one of the sides of the grotto, in a spot where it could run no risk of harm.

The storm had ceased during the night. The last low mutterings of the thunder died away in the west. Rain fell no longer, but the sky was yet obscured by clouds. On the whole, this month of October, the first of the southern spring, was not ushered in by satisfactory tokens, and the wind had a tendency to shift from one point of the compass to another, which rendered it impossible to count upon settled weather.

Cyrus Harding and his companions, on leaving Dakkar Grotto, had taken the road to the corral. On their way Neb and Herbert were careful to preserve the wire which had been laid down by the captain between the corral and the grotto, and which might at a future time be of service.

The colonists spoke but little on the road. The various incidents of the night of October 15th had left a profound impression on their minds. The unknown being whose influence had so effectually protected them, the man whom their imagination had endowed with supernatural powers, Captain Nemo, was no more. His 'Nautilus' and he were buried in the depths of the abyss. To each one of them their existence seemed even more isolated than before. They had been accustomed to count upon the intervention of that power which existed no longer, and Gideon Spilett, and even Cyrus Harding, could not escape this impression. Thus they maintained a profound silence during their journey to the corral.

Towards nine in the morning the colonists arrived at Granite House.

It had been agreed that the construction of the vessel should be actively pushed forward, and Cyrus Harding more than ever devoted his time and labour to this object. It was impossible to divine what future lay before them. Evidently the advantage to the colonists would be great of having at their disposal a substantial vessel, capable of keeping the sea even in heavy weather, and large enough to attempt, in case of need, a voyage of some duration. Even if, when their vessel should be completed, the colonists should not resolve to leave Lincoln Island as yet, in order to gain either one of the Polynesian Archipelagoes of the Pacific or the shores of New Zealand, they might at least, sooner or later, proceed to Tabor Island, to leave there the notice relating to Ayrton. This was a precaution rendered indispensable by the possibility of the Scotch yacht reappearing in those seas, and it was of the highest importance that nothing should be neglected on this point.

The works were then resumed. Cyrus Harding, Pencroft, and Ayrton, assisted by Neb, Gideon Spilett, and Herbert, except when unavoidably called off by other necessary occupations, worked without cessation. It was important that the new vessel should be ready in five months—that is to say, by the beginning of March—if they wished to visit Tabor Island before the equinoctial gales rendered the voyage impracticable. Therefore the carpenters lost not a moment. Moreover, it was unnecessary to manufacture rigging, that of the 'Speedy' having been saved entire, so that the hull only of the vessel needed to be constructed.

The end of the year 1868 found them occupied by these important labours, to the exclusion of almost all others. At the expiration of two months and a half the ribs had been set up and the first planks adjusted. It was already evident that the plans made by Cyrus Harding were admirable, and that the vessel would behave well at sea.

Pencroft brought to the task a devouring energy, and would even grumble when one or the other abandoned the carpenter's axe for the gun of the hunter. It was nevertheless necessary to keep up the stores of Granite House, in view of the approaching winter. But this did not satisfy Pencroft. The brave, honest sailor was not content when the workmen were not at the dockyard. When this happened he grumbled vigorously, and, by way of venting his feelings, did the work of six men.

The weather was very unfavourable during the whole of the summer season. For some days the heat was overpowering, and the atmosphere, saturated with electricity, was only cleared by violent storms. It was rarely that the distant growling of the thunder could not be heard, like a low but incessant murmur, such as is produced in the equatorial regions of the globe.

The 1st of January, 1869, was signalized by a storm of extreme violence, and the thunder burst several times over the island. Large trees were struck by the electric fluid and shattered, and among others one of those gigantic nettle-trees which had shaded the poultry-yard at the southern extremity of the lake. Had this meteor any relation to the phenomena going on in the bowels of the earth? Was there any connection between the commotion of the atmosphere and that of the interior of the earth? Cyrus Harding was inclined to think that such was the case, for the development of these storms was attended by the renewal of volcanic symptoms.

It was on the 3rd of January that Herbert, having ascended at daybreak to the plateau of Prospect Heights to harness one of the onagers, perceived an enormous hat-shaped cloud rolling from the summit of the volcano.

Herbert immediately apprised the colonists, who at once joined him in watching the summit of Mount Franklin.

'Ah!' exclaimed Pencroft, 'those are not vapours this time! It seems to me that the giant is not content with breathing; he must smoke!'

This figure of speech employed by the sailor exactly expressed the changes going on at the mouth of the volcano. Already for three months had the crater emitted vapours more or less dense, but which were as yet produced only by an internal ebullition of mineral substances. But now the vapours were replaced by a thick smoke, rising in the form of a grayish column, more than three hundred feet in width at its base, and which spread like an immense mushroom to a height of from seven to eight hundred feet above the summit of the mountain.

'The fire is in the chimney,' observed Gideon Spilett.

'And we can't put it out!' replied Herbert.

'The volcano ought to be swept,' observed Neb, who spoke as if perfectly serious.

'Well said, Neb!' cried Pencroft, with a shout of laughter; 'and you'll undertake the job, no doubt?'

Cyrus Harding attentively observed the dense smoke emitted by Mount Franklin, and even listened, as if expecting to hear some distant muttering. Then, turning towards his companions, from whom he had gone somewhat apart, he said,—

'The truth is, my friends, we must not conceal from ourselves that an important change is going forward. The volcanic substances are no longer in a state of ebullition, they have caught fire, and we are undoubtedly menaced by an approaching eruption.'

'Well, captain,' said Pencroft, 'we shall witness the eruption; and if it is a good one, we'll applaud it. I don't see that we need concern ourselves further about the matter.'

'It may be so,' replied Cyrus Harding, 'for the ancient track of the lava is still open; and thanks to this, the crater has hitherto overflowed towards the north. And yet—'

'And yet, as we can derive no advantage from an eruption, it might be better it should not take place,' said the reporter.

'Who knows?' answered the sailor. 'Perhaps there may be some valuable substance in this volcano, which it will spout forth, and which we may turn to good account!'

Cyrus Harding shook his head with the air of a man who augured no good from the phenomenon whose development had been so sudden. He did not regard so lightly as Pencroft the results of an eruption. If the lava, in consequence of the position of the crater, did not directly menace the wooded and cultivated parts of the island, other complications might present themselves. In fact, eruptions are not unfrequently accompanied by earthquakes; and an island of the nature of Lincoln Island, formed of substances so varied, basalt on one side, granite on the other, lava on the north, rich soil on the south, substances which consequently could not be firmly attached to each other, would be exposed to the risk of disintegration. Although, therefore, the spreading of the volcanic matter might not constitute a serious danger, any movement of the terrestrial structure which should shake the island might entail the gravest consequences.

'It seems to me,' said Ayrton, who had reclined so as to place his ear to the ground, 'it seems to me that I can hear a dull, rumbling sound, like that of a wagon loaded with bars of iron.'

The colonists listened with the greatest attention, and were convinced that Ayrton was not mistaken. The rumbling was mingled with a subterranean roar, which formed a sort of rinforzando, and died slowly away, as if some violent storm had passed through the profundities of the globe. But no explosion properly so termed, could be heard. It might therefore be concluded that the vapours and smoke found a free passage through the central shaft; and that the safety-valve being sufficiently large, no convulsion would be produced, no explosion was to be apprehended.

'Well, then!' said Pencroft, 'are we not going back to work? Let Mount Franklin smoke, groan, bellow, or spout forth fire and flame as much as it pleases, that is no reason why we should be idle! Come, Ayrton, Neb, Herbert, Captain Harding, Mr. Spilett, every one of us must turn to at our work today! We are going to place the keelson, and a dozen pair of hands would not be too many. Before two months I want our new 'Bonadventure '— for we shall keep the old name, shall we not?—to float on the waters of Port Balloon! Therefore there is not an hour to lose!'

All the colonists, their services thus requisitioned by Pencroft, descended to the dockyard, and proceeded to place the keelson, a thick mass of wood which forms the lower portion of a ship and unites firmly the timbers of the hull. It was an arduous undertaking, in which all took part.

They continued their labours during the whole of this day, the 3rd of January, without thinking further of the volcano, which could not, besides, be seen from the shore of Granite House. But once or twice, large shadows, veiling the sun, which described its diurnal arc through an extremely clear sky, indicated that a thick cloud of smoke passed between its disc and the island. The wind, blowing on the shore, carried all these vapours to the westward. Cyrus Harding and Gideon Spilett remarked these sombre appearances, and from time to time discussed the evident progress of the volcanic phenomena, but their work went on without interruption. It was, besides, of the first importance from every point of view, that the vessel should be finished with the least possible delay. In presence of the eventualities which might arise, the safety of the colonists would be to a great extent secured by their ship. Who could tell that it might not prove some day their only refuge?

In the evening, after supper, Cyrus Harding, Gideon Spilett, and Herbert again ascended the plateau of Prospect Heights. It was already dark, and the obscurity would permit them to ascertain if flames or incandescent matter thrown up by the volcano were mingled with the vapour and smoke accumulated at the mouth of the crater.

'The crater is on fire!' said Herbert, who, more active than his companion, first reached the plateau.

Mount Franklin, distant about six miles, now appeared like a gigantic torch, around the summit of which turned fuliginous flames. So much smoke, and possibly scoriae and cinders were mingled with them, that their light gleamed but faintly amid the gloom of the night. But a kind of lurid brilliancy spread over the island, against which stood out confusedly the wooded masses of the heights. Immense whirlwinds of vapour obscured the sky, through which glimmered a few stars.

'The change is rapid!' said the engineer.

'That is not surprising,' answered the reporter. 'The reawakening of the volcano already dates back some time. You may remember, Cyrus, that the first vapours appeared about the time we searched the sides of the mountain to discover Captain Nemo's retreat. It was, if I mistake not, about the 15th of October.'

'Yes,' replied Herbert, 'two months and a half ago!'

'The subterranean fires have therefore been smoldering for ten weeks,' resumed Gideon Spilett, 'and it is not to be wondered at that they now break out with such violence!'

'Do not you feel a certain vibration of the soil?' asked Cyrus Harding.

'Yes,' replied Gideon Spilett, 'but there is a great difference between that and an earthquake.'

'I do not affirm that we are menaced with an earthquake,' answered Cyrus Harding, 'may God preserve us from that! No; these vibrations are due to the effervescence of the central fire. The crust of the earth is simply the shell of a boiler, and you know that such a shell, under the pressure of steam, vibrates like a sonorous plate. It is this effect which is being produced at this moment.'

'What magnificent flames!' exclaimed Herbert.

At this instant a kind of bouquet of flames shot forth from the crater, the brilliancy of which was visible even through the vapours. Thousands of luminous sheets and barbed tongues of fire were cast in various directions. Some, extending beyond the dome of smoke, dissipated it, leaving behind an incandescent powder. This was accompanied by successive explosions, resembling the discharge of a battery of machine-guns.

Cyrus Harding, the reporter, and Herbert, after spending an hour on the plateau of Prospect Heights, again descended to the beach, and returned to Granite House. The engineer was thoughtful and preoccupied, so much so, indeed, that Gideon Spilett inquired if he apprehended any immediate danger, of which the eruption might directly or indirectly be the cause.

'Yes, and no,' answered Cyrus Harding.

'Nevertheless,' continued the reporter, 'would not the greatest misfortune which could happen to us be an earthquake which would overturn the island? Now, I do not suppose that this is to be feared, since the vapours and lava have found a free outlet.'

'True,' replied Cyrus Harding, 'and I do not fear an earthquake in the sense in which the term is commonly applied to convulsions of the soil provoked by the expansion of subterranean gases. But other causes may produce great disasters.'

'How so, my dear Cyrus?'

'I am not certain. I must consider. I must visit the mountain. In a few days I shall learn more on this point.'

Gideon Spilett said no more, and soon, in spite of the explosions of the volcano, whose intensity increased, and which were repeated by the echoes of the island, the inhabitants of Granite House were sleeping soundly.

Three days passed by—the 4th, 5th, and 6th of January. The construction of the vessel was diligently continued, and without offering further explanations the engineer pushed forward the work with all his energy. Mount Franklin was now hooded by a sombre cloud of sinister aspect, and, amid the flames, vomiting forth incandescent rocks, some of which fell back into the crater itself. This caused Pencroft, who would only look at the matter in the light of a joke, to exclaim,—

'Ah! the giant is playing at cup and ball; he is a conjurer.'

In fact, the substances thrown up fell back again in to the abyss, and it did not seem that the lava, though swollen by the internal pressure, had yet risen to the orifice of the crater. At any rate, the opening on the northeast, which was partly visible, poured out no torrent upon the northern slope of the mountain.

Nevertheless, however pressing was the construction of the vessel, other duties demanded the presence of the colonists on various portions of the island. Before everything it was necessary to go to the corral, where the flocks of musmons and goats were enclosed, and replenish the provision of forage for those animals. It was accordingly arranged that Ayrton should proceed thither the next day, the 7th of January; and as he was sufficient for the task, to which he was accustomed, Pencroft and the rest were somewhat surprised on hearing the engineer say to Ayrton—

'As you are going tomorrow to the corral I will accompany you.'

'But, Captain Harding,' exclaimed the sailor, 'our working days will not be many, and if you go also we shall be two pair of hands short!'

'We shall return tomorrow,' replied Cyrus Harding, 'but it is necessary that I should go to the corral. I must learn how the eruption is progressing.'

'The eruption! always the eruption!' answered Pencroft, with an air of discontent. 'An important thing, truly, this eruption! I trouble myself very little about it.'

Whatever might be the sailor's opinion, the expedition projected by the engineer was settled for the next day. Herbert wished to accompany Cyrus Harding, but he would not vex Pencroft by his absence.

The next day, at dawn, Cyrus Harding and Ayrton, mounting the cart drawn by two onagers, took the road to the corral and set off at a round trot.

Above the forest were passing large clouds, to which the crater of Mount Franklin incessantly added fuliginous matter. These clouds, which rolled heavily in the air, were evidently composed of heterogeneous substances. It was not alone from the volcano that they derived their strange opacity and weight. Scoriae, in a state of dust, like powdered pumice-stone, and grayish ashes as small as the finest feculae, were held in suspension in the midst of their thick folds. These ashes are so fine that they have been observed in the air for whole months. After the eruption of 1783 in Iceland for upwards of a year the atmosphere was thus charged with volcanic dust through which the rays of the sun were only with difficulty discernible.

But more often this pulverized matter falls, and this happened on the present occasion. Cyrus Harding and Ayrton had scarcely reached the corral when a sort of black snow like fine gunpowder fell, and instantly changed the appearance of the soil. Trees, meadows, all disappeared beneath a covering several inches in depth. But, very fortunately, the wind blew from the northeast, and the greater part of the cloud dissolved itself over the sea.

'This is very singular, Captain Harding,' said Ayrton.

'It is very serious,' replied the engineer. 'This powdered pumice-stone, all this mineral dust, proves how grave is the convulsion going forward in the lower depths of the volcano.'

'But can nothing be done?'

'Nothing, except to note the progress of the phenomenon. Do you, therefore, Ayrton, occupy yourself with the necessary work at the corral. In the meantime I will ascend just beyond the source of Red Creek and examine the condition of the mountain upon its northern aspect. Then—'

'Well, Captain Harding?'

'Then we will pay a visit to Dakkar Grotto. I wish to inspect it. At any rate I will come back for you in two hours.'

Ayrton then proceeded to enter the corral, and, while awaiting the engineer's return, busied himself with the musmons and goats which seemed to feel a certain uneasiness in presence of these first signs of an eruption.

Meanwhile Cyrus Harding ascended the crest of the eastern spur, passed Red Creek, and arrived at the spot where he and his companions had discovered a sulphurous spring at the time of their first exploration.

How changed was everything! Instead of a single column of smoke he counted thirteen, forced through the soil as if violently propelled by some piston. It was evident that the crust of the earth was subjected in this part of the globe to a frightful pressure. The atmosphere was saturated with gases and carbonic acid, mingled with aqueous vapours. Cyrus Harding felt the volcanic tufa with which the plain was strewn, and which was but pulverized cinders hardened into solid blocks by time, tremble beneath him, but he could discover no traces of fresh lava.

The engineer became more assured of this when he observed all the northern part of Mount Franklin. Pillars of smoke and flame escaped from the crater; a hail of scoriae fell on the ground; but no current of lava burst from the mouth of the volcano, which proved that the volcanic matter had not yet attained the level of the superior orifice of the central shaft.

'But I would prefer that it were so,' said Cyrus Harding to himself. 'At any rate, I should then know that the lava had followed its accustomed track. Who can say that it may not take a new course? But the danger does not consist in that! Captain Nemo foresaw it clearly! No, the danger does not lie there!'

Cyrus Harding advanced towards the enormous causeway whose prolongation enclosed the narrow Shark Gulf. He could now sufficiently examine on this side the ancient channels of the lava. There was no doubt in his mind that the most recent eruption had occurred at a far-distant epoch.

He then returned by the same way, listening attentively to the subterranean mutterings which rolled like long-continued thunder, interrupted by deafening explosions. At nine in the morning he reached the corral.

Ayrton awaited him.

'The animals are cared for, Captain Harding,' said Ayrton.

'Good, Ayrton.'

'They seem uneasy, Captain Harding.'

'Yes, instinct speaks through them, and instinct is never deceived.'

'Are you ready?'

'Take a lamp, Ayrton,' answered the engineer; 'we will start at once.

Ayrton did as desired. The onagers, unharnessed, roamed in the corral. The gate was secured on the outside, and Cyrus Harding, preceding Ayrton, took the narrow path which led westward to the shore.

The soil they walked upon was choked with the pulverized matter fallen from the cloud. No quadruped appeared in the woods. Even the birds had fled. Sometimes a passing breeze raised the covering of ashes, and the two colonists, enveloped in a whirlwind of dust, lost sight of each other. They were then careful to cover their eyes and mouths with handkerchiefs, for they ran the risk of being blinded and suffocated.

It was impossible for Cyrus Harding and Ayrton, with these impediments, to make rapid progress. Moreover, the atmosphere was close, as if the oxygen had been partly burned up, and had become unfit for respiration. At every hundred paces they were obliged to stop to take breath. It was therefore past ten o'clock when the engineer and his companion reached the crest of the enormous mass of rocks of basalt and porphyry which composed the northwest coast of the island.

Ayrton and Cyrus Harding commenced the descent of this abrupt declivity, following almost step for step the difficult path which, during that stormy night, had led them to Dakkar Grotto. In open day the descent was less perilous, and, besides, the bed of ashes which covered the polished surface of the rock enabled them to make their footing more secure.

The ridge at the end of the shore, about forty feet in height, was soon reached. Cyrus Harding recollected that this elevation gradually sloped towards the level of the sea. Although the tide was at present low, no beach could he seen, and the waves, thickened by the volcanic dust, beat upon the basaltic rocks.

Cyrus Harding and Ayrton found without difficulty the entrance to Dakkar Grotto, and paused for a moment at the last rock before it.

'The iron boat should be there,' said the engineer.

'It is here, Captain Harding,' replied Ayrton, drawing towards him the fragile craft, which was protected by the arch of the vault.

'On board, Ayrton!'

The two colonists stepped into the boat. A slight undulation of the waves carried it farther under the low arch of the crypt, and there Ayrton, with the aid of flint and steel, lighted the lamp. He then took the oars, and the lamp having been placed in the bow of the boat, so that its rays fell before them, Cyrus Harding took the helm and steered through the shades of the grotto.

The 'Nautilus' was there no longer to illuminate the cavern with its electric light. Possibly it might not yet be extinguished, but no ray escaped from the depths of the abyss in which reposed all that was mortal of Captain Nemo.

The light afforded by the lamp, although feeble, nevertheless enabled the engineer to advance slowly, following the wall of the cavern. A deathlike silence reigned under the vaulted roof, or at least in the anterior portion, for soon Cyrus Harding distinctly heard the rumbling which proceeded from the bowels of the mountain.

'That comes from the volcano,' he said.

Besides these sounds, the presence of chemical combinations was soon betrayed by their powerful odour, and the engineer and his companion were almost suffocated by sulphurous vapours.

'This is what Captain Nemo feared,' murmured Cyrus Harding, changing countenance. 'We must go to the end, notwithstanding.'

'Forward!' replied Ayrton, bending to his oars and directing the boat towards the head of the cavern.

Twenty-five minutes after entering the mouth of the grotto the boat reached the extreme end.

Cyrus Harding then, standing up, cast the light of the lamp upon the walls of the cavern which separated it from the central shaft of the volcano. What was the thickness of this wall? It might be ten feet or a hundred feet—it was impossible to say. But the subterranean sounds were too perceptible to allow of the supposition that it was of any great thickness.

The engineer, after having explored the wall at a certain height horizontally, fastened the lamp to the end of an oar, and again surveyed the basaltic wall at a greater elevation.

There, through scarcely visible clefts and joinings, escaped a pungent vapour, which infected the atmosphere of the cavern. The wall was broken by large cracks, some of which extended to within two or three feet of the water's edge.

Cyrus Harding thought for a brief space. Then he said in a low voice,—

'Yes! the captain was right! The danger lies there, and a terrible danger!'

Ayrton said not a word, but, upon a sign from Cyrus Harding, resumed the oars, and half an hour later the engineer and he reached the entrance of Dakkar Grotto.

Chapter 19

The next day, the 8th day of January, after a day and night passed at the corral, where they left all in order, Cyrus Harding and Ayrton arrived at Granite House.

The engineer immediately called his companions together, and informed them of the imminent danger which threatened Lincoln Island, and from which no human power could deliver them.

'My friends,' he said, and his voice betrayed the depth of his emotion, 'our island is not among those which will endure while this earth endures. It is doomed to more or less speedy destruction, the cause of which it bears within itself, and from which nothing can save it.'

The colonists looked at each other, then at the engineer. They did not clearly comprehend him.

'Explain yourself, Cyrus!' said Gideon Spilett.

'I will do so,' replied Cyrus Harding, 'or rather I will simply afford you the explanation which, during our few minutes of private conversation, was given me by Captain Nemo.'

'Captain Nemo!' exclaimed the colonists.

'Yes, and it was the last service he desired to render us before his death!'

'The last service!' exclaimed Pencroft, 'the last service! You will see that though he is dead he will render us others yet!'

'But what did the captain say?' inquired the reporter.

'I will tell you, my friends,' said the engineer. 'Lincoln Island does not resemble the other islands of the Pacific, and a fact of which Captain Nemo has made me cognizant must sooner or later bring about the subversion of its foundation.'

'Nonsense! Lincoln Island, it can't be!' cried Pencroft, who, in spite of the respect he felt for Cyrus Harding, could not prevent a gesture of incredulity.

'Listen, Pencroft,' resumed the engineer, 'I will tell you what Captain Nemo communicated to me, and which I myself confirmed yesterday, during the exploration of Dakkar Grotto.

This cavern stretches under the island as far as the volcano, and is only separated from its central shaft by the wall which terminates it. Now, this wall is seamed with fissures and clefts which already allow the sulphurous gases generated in the interior of the volcano to escape.'

'Well?' said Pencroft, his brow suddenly contracting.

'Well, then, I saw that these fissures widen under the internal pressure from within, that the wall of basalt is gradually giving way and that after a longer or shorter period it will afford a passage to the waters of the lake which fill the cavern.'

'Good!'replied Pencroft, with an attempt at pleasantry. 'The sea will extinguish the volcano, and there will be an end of the matter!'

'Not so!' said Cyrus Harding, 'should a day arrive when the sea, rushing through the wall of the cavern, penetrates by the central shaft into the interior of the island to the boiling lava, Lincoln Island will that day be blown into the air—just as would happen to the island of Sicily were the Mediterranean to precipitate itself into Mount Etna.'

The colonists made no answer to these significant words of the engineer. They now understood the danger by which they were menaced.

It may be added that Cyrus Harding had in no way exaggerated the danger to be apprehended. Many persons have formed an idea that it would be possible to extinguish volcanoes, which are almost always situated on the shores of a sea or lake, by opening a passage for the admission of the water. But they are not aware that this would be to incur the risk of blowing up a portion of the globe, like a boiler whose steam is suddenly expanded by intense heat. The water, rushing into a cavity whose temperature might be estimated at thousands of degrees, would be converted into steam with a sudden energy which no enclosure could resist.

It was not therefore doubtful that the island, menaced by a frightful and approaching convulsion, would endure only so long as the wall of Dakkar Grotto itself should endure. It was not even a question of months, nor of weeks, but of days; it might be of hours.

The first sentiment which the colonists felt was that of profound sorrow. They thought not so much of the peril which menaced themselves personally, but of the destruction of the island which had sheltered them, which they had cultivated, which they loved so well, and had hoped to render so flourishing. So much effort ineffectually expended, so much labour lost.

Pencroft could not prevent a large tear from rolling down his cheek, nor did he attempt to conceal it.

Some further conversation now took place. The chances yet in favour of the colonists were discussed; but finally it was agreed that there was not an hour to be lost, that the building and fitting of the vessel should be pushed forward with their utmost energy, and that this was the sole chance of safety for the inhabitants of Lincoln Island.

All hands, therefore, set to work on the vessel. What could it avail to sow, to reap, to hunt, to increase the stores of Granite House? The contents of the storehouse and outbuildings contained more than sufficient to provide the ship for a voyage, however long might be its duration. But it was imperative that the ship should be ready to receive them before the inevitable catastrophe should arrive.

Their labours were now carried on with feverish ardour. By the 23rd of January the vessel was half-decked over. Up to this time no change had taken place on the summit of the volcano. Vapour and smoke mingled with flames and incandescent stones were thrown up from the crater. But during the night of the 23rd, in consequence of the lava attaining the level of the first stratum of the volcano, the hat-shaped cone which formed over the latter disappeared. A frightful sound was heard. The colonists at first thought the island was rent asunder, and rushed out of Granite House.

This occurred about two o'clock in the morning.

The sky appeared on fire. The superior cone, a mass of rock a thousand feet in height, and weighing thousands of millions of pounds, had been thrown down upon the island, making it tremble to its foundation. Fortunately, this cone inclined to the north, and had fallen upon the plain of sand and tufa stretching between the volcano and the sea. The aperture of the crater being thus enlarged projected towards the sky a glare so intense that by the simple effect of reflection the atmosphere appeared red-hot. At the same time a torrent of lava, bursting from the new summit, poured out in long cascades, like water escaping from a vase too full, and a thousand tongues of fire crept over the sides of the volcano.

'The corral! the corral!' exclaimed Ayrton.

It was, in fact, towards the corral that the lava was rushing as the new crater faced the east, and consequently the fertile portions of the island, the springs of Red Creek and Jacamar Wood, were menaced with instant destruction.

At Ayrton's cry the colonists rushed to the onagers' stables. The cart was at once harnessed. All were possessed by the same thought-to hasten to the corral and set at liberty the animals it enclosed.

Before three in the morning they arrived at the corral. The cries of the terrified musmons and goats indicated the alarm which possessed them. Already a torrent of burning matter and liquefied minerals fell from the side of the mountain upon the meadows as far as the side of the palisade. The gate was burst open by Ayrton, and the animals, bewildered with terror, fled in all directions.

An hour afterwards the boiling lava filled the corral, converting into vapour the water of the little rivulet which ran through it, burning up the house like dry grass, and leaving not even a post of the palisade to mark the spot where the corral once stood.

To contend against this disaster would have been folly—nay, madness. In presence of Nature's grand convulsions man is powerless.

It was now daylight—the 24th of January. Cyrus Harding and his companions, before returning to Granite House, desired to ascertain the probable direction this inundation of lava was about to take. The soil sloped gradually from Mount Franklin to the east coast, and it was to be feared that, in spite of the thick Jacamar Wood, the torrent would reach the plateau of Prospect Heights.

'The lake will cover us,' said Gideon Spilett.

'I hope so!' was Cyrus Harding's only reply.

The colonists were desirous of reaching the plain upon which the superior cone of Mount Franklin had fallen, but the lava arrested their progress. It had followed, on one side, the valley of Red Creek, and on the other that of Falls River, evaporating those watercourses in its passage. There was no possibility of crossing the torrent of lava; on the contrary, the colonists were obliged to retreat before it. The volcano, without its crown, was no longer recognizable, terminated as it was by a sort of flat table which replaced the ancient crater. From two openings in its southern and eastern sides an unceasing flow of lava poured forth, thus forming two distinct streams. Above the new crater a cloud of smoke and ashes, mingled with those of the atmosphere, massed over the island. Loud peals of thunder broke, and could scarcely be distinguished from the rumblings of the mountain, whose mouth vomited forth ignited rocks, which, hurled to more than a thousand feet, burst in the air like shells. Flashes of lightning rivalled in intensity the volcano's eruption.

Towards seven in the morning the position was no longer tenable by the colonists, who accordingly took shelter in the borders of Jacamar Wood. Not only did the projectiles begin to rain around them, but the lava, overflowing the bed of Red Creek, threatened to cut off the road to the corral. The nearest rows of trees caught fire, and their sap, suddenly transformed into vapour, caused them to explode with loud reports, while others, less moist, remained unhurt in the midst of the inundation.

The colonists had again taken the road to the corral. They proceeded but slowly, frequently looking back; but, in consequence of the inclination of the soil, the lava gained rapidly in the east, and as its lower waves became solidified others, at boiling heat, covered them immediately.

Meanwhile, the principal stream of Red Creek Valley became more and more menacing. All this portion of the forest was on fare, and enormous wreaths of smoke rolled over the trees, whore trunks were already consumed by the lava.

The colonists halted near the lake, about half a mile from the mouth of Red Creek. A question of life or death was now to be decided.

Cyrus Harding, accustomed to the consideration of important crises, and aware that he was addressing men capable of hearing the truth, whatever it might be, then said,—

'Either the lake will arrest the progress of the lava, and a part of the island will be preserved from utter destruction, or the stream will overrun the forests of the Far West, and not a tree or plant will remain on the surface of the soil. We shall have no prospect but that of starvation upon these barren rocks—a death which will probably be anticipated by the explosion of the island.'

'In that case,' replied Pencroft, folding his arms and stamping his foot, 'what's the use of working any longer on the vessel?'

'Pencroft,' answered Cyrus Harding, 'we must do our duty to the last!'

At this instant the river of lava, after having broken a passage through the noble trees it devoured in its course, reached the borders of the lake. At this point there was an elevation of the soil which, had it been greater, might have sufficed to arrest the torrent.

'To work!' cried Cyrus Harding.

The engineer's thought was at once understood. It might be possible to dam, as it were, the torrent, and thus compel it to pour itself into the lake.

The colonists hastened to the dockyard. They returned with shovels, picks, axes, and by means of banking the earth with the aid of fallen trees they succeeded in a few hours in raising an embankment three feet high and some hundreds of paces in length. It seemed to them, when they had finished, as if they had scarcely been working more than a few minutes.

It was not a moment too soon. The liquefied substances soon after reached the bottom of the barrier. The stream of lava swelled like a river about to overflow its banks, and threatened to demolish the sole obstacle which could prevent it from overrunning the whole Far West. But the dam held firm, and after a moment of terrible suspense the torrent precipitated itself into Grant Lake from a height of twenty feet.

The colonists, without moving or uttering a word, breathlessly regarded this strife of the two elements.

What a spectacle was this conflict between water and fare! What pen could describe the marvellous horror of this scene—what pencil could depict it? The water hissed as it evaporated by contact with the boiling lava. The vapour whirled in the air to an immeasurable height, as if the valves of an immense boiler had been suddenly opened. But, however considerable might be the volume of water contained in the lake, it must eventually be absorbed, because it was not replenished, while the stream of lava, fed from an inexhaustible source, rolled on without ceasing new waves of incandescent matter.

The first waves of lava which fell in the lake immediately solidified and accumulated so as speedily to emerge from it. Upon their surface fell other waves, which in their turn became stone, but a step nearer the centre of the lake. In this manner was formed a pier which threatened to gradually fill up the lake, which could not overflow, the water displaced by the lava being evaporated. The hissing of the water rent the air with a deafening sound, and the vapour, blown by the wind, fell in rain upon the sea. The pier became longer and longer, and the blocks of lava piled themselves one on another. Where formerly stretched the calm waters of the lake now appeared an enormous mass of smoking rocks, as if an upheaving of the soil had formed immense shoals. Imagine the waters of the lake aroused by a hurricane, then suddenly solidified by an intense frost, and some conception may be formed of the aspect of the lake three hours alter the eruption of this irresistible torrent of lava.

This time water would be vanquished by fire.

Nevertheless it was a fortunate circumstance for the colonists that the effusion of lava should have been in the direction of Lake Grant. They had before them some days' respite. The plateau of Prospect Heights, Granite House, and the dockyard were for the moment preserved. And these few days it was necessary to employ in planking and carefully calking the vessel, and launching her. The colonists would then take refuge on board the vessel, content to rig her after she should be afloat on the waters. With the danger of an explosion which threatened to destroy the island there could be no security on shore. The walls of Granite House, once so sure a retreat, might at any moment fall in upon them.

During the six following days, from the 25th to the 30th of January, the colonists accomplished as much of the construction of their vessel as twenty men could have done. They hardly allowed themselves a moment's repose, and the glare of the flames which shot from the crater enabled them to work night and day. The flow of lava continued, but perhaps less abundantly. This was fortunate, for Lake Grant was almost entirely choked up, and if more lava should accumulate it would inevitably spread over the plateau of Prospect Heights, and thence upon the beach.

But if the island was thus partially protected on this side, it was not so with the western part.

In fact, the second stream of lava, which had followed the valley of Falls River, a valley of great extent, the land on both sides of the creek being flat, met with no obstacle. The burning liquid had then spread through the forest of the Far West. At this period of the year, when the trees were dried up by a tropical heat, the forest caught fire instantaneously, in such a manner that the conflagration extended itself both by the trunks of the trees and by their higher branches, whose interlacement favoured its progress. It even appeared that the current of flame spread more rapidly among the summits of the trees than the current of lava at their bases.

Thus it happened that the wild animals, jaguars, wild boars, capybaras, koalas, and game of every kind, mad with terror, had fled to the banks of the Mercy and to the Tadorn Marsh, beyond the road to Port Balloon. But the colonists were too much occupied with their task to pay any attention to even the most formidable of these animals. They had abandoned Granite House, and would not even take shelter at the Chimneys, but encamped under a tent, near the mouth of the Mercy.

Each day Cyrus Harding and Gideon Spilett ascended the plateau of Prospect Heights. Sometimes Herbert accompanied them, but never Pencroft, who could not bear to look upon the prospect of the island now so utterly devastated.

It was, in truth, a heart-rending spectacle. All the wooded part of the island was now completely bare. One single clump of green trees raised their heads at the extremity of Serpentine Peninsula. Here and there were a few grotesque blackened and branchless stumps. The side of the devastated forest was even more barren than Tadorn Marsh. The eruption of lava had been complete. Where formerly sprang up that charming verdure, the soil was now nothing but a savage mass of volcanic tufa. In the valleys of the Falls and Mercy rivers no drop of water now flowed towards the sea, and should Lake Grant be entirely dried up, the colonists would have no means of quenching their thirst. But, fortunately the lava had spared the southern corner of the lake, containing all that remained of the drinking water of the island. Towards the northwest stood out the rugged and well-defined outlines of the sides of the volcano, like a gigantic claw hovering over the island. What a sad and fearful sight, and how painful to the colonists, who, from a fertile domain covered with forests, irrigated by watercourses, and enriched by the produce of their toils, found themselves, as it were, transported to a desolate rock, upon which, but for their reserves of provisions, they could not even gather the means of subsistence!

'It is enough to break one's heart!' said Gideon Spilett, one day.

'Yes, Spilett,' answered the engineer. 'May God grant us the time to complete this vessel, now our sole refuge!'

'Do not you think, Cyrus, that the violence of the eruption has somewhat lessened? The volcano still vomits forth lava, but somewhat less abundantly, if I mistake not.'

'It matters little,' answered Cyrus Harding. 'The fire is still burning in the interior of the mountain, and the sea may break in at any moment. We are in the condition of passengers whose ship is devoured by a conflagration which they cannot extinguish, and who know that sooner or later the flames must reach the powder-magazine. To work, Spilett, to work, and let us not lose an hour!'

During eight days more, that is to say until the 7th of February, the lava continued to flow, but the eruption was confined within the previous limits. Cyrus Harding feared above all lest the liquefied matter should overflow the shore, for in that event the dockyard could not escape. Moreover, about this time the colonists felt in the frame of the island vibrations which alarmed them to the highest degree.

It was the 20th of February. Yet another month must elapse before the vessel would be ready for sea. Would the island hold together till then? The intention of Pencroft and Cyrus Harding was to launch the vessel as soon as the hull should be complete. The deck, the upperworks, the interior woodwork and the rigging might be finished afterwards, but the essential point was that the colonists should have an assured refuge away from the island. Perhaps it might be even better to conduct the vessel to Port Balloon, that is to say, as far as possible from the centre of eruption, for at the mouth of the Mercy, between the islet and the wall of granite, it would run the risk of being crushed in the event of any convulsion. All the exertions of the voyagers were therefore concentrated upon the completion of the hull.

Thus the 3rd of March arrived, and they might calculate upon launching the vessel in ten days.

Hope revived in the hearts of the colonists, who had, in this fourth year of their sojourn on Lincoln island, suffered so many trials. Even Pencroft lost in some measure the sombre taciturnity occasioned by the devastation and ruin of his domain. His hopes, it is true, were concentrated upon his vessel.

'We shall finish it,' he said to the engineer, 'we shall finish it, captain, and it is time, for the season is advancing and the equinox will soon be here. Well, if necessary, we must put in to Tabor island to spend the winter. But think of Tabor island after Lincoln Island. Ah, how unfortunate! Who could have believed it possible?'

'Let us get on,' was the engineer's invariable reply.

And they worked away without losing a moment.

'Master,' asked Neb, a few days later, 'do you think all this could have happened if Captain Nemo had been still alive?'

'Certainly, Neb,' answered Cyrus Harding.

'I, for one, don't believe it!' whispered Pencroft to Neb.

'Nor I!' answered Neb seriously.

During the first week of March appearances again became menacing. Thousands of threads like glass, formed of fluid lava, fell like rain upon the island. The crater was again boiling with lava which overflowed the back of the volcano. The torrent flowed along the surface of the hardened tufa, and destroyed the few meagre skeletons of trees which had withstood the first eruption. The stream, flowing this time towards the southwest shore of Lake Grant, stretched beyond Creek Glycerine, and invaded the plateau of Prospect Heights. This last blow to the work of the colonists was terrible. The mill, the buildings of the inner court, the stables, were all destroyed. The affrighted poultry fled in all directions. Top and Jup showed signs of the greatest alarm, as if their instinct warned them of an impending catastrophe. A large number of the animals of the island had perished in the first eruption. Those which survived found no refuge but Tadorn Marsh, save a few to which the plateau of Prospect Heights afforded asylum. But even this last retreat was now closed to them, and the lava- torrent, flowing over the edge of the granite wall, began to pour down upon the beach its cataracts of fire. The sublime horror of this spectacle passed all description. During the night it could only be compared to a Niagara of molten fluid, with its incandescent vapours above and its boiling masses below.

The colonists were driven to their last entrenchment, and although the upper seams of the vessel were not yet calked, they decided to launch her at once.

Pencroft and Ayrton therefore set about the necessary preparations for the launching, which was to take place the morning of the next day, the 9th of March.

But during the night of the 8th an enormous column of vapour escaping from the crater rose with frightful explosions to a height of more than three thousand feet. The wall of Dakkar Grotto had evidently given way under the pressure of gases, and the sea, rushing through the central shalt into the igneous gulf, was at once converted into vapour. But the crater could not afford a sufficient outlet for this vapour. An explosion, which might have been heard at a distance of a hundred miles, shook the air. Fragments of mountains fell into the Pacific, and, in a few minutes, the ocean rolled over the spot where Lincoln island once stood.

Chapter 20

An isolated rock, thirty feet in length, twenty in breadth, scarcely ten from the water's edge, such was the only solid point which the waves of the Pacific had not engulfed.

It was all that remained of the structure of Granite House! The wall had fallen headlong and been then shattered to fragments, and a few of the rocks of the large room were piled one above another to form this point. All around had disappeared in the abyss; the inferior cone of Mount Franklin, rent asunder by the explosion; the lava jaws of Shark Gulf, the plateau of Prospect Heights, Safety Islet, the granite rocks of Port Balloon, the basalts of Dakkar Grotto, the long Serpentine Peninsula, so distant nevertheless from the centre of the eruption. All that could now be seen of Lincoln Island was the narrow rock which now served as a refuge to the six colonists and their dog Top.

The animals had also perished in the catastrophe; the birds, as well as those representing the fauna of the island—all either crushed or drowned, and the unfortunate Jup himself had, alas! found his death in some crevice of the soil.

If Cyrus Harding, Gideon Spilett, Herbert, Pencroft, Neb, and Ayrton had survived, it was because, assembled under their tent, they had been hurled into the sea at the instant when the fragments of the island rained down on every side.

When they reached the surface they could only perceive, at half a cable's length, this mass of rocks, towards which they swam and on which they found footing.

On this barren rock they had now existed for nine days. A few provisions taken from the magazine of Granite House before the catastrophe, a little fresh water from the rain which had fallen in a hollow of the rock, was all that the unfortunate colonists possessed. Their last hope, the vessel, had been shattered to pieces. They had no means of quitting the reef; no fire, nor any means of obtaining it. It seemed that they must inevitably perish.

This day, the 18th of March, there remained only provisions for two days, although they limited their consumption to the bare necessaries of life. All their science and intelligence could avail them nothing in their present position. They were in the hand of God.

Cyrus Harding was calm, Gideon Spilett more nervous, and Pencroft, a prey to sullen anger, walked to and fro on the rock. Herbert did not for a moment quit the engineer's side, as if demanding from him that assistance he had no power to give. Neb and Ayrton were resigned to their fate.

'Ah, what a misfortune! what a misfortune!' often repeated Pencroft. 'If we had but a walnut-shell to take us to Tabor Island! But we have nothing, nothing!'

'Captain Nemo did right to die,' said Neb.

During the five ensuing days Cyrus Harding and his unfortunate companions husbanded their provisions with the most extreme care, eating only what would prevent them from dying of starvation. Their weakness was extreme. Herbert and Neb began to show symptoms of delirium.

Under these circumstances was it possible for them to retain even the shadow of a hope? No! What was their sole remaining chance? That a vessel should appear in sight of the rock? But they knew only too well from experience that no ships ever visited this part of the Pacific. Could they calculate that, by a truly providential coincidence, the Scotch yacht would arrive precisely at this time in search of Ayrton at Tabor Island? It was scarcely probable; and, besides, supposing she should come there, as the colonists had not been able to deposit a notice pointing out Ayrton's change of abode, the commander of the yacht, after having explored Tabor Island without results, would again set sail and return to lower latitudes.

No! no hope of being saved could be retained, and a horrible death, death from hunger and thirst, awaited them upon this rock.

Already they were stretched on the rock, inanimate, and no longer conscious of what passed around them. Ayrton alone, by a supreme effort, from time to time raised his head, and cast a despairing glance over the desert ocean.

But on the morning of the 24th of March Ayrton's arms were extended toward a point in the horizon; he raised himself, at first on his knees, then upright, and his hand seemed to make a signal.

A sail was in sight off the rock. She was evidently not without an object. The reef was the mark for which she was making in a direct line, under all steam, and the unfortunate colonists might have made her out some hours before if they had had the strength to watch the horizon.

'The 'Duncan'!' murmured Ayrton—and fell back without sign of life.

When Cyrus Harding and his companions recovered consciousness, thanks to the attention lavished upon them, they found themselves in the cabin of a steamer, without being able to comprehend how they had escaped death.

A word from Ayrton explained everything.

'The 'Duncan'!' he murmured.

'The 'Duncan'!' exclaimed Cyrus Harding. And raising his hand to Heaven, he said, 'Oh! Almighty God! mercifully hast Thou preserved us!'

It was, in fact, the 'Duncan,' Lord Glenarvan's yacht, now commanded by Robert, son of Captain Grant, who had been despatched to Tabor Island to find Ayrton, and bring him back to his native land alter twelve years of expiation.

The colonists were not only saved, but already on the way to their native country.

'Captain Grant,' asked Cyrus Harding, 'who can have suggested to you the idea, after having left Tabor Island, where you did not find Ayrton, of coming a hundred miles farther northeast?'

'Captain Harding,' replied Robert Grant, 'it was in order to find, not only Ayrton, but yourself and your companions.'

'My companions and myself?'

'Doubtless, at Lincoln Island.'

'At Lincoln Island!' exclaimed in a breath Gideon Spilett, Herbert, Neb, and Pencroft, in the highest degree astonished.

'How could you be aware of the existence of Lincoln Island?' inquired Cyrus Harding, 'it is not even named in the charts.'

'I knew of it from a document left by you on Tabor Island,' answered Robert Grant.

'A document!' cried Gideon Spilett.

'Without doubt, and here it is,' answered Robert Grant, producing a paper which indicated the longitude and latitude of Lincoln Island, 'the present residence of Ayrton and five American colonists.'

'It is Captain Nemo!' cried Cyrus Harding, after having read the notice, and recognized that the handwriting was similar to that of the paper found at the corral.

'Ah!' said Pencroft, 'it was then he who took our 'Bonadventure' and hazarded himself alone to go to Tabor Island!'

'In order to leave this notice,' added Herbert.

'I was then right in saying,' exclaimed the sailor, 'that even after his death the captain would render us a last service.'

'My friends,' said Cyrus Harding, in a voice of the profoundest emotion, 'may the God of mercy have had pity on the soul of Captain Nemo, our benefactor.'

The colonists uncovered themselves at these last words of Cyrus Harding, and murmured the name of Captain Nemo.

Then Ayrton, approaching the engineer, said simply, 'Where should this coffer be deposited?'

It was the coffer which Ayrton had saved at the risk of his life, at the very instant that the island had been engulfed, and which he now faithfully handed to the engineer.

'Ayrton! Ayrton!' said Cyrus Harding, deeply touched. Then, addressing Robert Grant, 'Sir,' he added, 'you left behind you a criminal; you find in his place a man who has become honest by penitence, and whose hand I am proud to clasp in mine.'

Robert Grant was now made acquainted with the strange history of Captain Nemo and the colonists of Lincoln Island. Then, observation being taken of what remained of this shoal, which must henceforward figure on the charts of the Pacific, the order was given to make all sail.

A few weeks afterwards the colonists landed in America, and found their country once more at peace alter the terrible conflict in which right and justice had triumphed.

Of the treasures contained in the coffer left by Captain Nemo to the colonists of Lincoln Island, the larger portion was employed in the purchase of a vast territory in the State of Iowa. One pearl alone, the finest, was reserved from the treasure and sent to Lady Glenarvan in the name of the castaways restored to their country by the 'Duncan.'

There, upon this domain, the colonists invited to labour, that is to say, to wealth and happiness, all those to whom they had hoped to offer the hospitality of Lincoln Island. There was founded a vast colony to which they gave the name of that island sunk beneath the waters of the Pacific. A river there was called the Mercy, a mountain took the name of Mount Franklin, a small lake was named Lake Grant, and the forests became the forests of the Far West. It might have been an island on terra firma.

There, under the intelligent hands of the engineer and his companions, everything prospered. Not one of the former colonists of Lincoln Island was absent, for they had sworn to live always together. Neb was with his master; Ayrton was there ready to sacrifice himself for all; Pencroft was more a farmer than he had ever been a sailor; Herbert, who completed his studies under the superintendence of Cyrus Harding, and Gideon Spilett, who founded the New Lincoln Herald, the best-informed journal in the world.

There Cyrus Harding and his companions received at intervals visits from Lord and Lady Glenarvan, Captain John Mangles and his wife, the sister of Robert Grant, Robert Grant himself, Major McNab, and all those who had taken part in the history both of Captain Grant and Captain Nemo.

There, to conclude, all were happy, united in the present as they had been in the past; but never could they forget that island upon which they had arrived poor and friendless, that island which, during four years had supplied all their wants, and of which there remained but a fragment of granite washed by the waves of the Pacific, the tomb of him who had borne the name of Captain Nemo.
